Fundamentals of carpentry

Carpentry is an ancient and proud craft.
There is pride and dignity in being a safe and
competent workman.

Fundamentals of carpentry

tools, materials, and practices

volume 1

by **WALTER E. DURBAHN**

Chairman Emeritus, Vocational Department
Highland Park High School
Highland Park, Illinois

With the collaboration of American Technical Society
Editorial Staff

FOURTH EDITION

AMERICAN TECHNICAL SOCIETY
Chicago, U.S.A. 60637

Preface

The Fourth edition of *Fundamentals of Carpentry, Volume I—Tools, Materials, Practice* is designed to provide a comprehensive groundwork for the building tradesman. The carpentry fundamentals it presents are important not only for the conventional applications of carpentry to home building, but also for the applications of carpentry to the many closely related trades. For the pre-apprentice or apprentice the new edition offers clear cut instruction in the safe use of tools, materials, and rough and finish hardware. For upgrading and retraining of foremen and construction supervisors it offers a diversity of coverage with detailed up-to-date information.

The discussion of carpentry tools is organized to follow the actual trade practices in the field. Portable power tools frequently used by the carpenter are associated with the hand tools that do the same job. For example, the use of the hand saw, the portable power saw, and the stationary saws, along with the various types of blades, are grouped together. The tools and materials in the new edition are also directly related to their uses and applications in the building industry. Practical, easy to follow instructions with explanatory text have been added to show how tools are used by the experienced carpenter.

Technological changes and developments have modified the tools and materials used by the modern carpenter. New tools and modifications of old tools are constantly being introduced. New materials are being developed almost daily. Careful attention has been paid to the new developments in the building industry. New tools and materials that have been tested in the field and have been accepted by the carpenter are discussed in this new edition..

The carpenter will find the latest information on such tools as power screwdrivers, air-powered staplers and nailers, adhesive guns, manual and powder fasteners, power saws, etc. The more complicated power equipment, such as power saws, routers, jointers, sanders, etc., have detailed illustrations with the various parts labeled.

A new chapter has been added to discuss the many new wood products and building materials that have become accepted in the industry. Not only are plywoods, hardboards, fiberboards and gypsum board discussed, but also laminated woods, building components, steel studs, solid vinyl, etc.

An entire chapter is now devoted to the fast-growing field of adhesives, and the hardware chapter has been expanded into a chapter on rough hardware and one on finish hardware.

All tools, materials, practices and applications have been carefully checked against current usages and practices. Materials and practices discussed conform to the latest standards and codes.

An important consideration in the building industry is the safety of the workers. Accidents may be prevented by an awareness of safe on-the-job working conditions and by a knowledge of the proper use of tools both in the field and in the workshop. A new chapter has been added covering both general and specific accident prevention practices; general procedures for the safe use of tools are also included. In addition, throughout the text rules and procedures are given for the safe use of specific hand and power tools.

Safety rules and procedures for a specific tool are given just after the discussion of the tool.

The *Appendix* offers the carpenter supplemental material that the instructor can use in adapting the book to individual and local needs. Devices that a carpenter might wish to make on the job, such as a sawhorse or a straightedge, are covered. Advanced steel square work is included to supplement the text coverage. The latest softwood standards are given, and first aid kit materials are discussed. In addition, a concise explanation of floor plans, elevations, details, sections, symbols, conventions, etc., is presented so the student may review any area in which he feels a need for his particular job.

An extensive *Glossary of Carpentry Terms* is given at the end of the book. Here, terms which relate to the actual work of the carpenter are explained. Terms used by those related trades that the carpenter will work with are also discussed. Illustrations are provided to clarify the more difficult terms.

This book provides an understandable and thorough training in building supplies, tools, safety, and construction terminology and nomenclature. This background enables the student to approach the companion volume, *Practical Construction*, with increased skill and greater comprehension.

THE PUBLISHERS

Contents

Chapter

1 Carpentry as a Trade, 1

2 Introduction to Accident Prevention, 14

3 Tools: Part I, 22
   Hammering, Turning, Supporting, Layout and Measuring Tools

4 Tools: Part II, 72
   Cutting Tools: Saws, Borers, Planers and Sanders

5 Construction Lumber, 138

6 Wood Products and Other Building Materials, 173

7 Building Insulation, 196

8 Hardware: Rough, 222

9 Hardware: Finish, 257

10 Adhesives, 271

Appendix

A Devices Made on the Job, 282

B Advanced Work on the Steel Square, 304

C Softwood Standards, 317

D First Aid Kit, 323

E Review of Blueprints, Conventions and Symbols, 325

Glossary of Building Terms, 342

Index, 400

An understanding of basic tools and materials, along with a knowledge of standard practices, is essential to quality construction.

Carpentry as a Trade

"Which came first, the carpenter or the farmer?" No one knows, of course, as both occupations started in prehistoric times. Records do show, however, that ancient man did not become a civilized being until he erected permanent homes and started growing crops.

Civilization, from prehistoric time to today, to a great extent has been made possible by the carpenter. Every building, whether of stone, concrete, or steel, depends on the carpenter. Today the modern carpenter is a respected craftsman. His work is basic to all the other building trades; he is the first and the last man on the job. He is concerned with the safety and comfort of workers on the job as well as the persons who will use and occupy the buildings.

Carpentry, today as in the past, is one of the cornerstones of our way of life.

Carpentry as an Ancient Craft

Carpentry is the art of working with wood, in the construction of buildings in which men live or work, the making of furniture, and many other devices of wood, to help man adapt himself to his environment. The art of carpentry is thousands of years old. We might say that carpentry began when man first left the caves in which he had lived until then; driven out perhaps by hunger and the need to seek better hunting grounds, he made for himself crude shelters of branches which he covered with leaves and grass.

However, this early ancestor had no tools, as we know them today, and since tools are so vital a part of carpentry, it would perhaps be more correct to say that carpentry began when men first fashioned crude tools from bronze and iron. With these tools, wood that was used for building and making could be cut instead of broken. Men then began to shape wood into useful objects and to improve the shelters which protected them from their enemies and the weather.

The Modern Carpenter

At one time the carpenter's work was almost entirely with wood. However, in recent years many substitutes for wood have been put on the market, and, in order to protect his interests, the carpenter has claimed the right to work in many of the newer materials, on the basis that such work requires the use of carpentry tools.

When a jurisdictional dispute arises among the different trades as to which trade is to do certain work, each trade in question selects a representative to present its case and the dispute is referred to a joint arbitration board, a permanent body, ready to analyze the facts and render a decision in favor of one trade or the other.

However, the carpenter's work is not confined to the erection of buildings; this is only one phase of carpentry. Carpenters are employed in the building of bridges, piers, docks, and wharfs. A large number of men are employed as boat or ship carpenters, work requiring training which is different from that for building and construction work.

In the metropolitan areas where labor is more highly organized, the work of the various trades must be carefully defined. In small communities, a carpenter is likely to be called upon to do work which in a city would be done by another tradesman.

Though persons unfamiliar with trade classifications are apt to assume that everyone who works in wood is a carpenter, this is not so. There was a time when the carpenter not only built the house, but also made the trim, the built-in cabinet work, and even in some cases, the furniture. However, today, a builder of furniture is a cabinetmaker, while the man who makes the interior trim and builds stairs is a millman. In general, millmen and cabinetmakers, together with similar woodworking craftsmen, belong to the large group of men who work in factories; whereas the carpenter is employed on what is known as *outside work*.

The carpenter is a *key man* in the building field and must be a versatile person. Practically every phase of building requires his skill and knowledge. He is of the utmost importance in running accurate lines for the foundation and in building the forms that will permit the pouring of true foundation walls. He takes part in every phase of the building of the structure, and after the owner has moved in he comes back to make minor adjustments in doors, windows, and hardware. Among the skills he must acquire are the ability to use hand tools with precision and speed, and to use power tools to the greatest advantage. Many carpenters are also skilled in the practical use of some of the common woodworking machines such as the table saw, the jointer, the planer, and so on. Not only must he have great skill with his hands, but the carpenter must also be familiar with a wide range of materials, knowing how each can be cut and shaped and where each is best used. He must know about hardware and fastenings, and about a great number of new products, which reach the market continually.

Considering the key importance of the carpenter, and the responsibility assumed by the carpenter, it is just that carpenters be called "la-bor's aristocracy." Carpentry is an ancient and proud craft. There is pride and dignity in being a safe and competent craftsman.

Training

The practical way of entering the trade is through an apprenticeship. To begin with, one requisite is a background experience with tools, through training obtained in the industrial arts programs and the vocational training courses that are offered in most modern schools.

A student interested in carpentry should take all the work offered in the industrial arts, drafting, mathematics and science in junior and senior high school.

If this training is then followed by two or three years of vocational trade training and an apprenticeship after graduation, the young carpenter should be well qualified as a journeyman.

A carpenter should be familiar, at least to some extent, with the work of the other building trades. Therefore, it is recommended that his vocational study in high school includes general trades training. He should take the allied courses offered in bricklaying, concrete work, plumbing, sheet-metal work, painting, welding, and electrical wiring. This training should be secured while the student is still in school because he will probably not have an opportunity for training in these fields after he has indentured himself as a carpenter's apprentice. The value of experience in other trades can scarcely be overemphasized; this is especially true if he wishes to advance to the position of foreman. As a foreman, he must assume some of the responsibility for the work of other trades on the building, for often the workmen in other trades will come to the foreman for information regarding procedure in their work.

The Carpenter Apprentice

The apprentice should have a good high school education. The age of carpentry apprentices varies from seventeen to twenty-seven. In order to become an apprentice a written indentureship agreement must be signed with an employer or with the Joint Apprenticeship Council. The employer must be one who regularly maintains a force of qualified carpenters. The agreement must be approved by the state or by a trade organization. In accordance with the indenture, the apprentice agrees to work at and to learn the carpentry trade, while his employer agrees to teach him the trade. The employer also agrees to send the apprentice to school to receive technical instruction in the trade and related subjects. The frequency of his attendance varies in different areas. This training is usually provided by the local Board of Educa-

tion or by the public school system.

When the apprentice completes this training period and passes an examination satisfactorily, he becomes a journeyman carpenter. He can then work anywhere he wishes, and it is assumed that his qualifications entitle him to journeyman's wages.

The trade offers an ambitious young man many opportunities for advancement. Progress is usually achieved by supplementary practical experience on the job, with evening school courses or correspondence courses, by reading books and trade journals, and by contact with skilled craftsmen. Those adept at the trade become foremen and superintendents in due course, then perhaps carpentry contractors, or general contractors. Others may continue their training to become architects.

The well informed carpenter will not limit his knowledge to the skillful handling of the tools of his trade and the building procedures. He will also keep up to date by subscribing to the periodicals of the trade, by studying local building codes and safety regulations, and by acquainting himself with such things as lot selection, financing, contracts, specifications, and other topics that are trade related.

The Building Industry

The building industry is one of the largest industries in the country. Housing is a basic need, and the continuously increasing number and expanding activities of the industrial and business world also make steady demands on construction. Repairs and alterations, too, play an important part in the building field.

Opportunities

The rising volume of construction causes an increasing need for carpenters. Almost every aspect of our modern civilization depends on the skill of the carpenter. The homes we live in; the buildings we work in; the churches, schools, stores, hospitals, streets and highways; the piers, docks and wharves; the launching pads for the exploration of outer space—all depend on the skill of the carpenter.

Carpenters are also needed for maintenance services in factories, commercial establishments, and government agencies. Remodeling, repairing and altering require more men every year. Factory prefabrication of parts and building components are also likely to increase the job prospects.

Carpenters, then, are needed in every branch and walk of life. As the country grows, the need for carpenters also grows.

The Carpenter as an Adviser

Carpenters are familiar figures on every building job from the time the batter boards are set to guide the foundation work to the last nail in the finish trim and the last lock on the door. Other tradesmen come, spend a short time performing their special tasks, and leave. Carpenters are there assisting the other trades as well as performing their own work. In home building, carpenters may be the only workmen on the job for days.

The home builder or buyer will often become familiar with carpenters as the craftsmen that are always present on the job. He will turn to them as the ones who have the widest knowledge of the work and who are most accessible.

As carpenters become acquainted with the home builder they will learn about the desires, ideas, plans, and hopes of the family that will occupy the home. They will often be looked to as experts on all phases of construction and their advice will be sought.

Carpenters, in the role of advisers to the home builder, can become invaluable members of the building team. They can be of real service to the architect, contractor, other tradesmen, financial institution, and the community. Carpenters, by explaining the reasons for certain methods or materials, can enlighten the home buyer and add to his feeling of satisfaction. They can, likewise, pass on ideas to the contractor and architect based on their contact with the buyer. Carpenters can be a unifying and coordinating factor between the elements in the construction field.

While carpenters can be of great aid in the role of advisers and coordinators, they should carefully avoid any actions that might infringe on the relations of the home buyer with the contractor and architect. All questions of major or expensive changes should be tactfully referred to the proper party for settlement.

When building a house a large item of expense is the amount the carpenter receives. This is especially true of the small house. Because so large a share of the cost of a building goes to the carpenter, he is considered by many as the builder, and by others as a building expert. Hence, he is called upon frequently for counsel and advice on general building and homeownership problems. These may include legal and financial advice as well as matters regarding community and personal obligations of the homeowner. In many cases the prospective home-

owner is so engrossed with the idea of homeownership and his future happiness in the new house that he does not give sufficient nor reasonable consideration to the many relatively important factors necessary in preparation for the actual construction of the home.

Building of a home is an undertaking which the average individual is not likely to repeat during his lifetime. Home building is an investment which perhaps will require all or at least most of the owner's savings. Should the venture prove to be a failure or one of disappointment, others might be discouraged by the failure. Therefore, a carpenter can render a service to a future homeowner by taking an interest in his building problems and by being prepared to give him helpful and much needed advice. This service will give the carpenter a good reputation in the community and will encourage others to undertake home building.

Location and Type of Home

Selection of Location. The type of family that is to occupy the home should govern the selection of a location. If there are one or more members of the family employed outside the home and there are growing children in the family, careful consideration should be given to accessibility to suitable employment areas, transportation, schools, and recreational facilities. A home always should be near market centers if possible.

Title to Property. There are many problems which must be satisfactorily solved by the future property owner before purchasing a lot on which to build his new home. Acquiring a piece of property is a legal transaction which should be handled by an experienced lawyer or a competent real-estate broker. An efficient lawyer or broker will check delinquent taxes, mortgages, liens, or any other irregularities which may be held against the property. Such a procedure will insure the buyer a clear and unquestionable title to the land he buys. This is not only a future protection to the purchaser but is also essential for the acquisition of a loan for financing of a building project.

Lot Survey. A lot survey shuld be made by a licensed land surveyor who is qualified to certify the accuracy of his report. The making of such a survey is strongly advised because it assures the property owner that the prospective building will be erected upon the right plot of ground and within the bounds of that plot. Due to the lack of a survey many an individual has been plunged into costly legal entanglements. Court records show that buildings have been erected on the wrong lot or have extended partly onto an adjoining lot to which the owner of

the building had no title. Such a situation places the builder or house owner at the mercy of the neighboring landowner who may sue for infringement of property rights. In case a building project is to be financed by a loan, a lot survey is imperative because financing companies demand a certified survey before lending money for the erection of a building on a plot of ground. Furthermore, before issuing a building permit, city building departments demand a lot survey.

Water and Sewerage. Adequate water supply, drainage, and sewerage disposal are extremely important, not only for household needs but also from the standpoint of health and sanitation. If city water is not available plans for a well must be made before building operations begin. If low land does not have natural drainage facilities, but otherwise is a desirable location for a home, consideration must be given to providing adequate drainage before a house is built. The sewer level should be checked with the city engineer to determine the height of the sewer, its adequacy, and record of performance. This information will be a great help in determining the depth the basement should be in order to insure proper drainage. Where sewers are not available attention must be given to septic tanks, and existing laws governing them and their drainage.

Electric, Gas, and Telephone Services. Public utility services must be checked as to their availability and the possibilities for connections with service lines. Sometimes building locations are so remote from such conveniences that special provisions must be made with the utility companies in order to secure their services.

Building Codes and Zoning Laws

Whenever people live together in a community certain regulations must be established which will work to the best interests of the majority. These regulations or laws are commonly called *city codes*. Those which should be of special interest to the contractor or builder are the *zoning laws* and *building codes*. These codes are written and passed upon by the people of the community to help make it a better and more desirable place in which to live. The codes are also intended to protect health, insure safety, to promote beauty and recreational facilities, and to assure the maintaining of reasonable property values for landowners.

Frequently people look upon these zoning and building codes as restrictions upon their rights. It is true codes do restrict the individual who fails to take into account the rights of others. However, in reality codes are designed to give the greatest amount of freedom to the greatest number of people.

The primary purpose of the zoning law in a community is: to divide the city into districts, such as residential and apartment house, commercial and business, industrial and manufacturing, and recreational zones; to promote health and safety; to protect property values; to eliminate or minimize fire hazards; and to control density of population. Zoning laws also govern the height of buildings and the size of open spaces required around buildings in accordance with the type of occupancy classifications.

Building codes promote safe engineering practices in the use of materials and establish standards which have been proved the most effective. To insure safety, buildings should not only conform to the best-known practices for sturdy construction, but safety precautions must also be taken against fire hazards due to imperfect heating equipment, defective chimneys, oil burners, and electrical devices. As the amount of open space around a building decreases, the fire hazard increases and fire-resisting features of a building must be increased. This safety of construction and precaution against fire hazards is equally as important for the private dwelling as it is for a public assembling place, such as churches, theaters, and other auditoriums. Other important phases of building codes pertain to sanitation, control of plumbing in buildings, ventilation, amount of glass area in the windows, and the height of ceilings. All of these factors are vitally important to the general welfare of a community as well as to individual members of the community.

Many states also exercise some degree of control over the most densely populated areas through zoning and building laws; however, state laws are formulated mainly from the viewpoint of sanitation; because unsanitary conditions in one community may affect neighboring communities. The licensing of architects is controlled by state legislation. Some states have an architectural-practice law which demands that licensed architects be employed for all public buildings, and in residential construction which exceeds a value of $10,000.

As a rule, licensed architects become familiar with zoning and build-ing laws during the process of training. However, the builder or contractor frequently is either unaware of, or minimizes the value of, existing building laws and codes. Ignoring zoning laws and building codes may work a great hardship upon both the carpenter and owner of a building. Therefore, before beginning construction work a wise builder will inform himself regarding all prevailing laws or codes, including state laws, which might cause him trouble later. In addition, every carpenter should utilize the opportunities offered by the office of building commissioners, or building inspector, and obtain all possible information and assistance necessary for interpreting any laws or codes which would in any way affect a building enterprise which he is preparing to undertake. The prospective owner rarely is informed concerning various legal requirements and practices and usually depends upon the architect or builder to supply information essential for protecting their mutual interests.

Drawing Up Specifications

Oftentimes a homeowner is disappointed in a new house because it has been erected without expert advice. Sometimes a carpenter must proceed with his construction work without definite instructions. In many cases the only specifications the builder receives is the meager information furnished him in a few sketchy drawings. These may have been made by someone totally ignorant of the varied and numerous details of a building project and the proper procedure to follow in dealing with them. Such laxity results invariably in costly changes during construction and gives rise to misunderstandings between the parties involved, especially between the builder and the homeowner. The drawings and building specifications, prepared by a competent architect, are well worth his fees. His expert knowledge of materials and methods of construction, as well as his training and experience, are valuable to a new homeowner unfamiliar with architectural procedure. A trained architect not only assumes responsibility for drawing up specifications and contracts but also takes over supervision of the work during the process of construction. In addition

he is able to protect the owner's interests by his understanding of how to plan economically to avoid waste in time and materials. The average new homeowner is unfamiliar with all such details.

Frequently carpenters have the ability required for looking after all details of construction and giving expert advice to their clients. Sometimes the owner has had training and experience which fits him to assume the responsibility for details himself. Regardless of how adequate drawings and building specifications are prepared, this is an important phase of home building which justifies the investment of ample time and effort in order to avoid misunderstandings between the builder and owner as to how the work is to be done.

Financing

The prospective homeowner should not obligate himself in any way by signing any contracts until final settlement has been made regarding financing of the new-building project. Before considering making a loan, finance companies demand adequate proof of a clear title to the property on which the building is to be erected. In addition these companies require several sets of drawings and building specifica-

tions together with figures showing the actual costs involved. When the loan has been granted, the owner or his agent can proceed to sign contracts; and construction work on the house may begin without undue risk.

Family needs and the quality of the proposed house must be considered carefully, so that the investment will be in keeping with the owner's individual resources. The cost of maintaining the home after it is completed should be taken into account also. This item of expense is governed by the prospective annual income of the owner.

If the carpenter is also acting as a general contractor he will have gone into the matter of financing before starting work or even signing a contract.

When work starts on a building the major elements of financing have been worked out. However, as work progresses the new home owner may discover many items that he might need: landscaping, changes in closets, more cabinets, different hardware, changes in doors and windows, recreation room, tool shed, shelving, patio, fences, etc., that were not originally considered important. These modifications are usually worked out with the contractor.

Table I gives a suggested monthly and yearly income in relation to total house cost. This will give the carpenter some idea of what the homeowner can afford.

Contracts

A prospective homeowner, or his agent, usually his lawyer, should draw up contracts and have them signed by the architect and the contractor, who sub-contracts to the tradesmen hired to perform services for the construction of the house. The general contractor assumes responsibility for materials delivered

TABLE I

APPROXIMATE HOUSE COST IN RELATION TO INCOME

INCOME*		TOTAL HOUSE COST
MONTH	YEAR	
$ 333	$ 4,000	$ 9,100
416	5,000	12,000
500	6,000	14,500
583	7,000	16,500
666	8,000	19,700
750	9,000	22,500
833	10,000	25,500
916	11,000	27,500
1,000	12,000	30,000
1,250	15,000	35,000

*Gross income or income before deductions.

to the job. Contracts may be verbal but, if carefully prepared, written contracts are more desirable. In case a question arises regarding either the material or the construction work, the evidence furnished in a written contract will remove all doubt as to the original agreement made between the owner and any contractor.

When competitive bids are called for on a construction job, it is advisable for a prospective homeowner to reserve the right to reject any or all bids and to investigate carefully the integrity, ability, and record of performance of every bidder. An important fact to remember is: *the lowest bid is not always the best bid.*

If complete, the contract figures will furnish the owner with definite assurance of the total cost of his home-building project, providing no changes in construction are made later. Such figures are not only a protection to the home builder but are necessary in making application for a loan to finance the proposed project.

Checking on your Knowledge

The following questions give you the opportunity to check up on yourself. If you have read the chapter carefully, you should be able to answer the questions. If you have any difficulty, read the chapter over once more so that you have the information well in mind before you read on.

DO YOU KNOW

1. What carpentry is?
2. When carpentry first began?
3. What work has been adjudged to be carpentry?
4. What a millman is?
5. What a cabinetmaker does?
6. What is required of a man who wishes to become a carpenter?
7. How a man becomes an apprentice in this work?
8. How a man becomes a journeyman carpenter?
9. The opportunities for carpenters in the United States?
10. The most essential factors included in the preparations for building a new home?
11. Why some home-building projects are failures as financial investments?
12. Why a homeowner is sometimes disappointed in his new home after it is completed?
13. Why the average man is not qualified to handle all the difficult problems connected with the preparation of building a new home?
14. How a carpenter can be of service in helping the prospective homeowner to solve his home-building problems?
15. Why a surveyor should be engaged to make a lot survey of the land on which a new home is to be erected?
16. Why the proper drainage of such a lot is of first importance to the home-owner?
17. Why some states have laws regulating the location of homes in relation to industrial and manufacturing centers?

18. How certain factors connected with the location of a new home may affect various members of the family concerned and, therefore, are of vital importance to the property owner?

19. What factors are more important, when choosing a building location, than a pleasing view from the front porch?

20. Who should be engaged to prepare architectural drawings and building specifications?

21. How the prospective homeowner can protect himself when seeking legal advice?

22. Why financial companies are interested in the property owner having a clear title to his home?

23. The primary purpose of zoning laws? In what way zoning laws and building codes restrict the rights of an individual homeowner?

24. Why it is important for the property owner to be informed regarding existing zoning laws and building codes in his community before beginning a building project?

25. Why it is important for the prospective homeowner to study carefully all financial matters involved in connection with the cost of building a new house?

26. What financial problems, in addition to the actual cost of building a new house, should be considered in connection with the cost of building?

27. Why the location of public utilities in relation to a new home is important to the homeowner?

28. What precautions the home builder should take before signing contracts with an architect, carpenters, building material dealers, and other interested parties? Why the lowest bid is not always the best bid?

Introduction to Accident Prevention

Before beginning actual work on a building, the carpenter should carefully consider the safety measures necessary to protect himself and his fellow workers against accidents. Every building mechanic should be aware of the particular hazards of his own trade, as well as those of associated trades. The accident rate is comparatively high in the building industry. Accidents often result in partial or total disability and are sometimes fatal. In addition to these serious accidents there is the possibility of sustaining innumerable minor cuts and bruises that are not only painful but temporarily handicap the workman. To reduce this accident rate to a minimum, the carpenter must become safety conscious; he must learn to think of the safety of his fellow workers as well as his own. Every man on the job must know how to prevent accidents, and must have a keen sense of responsibility toward his fellow workmen.

Safety on the Job

Safety education today has become an important phase of every training program. The safety rules that are important to the carpenter are outlined briefly. For your own safety and the safety of others, you must study, know, and practice these safety rules.

"Safety First" is a slogan adopted on a national scale by all branches of industry. Laws and regulations governing manufacturing, construc-

National Safety Council

National Safety Council

tion, and transportation are enforced by departments of safety in each state. However, instruction in safety regulations, by industry itself, pays dividends by reducing injuries and loss of time.

Of first importance in a "Safety First" campaign is the education of the worker. This education must become a part of his daily training as he learns the technical and manipulative skills of his job. Generally, a person becomes injured because of his own carelessness or the carelessness of some other person. To prevent accidents and injuries, observe all safety regulations, use all safety devices and guards when working with machines, and learn to control your work and actions so as to avoid danger. Training for safety is every bit as important as learning to be a skillful craftsman and should be a part of the worker's education.

In the performance of his work, the carpenter handles materials, manipulates hand tools, and operates machines which if improperly handled or used may result in serious injury. If an injury should occur, seek first aid no matter how slight the injury. Blood poisoning may result from an insignificant sliver. It is advisable to take a first aid course at the first opportunity.

Appendix *D* lists some of the common first aid equipment that a carpenter should carry.

General Safety on the Job

Safety is a combination of knowledge and awareness, *knowledge* and *skill* in the use and care of your tools, and *awareness* on the job of the particular hazards and safety procedures involved. Tool skills may be learned; awareness, however, depends on attitude. An attitude of care and concern while

15

on the job will help prevent injuries not only to yourself, but also to your fellow workers. Always be alert while on the job and follow recommended safety procedures. If in doubt, ask questions.

1. Wrestling, throwing objects, and other forms of horseplay should be avoided. Serious injuries may be the result.

2. Provide a place for everything and keep everything in its place.

3. Keep the arms and body as nearly straight as possible when lifting heavy objects. Place your feet close to the object. Bend your knees, squat, and keep your back as straight as possible. Lift with the legs—not with the back. If the object is too heavy or too bulky, get help.

YOUR BACK CAN CRACK!

LIFT WITH YOUR LEGS

National Safety Council

4. Never place articles on window sills, stepladders, or other high places where they may fall and cause injuries. Check a ladder for

articles before it is moved.

5. Oil, water, and other slippery substances left on the floor may cause a serious accident.

6. Keep all work spaces clear of scraps of lumber, tools, and material. Things left scattered on the floor may cause stumbling and result in serious injury from a fall.

7. Remove or bend down all protruding nails to eliminate the hazard of their being stepped on or brushed against.

Accidents don't just happen.... THEY ARE CAUSED!

National Safety Council

8. Notify your immediate superior of any known violations of safety rules or of conditions you think may be dangerous.

9. When loading factory trucks with lumber, cross-stack the load at intervals. When the truck stakes are removed, the lumber will not fall off. Employ this practice for all large stacks of lumber.

10. Inspect ladders carefully before mounting. Weak rungs or steps

construction methods for erecting a scaffold. Use quality lumber as specified by local and state codes. Wear a safety belt when required.

13. Replace faulty tools and equipment.

14. Immediately report all accidents, no matter how slight, to your superior, and report for first aid treatment.

15. Don't take chances.

may cause a fall. Remove defective ladders from service. Never paint a ladder—paint may hide dangerous defects.

11. When using a ladder, be sure that the bottom rests on solid footing so that it cannot slip. Do not slant it at such an acute angle that the weight of the body would pull the top of the ladder from the wall. Face the ladder when going up or down; grip with both hands.

12. Be familiar with the correct

Safety: Clothing and Personal Protective Equipment

1. Wear well-fitting carpenter's overalls. Keep them in good repair. Pockets and hatchet loop must be in good condition. Tailor the trousers to eliminate cuffs; do *not* turn up trouser cuffs as they may catch on protruding objects.

2. Do not wear ragged sleeves, neckties, or loose clothing of any sort, as they may get caught in machinery or on sharp projections. Button or zip up any jackets that are worn.

3. Roll up your shirt sleeves above your elbows. Loose cuffs are especially dangerous around moving machinery.

4. Wear thick-soled work shoes for protection against sharp objects such as nails. Wear work shoes with safety toes if the job requires.

5. Wear gloves when working with rough material or material with sharp edges or projections.

National Safety Council

6. Wear a hat or cap. Wear a safety helmet (hard hat) if the job requires. Keep your hair trimmed and be careful to avoid placing your head too near rotating machinery.

7. Wear safety goggles around abrading, scraping, or sawing equipment where chips or flying pieces of material usually occur. (Consult state laws and local codes for the requirements and specifications on eye-protective devices).

8. Wear a dust mask or respirator when working in dusty areas.

National Safety Council

The Carpenter's Tools and Safety

It is obvious that without good, quality tools the carpenter cannot do his job. It is equally obvious that without knowledge and skill in the use of his tools the carpenter cannot do a *competent* job. What is more important, and often forgotten, is that the carpenter must also use his tools *safely*.

Each tool has individual safety practices associated with it. A carpenter in learning the proper use of a tool must also learn the safe use of the tool. He must *learn* the safe use and he must *practice* the safe use. But knowledge and practice of individual tool safety, by itself, will not guarantee safe working conditions. The carpenter must also work in a safe environment and act in a safe manner. A safe environment includes such things as the proper installation of safety rails, sound scaffolding, clean work spaces, etc. Most on-the-job safety devices and conditions are covered by local and state safety codes. It is the duty and legal obligation of employers to provide these safety devices and safe working conditions. The carpenter, though, has the responsibility to use these safety devices. If safety devices are not provided or are not installed properly, this negligence must be reported and corrected. It is the carpenter's responsibility to correct unsafe conditions if possible. Such things as protruding nails and slippery or cluttered floors, for example, should be corrected by the carpenter.

If the carpenter learns to keep his tools in good condition and to use his tools properly and safely, he will go a long way towards preventing accidents. He must remember, however, that a tool is only as safe as the conditions under which it is used.

National Safety Council

SAFETY: HAND TOOLS

1. *Always focus your full attention on the work.*

2. *Use the right tool for the job.* Use not only the proper tool, but also the correct size. Use good, quality tools and use them for the job they were designed to accomplish.

3. *Learn how to use the tool properly.* Study your tools—learn the safe way of working with each tool. Never use tools beyond their capacity. Don't be afraid to ask questions on the proper and safe use of a tool.

4. *Keep tools in their best condition.* Always inspect a tool before using it. Do not use a tool which is in poor or faulty condition. Use only safe tools. Cutting tools should be sharp; tool handles should be free of cracks and splinters, and fastened securely to the working part.

5. *Keep each tool in its place.* Each tool should have a designated place in the tool box. Do not carry tools in your pockets unless the pocket is designed for that tool. Keep pencils in the pocket designed for them—do not place pencils behind your ear or under your hat or cap.

6. When using sharp-edged tools, cut away from the body. Keep your feet or free hand behind the direction of the cut in case the tool should slip.

7. Keep sharp-edged tools away from the edge of a bench or work area. Brushing against the tool may cause it to fall and injure a leg or foot.

8. Carry edge and sharply pointed tools with the cutting edge or point down.

9. Keep tools sharp and clean. Dull tools are dangerous. The extra force exerted in using dull tools often results

National Safety Council

in losing control of the tool. Dirt or oil on a tool may cause it to slip on the work and thus cause injury.

10. Always use a handle on a file. Otherwise, the tang may cut into your hand.

11. Do not strike hardened metal or tools with a hard-faced hammer. Chips of metal may break loose and cause injury.

12. Batter-heads of metal tools must be kept ground smooth and square to avoid mushrooming. When the head of a tool that has been allowed to mushroom is struck, bits of metal often break loose, causing serious injuries.

SAFETY: POWER TOOLS

Do not attempt to use any machinery without knowing its principles of operation, methods of use, and general and special safety precautions. Obtain authorization before using power tools.

National Safety Council

1. Be sure that all power tools are grounded. Power tools must have a 3-wire conductor cord. A 3-prong plug connects into a grounded outlet (receptacle). See Figs. 1 and 2 for the receptacle the tool will plug in and

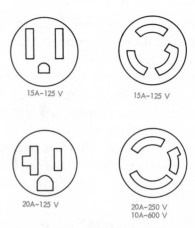

15A-125 V   15A-125 V

20A-125 V   20A-250 V
             10A-600 V

Fig. 1. Approved electrical outlets (receptacles) commonly used for 110 volt tools and equipment. (Amperage and voltage are given on a metal plate attached to the motor of the tool.)

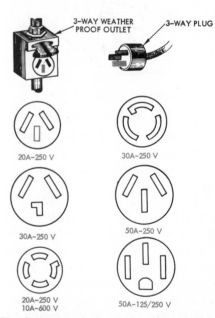

3-WAY WEATHER PROOF OUTLET   3-WAY PLUG

20A-250 V   30A-250 V

30A-250 V   50A-250 V

20A-250 V   50A-125/250 V
10A-600 V

Fig. 2. Approved electrical outlets, (receptacles) commonly used for 220 volt tools and equipment. (Amperage and voltage is given on a metal plate attached to the motor of the tool.)

consult local codes for proper grounding specifications.

2. Power tools should be inspected and serviced at regular intervals by a qualified repairman.

3. Know and understand all of the manufacturer's safety recommendations.

4. Be familiar with the operating principles of the tool. If you have any questions on safety or operation, check with your supervisor.

5. Inspect electrical cords to see that they are in good condition.

6. Do not leave electrical cords where they may be run over or damaged. Do not allow them to kink. Keep cords out of water.

7. Be sure that all safety guards are properly in place and in working order.

8. Remove tie, rings, wristwatch, and roll up sleeves before using power tools.

9. Be sure that your hands are dry. If you must work in a wet area, wear rubber gloves and rubber-soled shoes.

10. Make all adjustments and inspections with the power *off* and the cable *disconnected.*

11. Before connecting to a power source, be sure that the switch is in the OFF position.

12. Wear safety goggles and a dust mask when the work requires it.

13. Be sure that the material to be worked is free of obstructions and securely clamped.

14. Keep your attention focused on the work.

15. A change in sound during tool operation normally indicates trouble. Investigate immediately!

16. When work is completed. shut off the power. Wait until the operation of the tool ceases before leaving stationary tool or laying down portable tool.

17. When the operation of the tool has stopped, disconnect it from the power source.

18. After the tool is disconnected, remove blades, bits, etc., from the tool.

19. Store power tools and blades, bits, etc., in their proper, designated place.

20. When a power tool is defective remove it from service. Alert others of the situation.

Checking on Your Knowledge

If you have read the chapter carefully you should be able to answer the questions. If you have any difficulty, read the chapter over once more.

DO YOU KNOW

1. What is necessary to do a safe, competent job?
2. How to lift a heavy object?
3. What to do if safety violations are discovered on the job?
4. The safe use of a ladder?
5. What kind of clothing a carpenter should wear?

6. Three types of protective equipment a carpenter may use?
7. How to use sharp edged tools?
8. Three things to check for before using power tools?
9. What to do when you are through using a power tool?

Tools: Part 1

Hammering, turning, supporting, layout and measuring tools

"You can tell a craftsman by the way he handles his tools." This old saying points out a truth that every student of a trade should keep in mind. However, the point should be made that the handling of the tools applies to more than just the way in which they are used in performing a job. The way in which the tools are handled when they are not being used is equally as important as their actual use.

Tools are an indispensable part of the craft. As such they are an extension of the craftsman himself. The most skilled carpenter in the world will be handicapped by a dull saw. A nicked plane will never produce a smooth surface. A rounded screwdriver will mar and distort the head of the screw. An untrue square will never give a true mark.

Every carpenter should become familiar with the many kinds of tools he will need, and with their care. The sure mark of a poor workman is his disregard for the proper care and handling of his tools. Not only does this result in a poor performance by the tools, but also in an added expense in replacing them, and, most important, in causing them to become dangerous. The safety aspect of properly handled tools is mostly applied common sense once the potential hazards are known and appreciated.

This chapter and the following one cover the kinds of tools used in carpentry. Stress is laid on the correct care and safe use of them. Buy quality tools, take care of them and they will become part of your trade —an indispensable part.

Apprentice Tool Kit

The beginner's or apprentice's tool kit usually is limited to tools for rough work; as his training program takes him into finer work the need for other tools must be met. However, it is well for the beginner to exercise considerable care in the selection of these tools so that he may gradually build up a kit of tools of high quality and durability.

The tools that the apprentice will be required to own will depend to a certain extent on the particular job he is assigned to. Table I gives the hand tools most frequently used. The more common tools will be purchased first. Others should be purchased as required by the nature of his work.

Some of the carpenter's equipment, such as a sawhorse or straightedge, is frequently made on the job. *Appendix A* at the end of the book gives directions for making several of these common devices.

Such things as steel miter boxes, portable and stationary power tools, etc., will be furnished by the employer. The carpenter does *not* bring his own.

The carpenter's mode of dress and his grooming are important. Carpenter's overalls and a good pair of work shoes should be worn. A hat or cap, or a safety helmet, is also essential. Some jobs may require that the work shoes have safety toes.

TABLE I.   BASIC HAND TOOLS

Number Needed		Number Needed	
1	Tool Box 8"x8"x32" with lid, hasp, lock	1	Tape, 50'
2	Hammer, 13" overall length, 1 16 oz. curved and 1 20 oz. straight claw	1	Brace Bits: 1/4" to 1 1/2" augur. Planes, Block, Smooth or Bench Chisels, 1/8" to 1 1/4"
1	Pocket Rule, 10' (3/4" wide)		
3	Crosscut Saws, 2 - 8 pt. 1 - 10 pt.,	1	Sharpening Stone, coarse & fine
1	Ripsaw - 6 pt.	1	Compass Saw
1	Hatchet or hand axe	1	Screwdriver, "ratchet"
1	Nail Bar, 24" or 30"	1	Bevel T
1	Pliers, heavy-duty wire cutters	1	Twist Drill, Pencils, Plumb Bob, Chalker, Line, Scriber, Dividers, Nail Sets, Tin Snips, Hack Saw, Coping Sow, etc.
1	Wrench, 10" or 12"		
1	Spirit Level, 24"		
1	Combination Square		
1	Framing Square		

Figs. 1, 2, and 3. Types of tool boxes. The shoulder box (left) is most useful on a job, while the tool case (center) and the suitcase tool box (right) are best suited for storing or transporting tools. The suitcase tool box is made large enough to hold a framing square.

A good toolbox is also a necessity. Figs. 1, 2 and 3 illustrate some of the tool boxes used by the carpenter. (See *Appendix A* for how to build a tool box).

As an aid to the beginner, a brief description of various common hand tools and power tools is given in this text, together with a more detailed explanation of some of the important tools.

Tool Classification

The tools covered in Chapters III and IV are classified according to the type of work done by the tool. In Chapter III, for example, four types of tools are covered: (1) hammering and percussion tools; (2) turning tools and other miscellaneous tools: screwdrivers, wrenches, pliers, etc.; (3) supporting and holding tools; and (4) layout and measuring tools. In Chapter IV general cutting tools of all types are covered. These are also broken down into four types: (1) saws; (2) boring tools; (3) paring and shaving tools; and (4) abrading tools.

Hammering and Percussion Tools

In this group are tools used to drive nails or staples and tools (such as a mallet) that are used to strike other tools. Adhesive guns are also included in this grouping as they are used for fastening materials that were formerly fastened by nailing.

Hammering Tools

Curved Claw Hammer. Of all carpentry tools, this is the most used. See Fig. 4. Its weight should be about 16 ounces, for general all-around work. The steel in the head must be of such a quality that its face will withstand contact

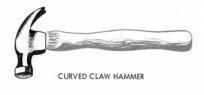

CURVED CLAW HAMMER

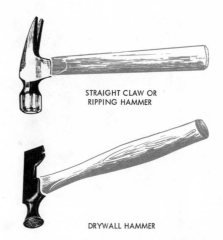

STRAIGHT CLAW OR
RIPPING HAMMER

FLOORING HAMMER

DRYWALL HAMMER

Fig. 4. Types of hammers.

with hard surfaces without marring or chipping. The claw must retain sufficient sharpness for pulling nails without heads. The handle is usually made of wood to absorb some of the shock instead of transmitting all of it to the worker's arm. This prevents the arm from tiring quickly. (Fig. 5 illustrates the proper use of the curved claw hammer.)

Straight Claw Hammer. For rough work the carpenter frequently has a straight claw or ripping hammer (Fig. 4), slightly heavier than the regular hammer, with which he can split pieces of wood as well as drive and pull nails. A 20 oz. hammer is recommended.

Flooring Hammer. This hammer (Fig. 4) is used in laying tongue and groove hardwood floors. A claw or half hatchet is sometimes used for this purpose.

Drywall Hammer. This is a specially designed hammer used for the application of drywall, such as gypsum panels. The rounded face of the hammer dimples the drywall surface without breaking the paper covering. See Fig. 4.

SAFETY: HAMMERS

1. Keep your attention focused on the work.

2. Be sure that the handle of the hammer is sound and without splinters. Check to see that the handle is securely set in the head. Replace loose or damaged handles.

3. Check the face of the hammer to see that it is clean and that it is not split, chipped, or mushroomed. Burrs from the head or claw may be ground off.

4. Use the hammer properly. See Fig. 5. Grasp the hammer handle firmly near the end. Use a light blow

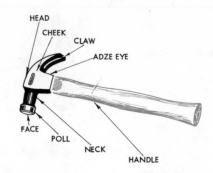

HEAD

CHEEK

CLAW

ADZE EYE

FACE

POLL

NECK

HANDLE

(A) CORRECT WAY TO HOLD A HAMMER.

(C)

ALWAYS STRIKE WITH THE FACE OF THE HAMMER. IT IS HARDENED FOR THAT PURPOSE. DO NOT DAMAGE THE FACE BY STRIKING STEEL HARDER THAN ITSELF. DO NOT STRIKE WITH THE CHEEK AS IT IS THE WEAKEST PART. STRIKE THE NAIL SQUARELY TO AVOID MARRING THE WOOD AND BENDING THE NAIL. KEEP THE FACE OF THE HAMMER CLEAN TO AVOID SLIPPING OFF THE NAIL. IF A NAIL BENDS DRAW IT AND START A NEW ONE IN A NEW PLACE.

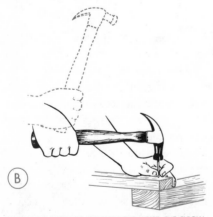

(B)

THE BLOW IS DELIVERED THROUGH THE WRIST, THE ELBOW AND THE SHOULDER, ONE OR ALL BEING BROUGHT INTO PLAY, ACCORDING TO THE STRENGTH OF THE BLOW TO BE STRUCK. REST THE FACE OF THE HAMMER ON THE NAIL, DRAW THE HAMMER BACK AND GIVE A LIGHT TAP TO START THE NAIL AND TO DETERMINE THE AIM.

(D)

USE A NAIL SET TO DRIVE NAILS BELOW THE SURFACE OF ALL FINE WORK. TO PREVENT THE NAIL SET SLIPPING OFF THE HEAD OF THE NAIL, REST THE LITTLE FINGER ON THE WORK AND PRESS THE NAIL SET FIRMLY AGAINST IT. SET NAILS ABOUT 1/16" BELOW THE SURFACE OF THE WOOD.

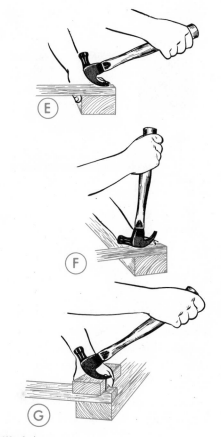

TO DRAW A NAIL: SLIP THE CLAW OF THE HAMMER UNDER THE NAIL HEAD; PULL UNTIL THE HANDLE IS NEARLY VERTICAL AND THE NAIL PARTLY DRAWN.

IF THE PULL IS CONTINUED, UNNECESSARY FORCE IS REQUIRED THAT WILL BEND THE NAIL, MAR THE WOOD AND PERHAPS BREAK THE HAMMER HANDLE.

SLIP A PIECE OF WOOD UNDER THE HEAD OF THE HAMMER TO INCREASE THE LEVERAGE AND TO RELIEVE THE UNNECESSARY STRAIN ON THE HANDLE.

Fig. 5. Use of the curved claw hammer. (Stanley Works)

to set the nail and to determine the aim. Strike the nail squarely.

5. Do not strike with the cheek of the hammer.

6. Do not strike a hardened steel surface with a hammer.

7. Use the claw for pulling nails; *not* as a pry or wedge, or for pulling spikes.

8. Do not use a hammer beyond its capacity.

9. Store hammers in a designated place in the toolbox.

Claw Hatchet. This hatchet (Fig. 6) has a flat head with a claw and may be used for driving and pulling *small* nails, and for cutting. This is a versatile and useful tool and may be used either like a hammer or like an axe. It has either a single bevel or a double bevel blade, see Fig. 6. The single bevel blade is useful for hewing off wood in a straight plane. The single bevel, however, may be used only by a right

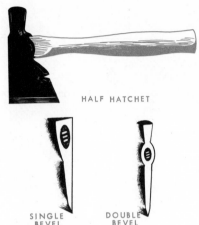

Fig. **6.** Types of hatchets.

handed person. The claw hatchet is sometimes used for laying flooring.

Half Hatchet. The half hatchet (Fig. 6) is lighter than the claw hatchet and is used for lighter work. It has a nail driving head and has a nail pulling slot on the back edge of the blade. The half hatchet comes with either a single or double bevel blade. It is also used for laying flooring.

Shingle Hatchet. The shingle hatchet or lathing hatchet (Fig. 6) is used in the application of cedar shingle roofs. It is similiar to, but lighter than, the half hatchet. The shingle hatchet has a sharp cutting blade useful in splitting the shingles to any desired width, and has a head suitable for driving shingle nails. It has a double bevel blade and is only used for light work.

SAFETY: HATCHETS AND AXES

1. Keep your attention focused on the work.

2. Keep blade edges sharp. (*Note*, however, that some hatchets are not used for cutting and are kept dull.) Inspect blade for nicks. When sharpening, be sure that the hatchet or axe is firmly secured in a vise or other holding device.

3. Be sure that the handle is sound and without splinters. Check to see that the handle is securely set in the head. Replace loose or damaged handles.

4. Use the right hatchet or axe for the job.

5. Use hatchets and axes properly. Be sure that there is room to swing. Do not use the side of the blade (the cheek) as a hammer. Never use a hatchet or an axe as a wedge.

6. Carry an unsheathed hatchet or axe at your side with the edge outward.

When handing, pass by the handle with the head down and facing outward.

7. Store hatchets and axes in a designated place in the toolbox. Fit into sheath if available. Never place a hatchet or axe anywhere where they could fall.

Sledge Hammers. The sledge hammer (Fig. 7) weighs between 2 pounds and 20 pounds and is used by the carpenter for driving layout stakes and batterboards in the laying out of a building. Two-pound hammers are used in timber construction when the wood is 3 or more inches thick, as in the construction of roofs. When using, be sure that there is room to swing and that you have a secure footing.

Fig. 7. Sledge hammer.

Mallets. A mallet (Fig. 8) is used for driving wood chisels and for striking nailing machines. A wooden mallet is commonly used, although mallets made of other materials are available. Various weights and handle lengths may be obtained. Use the mallet appropriate for the job.

WOODEN HEAD MALLET

RUBBER HEAD MALLET

Fig. 8. Mallets.

Hammer Fastening Tools. Pins and threaded studs may be set directly into concrete, building block, and light gauge steel by the use of a specially designed hammer and fastener holder. See Fig. 9. A solid steel hammer with a rubber encased han-

Fig. 9. Hammer fastening tool.

dle is used for striking. The fastener holding device allows the whole force of the hammer blow to be transmitted directly to the head of the fastener. Fasteners may be set into hard materials with a few quick blows. No drilling is necessary. The fasteners used with these tools are illustrated in the chapter on rough hardware, Chapter VIII. In using hammer fastening tools, observe the same safety rules as for an ordinary hammer.

Staplers

Mechanical Stapler. The mechanical stapler or gun tacker (Fig. 10) is used for a variety of operations that used to be done by hand nailing. Stapling is a quick and ef-

ficient method of tacking up insulation, wall planking, ceiling tile, metal lath, etc. Using the stapler leaves the other hand free for holding the material. Fig. 11 illustrates a stapler being used to put up metal lath. Staples come in a variety of sizes up to 9/16th of an inch. Staples should be chosen to fit the specific job.

Fig. 11. Stapler being used. (Duo-Fast Fastener Corp.)

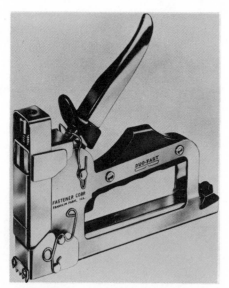

Fig. 10. Stapler. (Duo-Fast Fastener Corp.)

Roofing Hammer. The roofing hammer (Fig. 12) is used to drive staples into asphalt strip shingles. This stapling hammer uses staples 1 inch wide with ¾ inch legs; 16 gage wire is used. Other stapling hammers use a variety of smaller staples for lighter nailing jobs. Fig. 12, bottom, illustrates a roofing hammer being used.

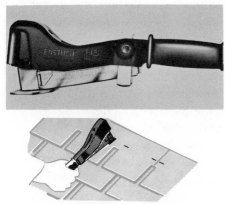

Fig. 12. Roofing hammer. (Bostitch)

Fig. 14. Nailing machine used for sheathing. (Rockwell Mfg. Co.)

Fig. 13. Nailing machines used for flooring. (Duo-Fast Fastener Corp.)

Nailing Machines. The manual nailing machine (Figs. 13 and 14) is used for applying underlayment to floors, and for laying finish flooring. It is operated by striking the plunger knob with a mallet. Staples up to 1⅛ to 1¾ inch long may be used, depending upon the model used, Fig. 13. Some models may be used to drive nails from 1¼ to 2 inches in length, Fig. 14.

Portable Air Staplers and Nailers

In addition to the hand operated staplers and nailers, a great variety of air-operated staplers and nailers are on the market. These come in several different sizes and shapes and are designed for many different, specific uses. Both the tool and the staple or nail used should be chosen to fit the job. A single stapler or

Fig. 15. Air-operated stapler. (Duo-Fast Fastener Corp.)

Fig. 16. Air stapler with extension. (Bostitch)

nailer, however, may do several different jobs by changing the staples or nail sizes. Electrically operated staplers are also available. All models may be operated as fast as the user desires, and most come equipped with safety devices to prevent accidental firing.

Air Stapler. The air-operated stapler (Fig. 15) depending on the staple used, can do many different jobs. It may be equipped with a guide, as in Fig. 15 to assure that the staples are accurately positioned. In addition to roofing shingles, air-operated staplers are used for fastening decking, insulation, ceiling tile, vapor barriers, building paper, metal lath, plywood and fiberboard sheathing, sub-flooring, etc. Some models are designed to be operated either by trigger action or by touch-trip action. With touch-trip action, pressure on the front nose causes the staple to release. Most air-operated staplers have safety devices to prevent accidental firing. The air-operated stapler may be equipped with an extension, Fig. 16, for operator comfort and ease of handling.

Electric Stapler. The electric stapler (Fig. 17) does the same job as the air-operated stapler. It has the advantage, however, that no air compressor is needed. It operates from an ordinary grounded outlet.

Air Nailer. The air-operated nailer (Fig. 18) is used for heavier

Fig. 17. Electric stapler. (Duo-Fast Fastener Corp.)

Fig. 18. Air-operated nailer. (Duo-Fast Fastener Corp.)

nailing jobs than the stapler. It drives 6d to 9d nails in the hardest wood and may be operated as fast as the user desires. Up to 300 nails may be loaded in the magazines of some models. The air-operated nailer may be operated by the trig-

ger or by the touch-trip method. Depending upon the model, various different kinds of nails may be used, such as common, finish, brad, or T-nails. Some models automatically countersink the nail, the depth of the countersink being controlled by the air pressure. All models are equipped with safety devices.

SAFETY: AIR-POWERED STAPLERS AND NAILERS

1. Keep your attention focused on the work.

2. Be familiar with the operating principles of the stapler or nailer; know where the safety features are and how they work.

3. Use the right stapler or nailer for the job. Follow manufacturer's recommendations.

4. Use the correct type and size of staple or nail for the job. Consult manufacturer's specifications.

5. Use no more air pressure than is required to do the job. Never use over 90 pounds of pressure. Follow manufacturer's recommendations.

6. Always keep the nose of the stapler or nailer pointed in the direction of the work. Keep nose pointed away from your body and *never* point an air stapler or nailer in the general direction of anyone.

7. Check to see that all safety features are functioning properly. Test fire the stapler or nailer into a block of wood or other appropriate material.

8. When using, place the nose of the stapler or nailer firmly against the surface to be stapled or nailed.

9. Keep free hand away from the spot to be stapled or nailed.

10. Disconnect stapler or nailer from the air supply when not in use.

Adhesive Gun

The adhesive gun (Fig. 19) is being used for installing wall paneling and ceiling panels and tiles. The adhesive used should be that recommended by the manufacturer of the product involved. The use of the adhesive gun cuts down the time element. Adhesives are particularly desirable where no visible nailing is required on panels.

Powder Fastener

The powder driven fastener (Fig. 20 and 21) is a tool that fires a specially designed cartridge which provides the power to sink fasteners into a wide variety of construction materials. The depth of penetration can be controlled to a fine degree, by a combination of adjustment and the use of charges of different power. Interchangeable barrels are used for different sizes of fastener. The powder actuated fastener is particularly suitable for securing fasteners in concrete and steel, and can penetrate up to an inch of steel.

Fig. 20. Powder-driven fastener: position and fire. (Ramset Fastening System)

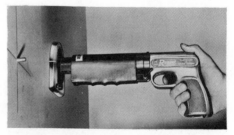

Fig. 21. Powder-driven fastener: pin is driven squarely in place. (Ramset Fastening System)

Fig. 19. Adhesive gun. (U. S. Gypsum Co.)

Variously shaped *drive pins* or fasteners, may be used (see Chapter VIII).

In using powder driven fasteners, be sure to follow all of the manufacturer's recommendations. Read and understand the instruction manual issued with each tool. Follow *all* of the safety precautions.

SAFETY: POWDER DRIVEN FASTENERS

Have a permit and obtain authorization before using the powder driven fastener.

1. Be *thoroughly* familiar with the operating principles and instructions for the powder driven fastener. Follow *all* of the manufacturers safety rules. (Most areas require certification for the use of this tool.)

2. Wear safety goggles and heavy gloves to protect against flying particles.

3. Do not use powder driven fasteners in an explosive or inflammable atmosphere.

4. Follow manufacturer's recommendations for firing into each different types of material. Do not fire into any material that can be nailed.

5. Determine if material is of sufficient density and thickness so that the fastener will not go completely through the material and do injury on the other side. Do *not*, for example, fire into concrete less than 2 inches thick.

6. Use the right type and size of drive pin for the job. Consult manufacturer's specifications.

7. Always use an alignment guide for firing through previously prepared holes in steel.

8. Do not use a fastener closer than ½" from the edge of steel or 3" from the edge of concrete.

9. Before loading the driver, be sure the cartridge is of proper powder load. (If the powder load is too great, the drive pin may go through the material and cause injury.) Select and position the powder cartridge according to manufacturer's recommendations. The stronger the powder charge, the stronger the force of the explosion. Learn the color code associated with the cartridge.

10. *Always* keep the powder driven fastener directed toward the work area. *Never* point away from the work area or in the general direction of anyone.

11. Keep your full attention focused on the work.

12. When loaded, position the gun and fire immediately—never leave lying around. Unload the tool if it is not possible to fire immediately.

13. When ready to fire, place the protective shield *evenly* against the work surface, press hard, and pull the trigger. (If the guard is not pressed against the work surface evenly, the driver may not fire.)

14. If the powder cartridge does not fire, keep the safety shield firmly pressed against the work surface for at least 30 seconds, then remove and safely dispose of the powder cartridge per manufacturer's recommendations.

15. Follow local and states codes for storing the powder cartridges. Store the powder driven fasteners in a designated location so that their use may be carefully controlled.

Screwdrivers, Pliers, Wrenches, Etc.

This group includes tools that are used for *turning* and other miscellaneous tools that are used for cutting, prying and punching. These are important tools, many of which the carpenter will wish to own. The portable power screwdriver, however, will be furnished by the contractor.

Hand Operated Screwdrivers

Screwdrivers. These (Fig. 22) are available with shanks from 1¼ inch to 12 inches in length. The blades also vary in size so that they may be matched to the screw being used. The tip should fit snugly into the slot of the screw head, and should not be any wider than the diameter of the screw head, or else it will damage the surrounding material. It is advisable for a carpenter to own three sizes of screwdrivers—a large, medium, and small size—to take care of any work which might require the use of different sizes of screws. Some screwdrivers have magnetic tips.

Phillips Screwdrivers. These are used for driving screws with a Phillip's head. See Fig. 22. They are similar to the conventional screw driver but the blade tip is shaped like a cross.

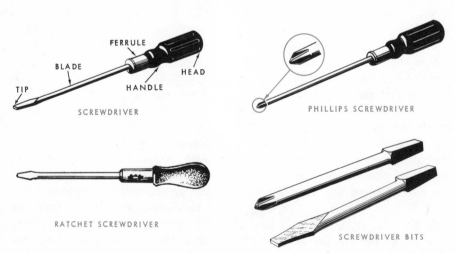

Fig. 22. Types of screwdrivers in common use.

Ratchet Screwdriver. The ratchet screwdriver (Fig. 22) has a blade from 1 to 8 inches long, and operates on the same principle as the spiral groove ratchet screw driver, except that it has no spiral and consequently must be turned by hand.

Screwdriver Bits. These bits (Fig. 22) are mainly used with large screws. They are held in a ratchet brace.

Spiral ratchet screwdrivers. These (Fig. 23) are generally available with three different size screw bits, and as additional accessories, a Phillips screwdriver bit and a countersink may be obtained. The spiral ratchet screwdriver is most useful for the rapid tightening of screws. It is especially practical where many screws are to be used at one time, as in the application of butts to doors. It can be steadied by holding the revolving chuck sleeve with the free hand. Screws can also be removed by changing the ratchet shift to the opposite direction.

Care should be exercised in using this tool as there is a powerful spring in the handle. When the screwdriver is shut and locked, it puts the spring in tension. If, by accident, the lock key is released, the base shoots out at great speed. Since this might happen accidentally, it is unwise to be careless with this tool. It should never be carried in a pocket and if used around glass it would be well to take the spring out of the handle and use the screw driver manually.

In using power screwdrivers, be sure to follow the safety rules.

SAFETY: SCREWDRIVERS

1. Keep your attention focused on the work.

2. Use only screwdrivers that are in good condition and of the correct size and length. Do not use a screwdriver with a rough or split handle. Be sure the blade tip fits the slot in the screw. The tip should not be wider than the screw head.

3. The blade tip should be properly ground and shaped; it should be free from grease. The tip should be straight and with parallel sides. It should not be beveled. Never grind a chisel edge on the tip.

4. Use a screwdriver properly (see Fig. 24). Hold the screwdriver in line

Fig. 23. Spiral ratchet screwdriver.

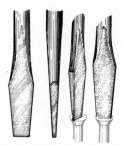

SELECT A SCREWDRIVER OF LENGTH AND TIP FITTED TO THE WORK. SCREWDRIVERS ARE SPECIFIED BY THE LENGTH OF THE BLADE. THE TIP SHOULD BE STRAIGHT AND NEARLY PARALLEL SIDED. IT SHOULD ALSO FIT THE SCREW SLOT AND BE NOT WIDER THAN THE SCREW HEAD.

IF THE TIP IS TOO WIDE IT WILL SCAR THE WOOD AROUND THE SCREW HEAD. IF THE SCREWDRIVER IS NOT HELD IN LINE WITH THE SCREW IT WILL SLIP OUT OF THE SLOT AND MAR BOTH THE SCREW AND THE WORK.

IF THE TIP IS ROUNDED OR BEVELED IT WILL RAISE OUT OF THE SLOT SPOILING THE SCREW HEAD. RE-GRIND OR FILE THE TIP TO MAKE IT AS SHOWN AT TOP.

USE THE LONGEST SCREWDRIVER CONVENIENT FOR THE WORK. MORE POWER CAN BE APPLIED TO A LONG SCREWDRIVER THAN A SHORT ONE, WITH LESS DANGER OF ITS SLIPPING OUT OF THE SLOT. HOLD THE HANDLE FIRMLY IN THE PALM OF THE RIGHT HAND WITH THE THUMB AND FOREFINGER GRASPING THE HANDLE NEAR THE FERRULE. WITH THE LEFT HAND STEADY THE TIP AND KEEP IT PRESSED INTO THE SLOT WHILE RENEWING THE GRIP ON THE HANDLE FOR A NEW TURN. IF NO HOLE IS BORED FOR THE THREADED PART OF THE SCREW THE WOOD IS OFTEN SPLIT OR THE SCREW IS TWISTED OFF. IF A SCREW TURNS TOO HARD, BACK IT OUT AND ENLARGE THE HOLE. A LITTLE SOAP ON THE THREADS OF THE SCREW MAKES IT EASIER TO DRIVE.

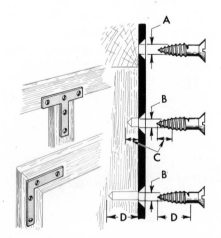

TO FASTEN HINGES OR OTHER HARDWARE IN PLACE WITH SCREWS:

1. LOCATE THE POSITION OF THE PIECE OF HARDWARE ON THE WORK.

2. RECESS THE WORK TO RECEIVE THE HARDWARE, IF IT IS NECESSARY.

3. LOCATE THE POSITIONS OF THE SCREWS.

4. SELECT SCREWS THAT WILL EASILY PASS THRU THE HOLES IN THE HARDWARE, AS AT **A**.

5. BORE THE PILOT HOLES (SECOND HOLE) SLIGHTLY SMALLER THAN THE DIAMETER OF THE THREADED PART OF THE SCREWS, AS AT **B**.

6. DRIVE THE SCREWS TIGHTLY IN PLACE.

IF THE WOOD IS SOFT, BORE AS DEEP AS HALF THE LENGTH OF THE THREADED PART OF THE SCREW, AS AT **C**. IF THE WOOD IS HARD (OAK), THE SCREW SOFT (BRASS), OR IF THE SCREW IS LARGE, THE HOLE MUST BE NEARLY AS DEEP AS THE SCREW, AS AT **D**. HOLES FOR SMALL SCREWS ARE USUALLY MADE WITH BRAD AWLS.

TO FASTEN TWO PIECES OF WOOD TOGETHER WITH SCREWS:

1. LOCATE THE POSITIONS OF THE SCREW HOLES.

2. BORE THE FIRST HOLE IN THE FIRST PIECE OF WOOD SLIGHTLY LARGER THAN THE DIAMETER OF THE SCREW SHANK, AS AT **A**.

3. BORE THE SECOND HOLE SLIGHTLY SMALLER THAN THE THREADED PART OF THE SCREWS, AS AT **B**. BORE AS DEEP AS HALF THE LENGTH OF THE THREADED PART.

4. COUNTERSINK THE FIRST HOLES TO MATCH THE DIAMETER OF THE HEADS OF THE SCREWS, AS AT **C**.

5. DRIVE THE SCREWS TIGHTLY IN PLACE WITH THE SCREWDRIVER.

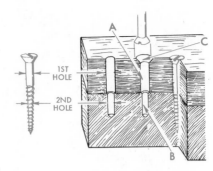

Fig. 24. How to use screwdrivers. (Stanley Works)

with the screw. Do not use a screwdriver as a punch or chisel; do not use as a pry or wedge.

5. Never hold work in your hand when tightening a screw. Lay the work on a bench or some other solid surface that will take the pressure. Use a bench vise for larger work.

6. Use an awl or nail to make the starting holes for small screws in soft wood.

7. Avoid holding a screw with your fingers when it is being started.

8. Keep fingers away from the tip of the screwdriver. When pilot holes have been drilled, it is not necessary to hold the screw.

9. Use insulated screwdrivers around electrical work.

10. Do not carry screwdrivers in your pocket.

11. Store screwdrivers in their designated place in the toolbox.

Portable Power Screwdrivers

Power Screwdriver. The portable power screwdriver (Fig. 25) is used for driving and removing screws quickly and efficiently. It is often employed in mounting wallboard, drywall, and acoustical tile. Some models are equipped with a screw depth locator so that screws are driven to an exact, pre-set depth. This is very useful in mounting acoustical tile and wallboard. The portable power screwdriver may also be used to remove screws by reversing the direction of turn. Various sized screw bits are available.

Ordinary variable-speed power drills are also sometimes equipped to use screw bits.

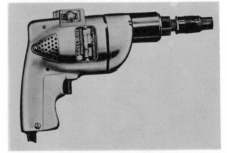

Fig. 25. Portable power screwdriver. (Black & Decker Mfg. Co.)

SAFETY: PORTABLE POWER SCREWDRIVERS

Do not use this tool unless you understand its operation and know the safety rules.

1. Be sure power screwdriver is properly grounded.

2. Remove tie, rings, wristwatch, and roll up sleeves.

3. Disconnect power screwdriver from power source and be sure that the switch is off before removing or installing bits.

4. Before connecting to power source, make sure that switch is in OFF position.

5. Before starting screwdriver, make certain that the bit is securely gripped in the chuck.

6. Check to see that the key has been removed from the chuck before starting screwdriver.

7. Adjust driving torque (clutch adjustment) to the tightness desired.

8. Keep your attention focused on the work.

9. When work is completed, turn off, disconnect screwdriver from power source, and remove the bit.

Pliers, Pincers, Snips, Wrenches, etc.

Combination Pliers. The combination or adjustable pliers (Fig. 26) are available in lengths from 8 to 10 inches. They are used for gripping and bending wire. Another common use for pliers is the removal of stubborn nails that resist extraction with a carpenter's hammer. By slipping the joint a larger jaw opening may be obtained. Combination pliers are also sometimes used for cutting wire.

Side Cutting Pliers. These are used most frequently for cutting wires. The flat nose affords a firm grip. See Fig. 26.

Carpenters Pincers. These are used for cutting wire, metal lath, etc., and for tying metal lath. See Fig. 26. They are particularly useful for cutting flush against a surface.

COMBINATION PLIERS

SIDE CUTTING PLIERS

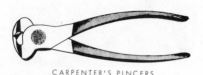

CARPENTER'S PINCERS

TIN SNIPS

Fig. 26. Pliers, pincers and snips.

SAFETY: PLIERS

1. Keep your attention focused on the work.

2. Use pliers properly. Grip them close to the ends to prevent being pinched by the hinge. When clipping the ends of wire, point the end downward. Wear goggles when cilpping wire ends.

3. Do *not* use pliers as a wrench. Do not use to tighten small nuts or bolts—the pliers will damage the nut or the bolt head, and they may slip and cause injury.

4. Store pliers in their designated place in the toolbox.

Tin Snips. These (Fig. 26) are used for cutting sheet metals, metal lath, etc. They come in various lengths; heavy duty snips with a cut of 3 to 3½ inches are desirable. They should be kept sharp and well oiled.

SAFETY: TIN SNIPS

1. Keep your attention focused on the work.

2. Keep fingers out of the space between the handles when a cut is completed, the handles snap together with considerable force.

3. Before cutting metal with the tin snips, be sure to remove all burrs on the metal with a file.

4. Hold metal firmly to prevent it from slipping and cutting the hand.

5. Store tin snips in their designated place in the toolbox.

Fig. 27A. Adjustable wrench.

Adjustable Wrenches. The adjustable wrench (Fig. 27A) is available in lengths from 4 to 18 inches and will open from ½ inch to $2\frac{1}{16}$ inches. This tool is used to tighten nuts and bolts in construction. Typical applications being the bolting of plates to a foundation wall, and the bolting of stanchions to beams. A 10 or 12 inch adjustable wrench is commonly used.

SAFETY: ADJUSTABLE WRENCHES

1. Keep your attention focused on the work.

2. Check your wrench to see that it is in good working condition, not bent or cracked, and the jaws are sharp and not damaged.

3. Always place your wrench so that each pull forces the jaws onto the nut. See Fig. 27B. Make sure that the jaws are tightened. Be sure that there is clearance for your fingers.

4. When much pressure is needed, hold both hands on the wrench, pushing or pulling with one hand while the other acts as a brake should the wrench slip. Be sure that your footing is secure.

5. Always pull a wrench unless it is absolutely necessary to push it. (If a wrench is pushed it may slip and injure hand.)

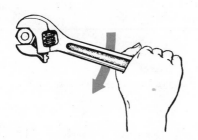

Fig. 27B. Safe way to use adjustable wrench.

6. Use the correct wrench for the job. Use the adjustable wrench on square heads such as carriage bolts and lag screws.

7. Never use a wrench as a hammer.

8. Never use a wrench beyond its capacity. Do not fit a pipe or any other extension on the handle to increase the leverage. Do not pound the handle of a wrench with a hammer. Do not open the jaws too far, they may be sprung.

9. Store wrenches in their designated place in the toolbox.

Wrecking Bars. The wrecking bar (Fig. 28) varies in length from 12 to 36 inches and is made from ½ to ⅞ inch stock steel. It is used to strip down forms and wood scaffolding, as well as a pry to tighten wood braces and to remove large nails and spikes. The 30 inch wrecking bar is considered to be a good, all around tool.

Nail Sets. These (Fig. 29) are used to sink the head of a nail below the surface of the wood in finish work. The resulting cavity is filled. The tip of the nail set ranges from $\frac{1}{32}$ of an inch to ⅛ of an inch in diameter, and the tool itself is usually 3⅜ inches long. (Fig. 5, showing the use of the curved claw hammer, illustrates how the nail set is commonly used.)

Center Punches. These are used for indenting or holing metal surfaces. See Fig. 29. They are useful in locating drill holes so that the point will be accurately centered. The length of the center punch varies from 3⅞ to 5 inches.

Fig. 28. Wrecking bar.

NAIL SET

CENTER PUNCH

Fig. 29. Nail set and center punch.

Tools for Supporting and Holding Work

In this group are tools or devices, some of which the carpenter may make on the job.

Miter Boxes. The miter box (Fig. 30) is a precision device used for guiding a backsaw at the proper angle for cutting a miter joint in wood. The carpenter usually makes his own miter box on the job, but more accurate manufactured boxes can be obtained. The standard miter box will cut wood up to 4 inches in thickness, and up to 8 inches in width if the cut is at right angles. The quadrant is graduated in degrees. (See *Appendix A* for how to build a wooden miter box.)

Vises. The portable vise (Fig. 31) which is clamped on a sawhorse or work bench can easily be carried in the carpenter's tool kit, and re-ceives heavy use. A typical vise of this type will clamp on a bench or saw horse up to 2½ inches in thickness. The L-shaped jaws are designed to hold work both horizontally and vertically, and open up to 3½ inches. This type of vise when clamped onto a sawhorse makes an excellent holding device for doors during the application of hardware. The *large vise* used by carpenters is too bulky to be easily carried around, and is therefore usually furnished by the contractor.

C-clamps. These, or other kinds of clamps, are also sometimes used by the carpenter. See Fig. 31. They are often used to secure material that is being worked on, such as for securing material that is to be sawn, planed, or routed.

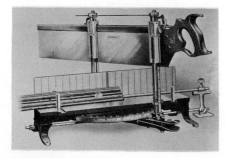

Fig. 30. Miter box.

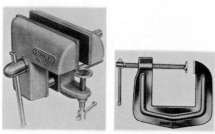

Fig. 31. Portable vise and C clamp. (Stanley Works)

Layout and Measuring Tools

The ease and accuracy with which a craftsman lays out his work depend not only upon his skill and training but also to a great extent upon the kind of tools he has available. A carpenter will own most of the tools in this group. Only well made, quality tools should be purchased.

Chalk Line. The chalk line and reel (Fig. 32) is used to strike a straight guide line on work, such as on boards and shingles. The chalked string is held taut, close to the work, by nails at each end of the string, and is then snapped with the fingers to strike a chalk line on the material. The reel contains a colored chalk dust which becomes attached

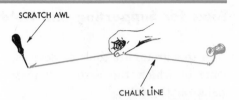

SCRATCH AWL

CHALK LINE

Fig. 33. The chalk line is used for long straight lines. Be sure to snap the taut line square to the surface. (Stanley Works)

to the line. A wooden spool and a chalk rubbed line is also used. Fig. 33 illustrates how the chalk line is used.

Plumb Bob. The plumb bob (Fig. 32), is a weighted tool, from 2¾ ounces to 16 ounces in weight, and ranging in length from 4 inches to 6 inches. It is commonly used in form construction, to ensure that the form is vertical. To plumb a vertical member, suspend the bob on a string long enough to stretch from the top to the bottom of the member. Attach the top of the string to a ruler placed on the *top* of the vertical member so that the string falls exactly 2 inches away from the side of the member to be plumbed. With another ruler measure the distance at the *bottom* from the side of the member to the centerline of the string. If the distance is exactly 2 inches then the vertical member is plumb. If it is not 2 inches then the member is not plumb and should be adjusted until

CHALK LINE
AND REEL

PLUMB BOB

Fig. 32. Chalk line and plumb bob.

the center of the line at the bottom is exactly 2 inches from the member.

The plumb bob is also used in conjunction with a transit (the tool that the carpenter uses in plotting a building). Here the bob is used to accurately locate points on the ground. For this the *point* of the plumb bob is used. This is possible because the point of the bob falls directly under the centerline of the string. The transit is attached directly to the string from which the plumb bob is suspended. The result is that the *center* of the transit itself is exactly over the point of the bob. This assures accuracy in plotting locations of house corners, etc.

Level. The level (Fig. 34), is a tool used by the carpenter to plumb and level building members. The 24 or 28-inch level is the most commonly used in the carpenter trade. The 24 inch is usually purchased first. Particular care should be taken not to drop the level, since the glass containing the fluid may shatter, or the level may be distorted. Some levels are adjustable so that the glass vial with the bubble may be accurately re-set if necessary. It is a good practice when using the level to reverse the ends and take two readings each time used. This will make sure that the reading is accurate.

Straightedge. The straightedge (Fig. 34) is used in connection with a level for plumbing door jambs and corner posts, or for leveling work when spans greater than the length of the level are encountered; northern white pine is a desirable wood to use for this purpose. When properly seasoned, white pine will not warp. The carpenter often makes his own straight edge. Information and dimensions for constructing straightedges are given in *Appendix A*. Accuracy in construction is all-essential. The size of the straightedge varies with the needs of the job. Fig. 35 illustrates how

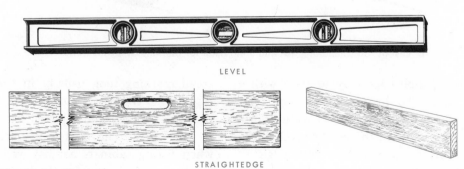

LEVEL

STRAIGHTEDGE

Fig. 34. Leveling tools.

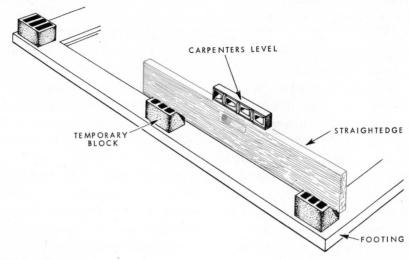

CARPENTERS LEVEL

TEMPORARY
BLOCK

STRAIGHTEDGE

FOOTING

Fig. 35. Leveling a wall.

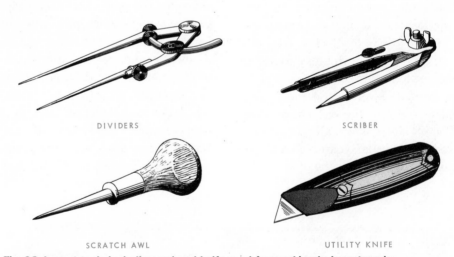

DIVIDERS

SCRIBER

SCRATCH AWL

UTILITY KNIFE

Fig. 36. Layout tools including awl and knife used for marking in layout work.

a straightedge may be used with a level. To be absolutely sure that the straightedge is accurate take a reading with the level placed on the bottom edge of the straightedge.

Scriber. A scriber (Fig. 36), is a small marking tool, usually in the form of a compass, with a metal point at one end and a pencil fixed to the other. The scriber is used when fitting cabinets against walls or other surfaces and for the laying

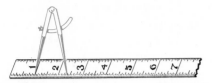

TO SET DIVIDERS HOLD BOTH POINTS ON THE MEASURING LINES OF THE RULE.

DIVIDERS ARE USED FOR SCRIBING CIRCLES OR AN ARC. ALSO FOR COMBINATIONS OF CIRCLES AND ARCS FOR MAKING LAYOUTS FOR CURVED DESIGNS, ETC.

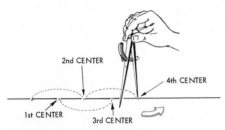

2nd CENTER

4th CENTER

1st CENTER

3rd CENTER

DIVIDERS ARE USED TO STEP OFF A MEASUREMENT SEVERAL TIMES ACCURATELY.

DIVIDERS MAY BE USED TO SCRIBE A LINE TO MATCH AN IRREGULAR SURFACE, MASONRY OR WOODWORK.

Fig. 37. How to use the wing dividers. When scribing take care to hold the dividers at the same angle to the surface being scratched. If the angle varies, the line will not be true.

out of coped joints. It may be used in the same way as the wing type dividers.

Wing type dividers. These are available in lengths from 6 inches to 8 inches. See Fig. 36. This tool is used to check layout work, by stepping off the hypotenuse of the rise and run on both rafters and stringers for stair construction. Both points should be periodically sharpened and the vertex oiled for accurate work. Fig. 37 illustrates how wing type dividers are used.

Scratch Awl. The scratch awl (Fig. 36) is a handy implement that is used by carpenters and other woodworkers for locating positions and starting screws, nails, and bits. The blade varies in length from $2\frac{3}{4}$ inches to $3\frac{1}{2}$ inches. Many carpenters also use the scratch awl for marking guide lines in layout work, and hence its classification as a layout tool. Fig. 38 illustrates the typical use of a scratch awl.

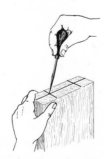

Fig. 38. The center for boring holes should be carefully sunk with the point of a scratch awl for accuracy in locating the bit. (Stanley Works)

Utility Knife. The utility knife (Fig. 36) is also used for cutting or scribing guide lines. Sometimes an ordinary pocket knife is used for this purpose. The utility knife and pocket knife are also used for cutting such materials as Formica, composition roofing materials, asbestos products, plastic flooring materials, linoleum, fiberboard, plaster board, and wallboard. The blade may be replaced and different types of blades are available. Choose the right blade for the specific job.

When scribing guide lines a knife with a longer, flat blade should be used. The flat blade assures that the line will not vary because of uneven blade thickness. A wood chisel with a flat back side is sometimes used for scribing.

SAFETY: KNIVES

1. Keep your attention focused on the work.

2. Keep knife blades sharp.

3. Select the right knife for the job.

4. Keep knife and hands clean, dry, and free from grease.

5. Use knife properly: do *not* use as a pry, screwdriver, wedge, etc.

6. Cut away from your body. Keep other hand away from the direction of the cut.

7. When passing an open knife, hold it by the blade so that the receiver grasps the knife by the handle. When passing a pocket knife, close it first.

8. Never try to catch a falling knife.

9.Store knives safely: keep knives in a designated place in the toolbox. Keep knives in a scabbard or closed when not using. *Never* place a knife where it could fall.

Marking Gage. The marking gage (Fig. 39) is used, as the name implies, for marking (scribing) a line at a set depth parallel to the edge of the work. The beam is graduated in 16th for 6 inches. Fig. 40 illustrates how to adjust, hold, and scribe with the marking gage. A simple gage can be made on the job from a scrap of wood by driving two nails through the wood. While a home made gage is not adjustable, it will hold its distance through heavy usage.

Butt Gage. The butt gage (Fig. 39), is used to lay out hinges on doors and door jambs. It has three marking knives (A, B and C) which can be set from $\frac{1}{16}$ of an inch to 2 inches. It should be kept free from dirt and lightly oiled.

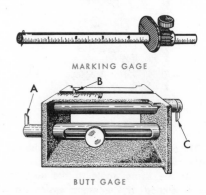

MARKING GAGE

BUTT GAGE

Fig. 39. Marking and butt gages.

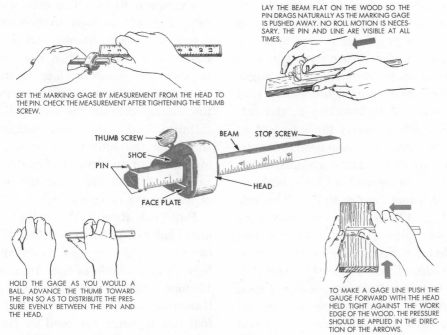

LAY THE BEAM FLAT ON THE WOOD SO THE PIN DRAGS NATURALLY AS THE MARKING GAGE IS PUSHED AWAY. NO ROLL MOTION IS NECESSARY. THE PIN AND LINE ARE VISIBLE AT ALL TIMES.

SET THE MARKING GAGE BY MEASUREMENT FROM THE HEAD TO THE PIN. CHECK THE MEASUREMENT AFTER TIGHTENING THE THUMB SCREW.

THUMB SCREW   BEAM   STOP SCREW
SHOE
PIN
HEAD
FACE PLATE

HOLD THE GAGE AS YOU WOULD A BALL. ADVANCE THE THUMB TOWARD THE PIN SO AS TO DISTRIBUTE THE PRESSURE EVENLY BETWEEN THE PIN AND THE HEAD.

TO MAKE A GAGE LINE PUSH THE GAUGE FORWARD WITH THE HEAD HELD TIGHT AGAINST THE WORK EDGE OF THE WOOD. THE PRESSURE SHOULD BE APPLIED IN THE DIRECTION OF THE ARROWS.

Fig. 40. How to use the marking gage. (Stanley Works)

Trammel Points. These are attached to a straight rod and are used to strike circles with diameters too large for the ordinary compass. See Fig. 41.

T-Bevel. The T-bevel (Fig. 41), has a blade which ranges in size from 6 inches to 12 inches, and is adjustable in length. Since the angle of the blade to the handle may be

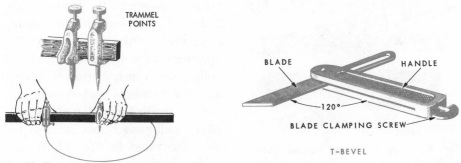

TRAMMEL POINTS

BLADE   HANDLE
120°
BLADE CLAMPING SCREW

T-BEVEL

Fig. 41. Trammel points and T-bevel. (Trammel points: Stanley Works)

adjusted as well as its length this tool is used a great deal in angular work. A protractor is used to obtain exact angles. When two pieces of wood are to fit together at an angle, the T-bevel is used to measure that angle, and by bisecting it, the cutting line necessary for a perfect fit is obtained. It is also used for transferring and marking a similar angle from one piece of work to another.

Six-foot Zig-Zag Rule. This rule (Fig. 42) is the first measuring tool which the carpenter will find that he needs. There are several grades of rulers available; and it is a wise investment to get one of good quality. A drop of fine machine oil in each joint of a new ruler will make its operation smoother and its life longer. A measure of care should be exercised when opening and closing the wood zig-zag ruler. Fig. 43 illustrates how to use the zig-zag rule.

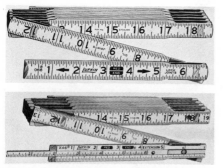

Fig. 42. Two types of zig-zag rulers. (Lufkin Rule Co.)

Extension Rule. The extension rule (Fig. 42) is used to measure inside of door frames, window frames, etc. To use, open the rule to within 6 inches or less of the opening to be measured and extend the sliding measure the rest of the distance. Add the measurement shown on the slide to the over-all measurement on the rest of the zig-zag rule. Fig. 43 illustrates the use of the zig-zag extension rule.

Pull-Push Rule. The pull-push metal ruler or pocket rule (Fig. 44) can occasionally be used to advantage. It is available in 6, 8, 10, and 12 foot lengths, and is a half or three-fourths of an inch wide. A 10 foot rule is commonly used by carpenters. Both the upper and lower edges are marked with inch readings; divisions are in 16ths and feet are marked. Most pull-push rules used by carpenters are marked every 16 inches to facilitate stud layout. The metal case of the ruler is exactly 2 inches, and may be used for making inside measurements. The 2 inches is added to the total reading shown on the blade. Often, pull-push rules have a self winding mechanism. Oil should be applied sparingly to metal rules, for oil will collect dirt which in turn will damage the numbers and divisions as well as impair the action of the rule. Many pull-push rulers, such as the one illustrated in Fig. 44, require no lubrication.

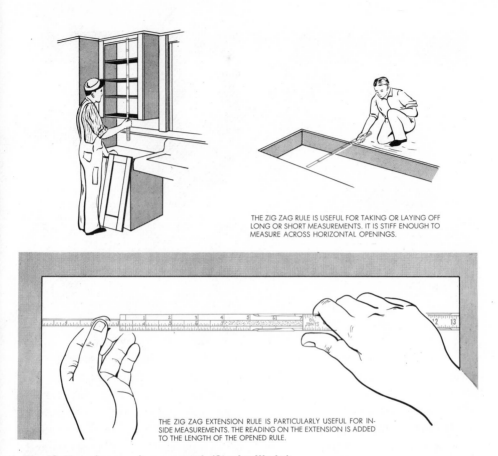

THE ZIG ZAG RULE IS USEFUL FOR TAKING OR LAYING OFF LONG OR SHORT MEASUREMENTS. IT IS STIFF ENOUGH TO MEASURE ACROSS HORIZONTAL OPENINGS.

THE ZIG ZAG EXTENSION RULE IS PARTICULARLY USEFUL FOR IN-SIDE MEASUREMENTS. THE READING ON THE EXTENSION IS ADDED TO THE LENGTH OF THE OPENED RULE.

Fig. 43. How zig-zag rulers are used. (Stanley Works)

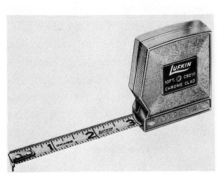

Fig. 44. Rule and tape used by carpenters. (Lufkin Rule Co.)

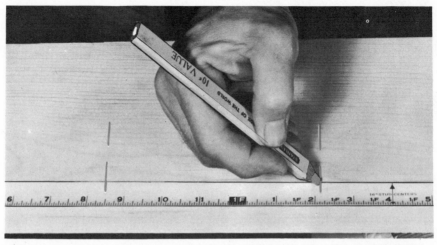

Fig. 45. Carpenter's pencil used on push-pull rule with blank edge. (Stanley Works)

Fig. 45 illustrates a *pull-push ruler* with one edge left *blank* for marking on. The user simply marks the needed length on the blank edge with a *carpenters pencil* (see Fig. 45). He then transfers the measurement directly to the material to be cut. This procedure eliminates the possibility of remembering or jotting down the wrong dimension. After the measurement is transferred the pencil mark on the tape is easily wiped off.

Steel Tape. The steel tape (Fig. 44), is an important tool for layout work; the measurement of rafter lengths, room lengths and diagonals. The measuring of wall diagonals is an aid to insuring that walls are square for framing. Steel tapes are available in lengths from twenty-five feet to one hundred feet. A 50 foot tape is commonly used. Oil should be applied sparingly as for the pull-push metal ruler.

Caliper Rule. The caliper rule (Fig. 46) is used for taking small measurements, such as board thickness, pipe and bolt diameters, and hole and opening widths. Two readings are given of the face of the caliper rule: outside and inside. *Outside readings* are for taking measurements of objects which are inserted between the caliper jaws. *Inside readings* are for taking the dimensions of holes and openings— here the caliper jaws are inserted into the opening to be measured. Fig. 46 illustrates both uses of the caliper rule.

Combination Square. The combination square (Fig. 47), is a steel tool, twelve inches long, with a 4½

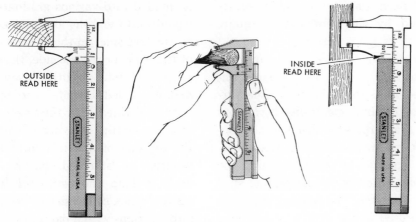

Fig. 46. Use of the caliper rule. (Stanley Works)

inch handle. The blade is either slotted or grooved. The handle and the blade are so joined as to allow measurement, on a go or no go basis, of both 45 degree and 90 degree angles. It is useful for short markings, and because of its size it can be carried in the hip pocket. Combination squares are sometimes made with a spirit level built into the handle. This tool should receive the same care as a framing square.

Try and Miter Square. This square (Fig. 47), has a blade ranging from 6 inches to 10 inches in length, with a 4 inch to 6 inch handle. Angles of 45 degrees and 90 degrees can be checked with the handle, but unlike the combination square, no adjustment can be made.

Try Square. The blade of the try square (Fig. 47), is between 6 inches and 12 inches long, with a 4⅜ inch to 8 inch handle. This tool

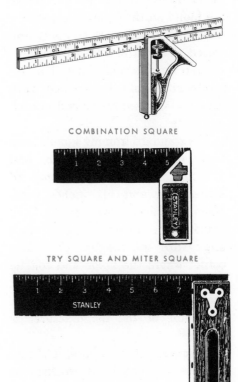

COMBINATION SQUARE

TRY SQUARE AND MITER SQUARE

STANLEY

TRY SQUARE

Fig. 47. Types of squares.

has been almost completely superseded by the combination square which is more versatile.

Framing Square. The framing square (Fig. 48), as its name implies, finds its main use in the various framing operations performed by the carpenter. Some of the operations are the framing of a house, the spacing of studs, framing for doors, windows, fireplaces, and similar openings. The framing square is also used in the layout of stringers and carriages in stair construction; rafter framing tables for all pitches are found on the square. In fact the uses of the square are so many and varied that entire books have been written on this tool alone. This instrument should be treated with care, and cleaned at the end of each day's use.

The standard framing square has a *blade*, or *body*, 24 inches long and 2 inches wide, and a *tongue* 16 inches long and 1½ inches wide. (Some squares have an 18 inch blade.) The blade forms a right angle with the tongue. The outer corner where the blade and tongue meet is called the *heel*. The *face* of the square is the side on which the name of the manufacturer is stamped.

A smaller steel square, 12″ x 8″ is sometimes used for working in close places, such as small windows, etc.

On a standard square the inch is divided into various graduations, usually into eighths and sixteenths on the face side; on the outside edge of the back, or reverse side, the inch is divided into twelfths, useful in making scaled layouts; the inside edge is divided into thirty-seconds and one-tenths. On some squares the division of one inch into hundredths is stamped on at the heel, to help the estimator when making quick conversion of decimals into fractions with a pair of dividers.

A framing square made of stainless steel will not rust, an item of great importance when selecting any tool. Galvanized, copper- or nickel-plated squares are also rust resistant; however, the plating on these squares is apt to wear off in the course of time.

In addition to the convenient division marks and the rust-resistant material, it is advisable to select a square which has useful tables stamped on it; for example, the *rafter-framing table, Essex board measure, octagon scale,* and *brace measure,* Fig. 48. Rafter-framing tables vary with different makes of squares. Some are unit-length tables while others are total-length tables for the most common roof pitches. Although these tables are not always used, it is convenient to have them at hand when the need for them arises. A book of instruction usually accompanies each square explaining its use.

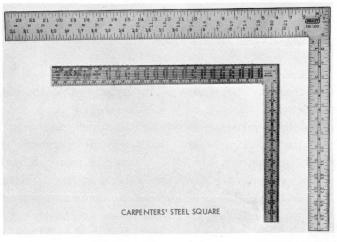

CARPENTERS' STEEL SQUARE

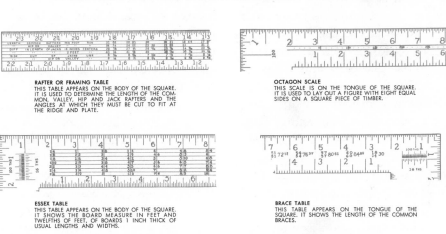

RAFTER OR FRAMING TABLE
THIS TABLE APPEARS ON THE BODY OF THE SQUARE. IT IS USED TO DETERMINE THE LENGTH OF THE COMMON, VALLEY, HIP AND JACK RAFTERS AND THE ANGLES AT WHICH THEY MUST BE CUT TO FIT AT THE RIDGE AND PLATE.

OCTAGON SCALE
THIS SCALE IS ON THE TONGUE OF THE SQUARE. IT IS USED TO LAY OUT A FIGURE WITH EIGHT EQUAL SIDES ON A SQUARE PIECE OF TIMBER.

ESSEX TABLE
THIS TABLE APPEARS ON THE BODY OF THE SQUARE. IT SHOWS THE BOARD MEASURE IN FEET AND TWELFTHS OF FEET, OF BOARDS 1 INCH THICK OF USUAL LENGTHS AND WIDTHS.

BRACE TABLE
THIS TABLE APPEARS ON THE TONGUE OF THE SQUARE. IT SHOWS THE LENGTH OF THE COMMON BRACES.

Fig. 48. Framing square and common tables on the square. (Stanley Works)

Stair Framing Square Gages. These are sometimes used with the framing square. See Fig. 49. They come in pairs and are used on the framing square to mark off different rises and runs for stringers, in stair construction, and also for rafter layout. They are available in two different styles. The set screw should be oiled regularly.

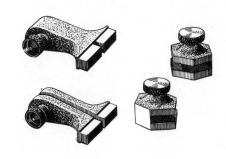

Fig. 49. Stair framing-square gages.

Framing Square—some of its Uses

Without a framing square in his tool kit, the present-day carpenter would be seriously handicapped in his work. To a skilled craftsman in the trade, the square is almost as indispensable as the hammer, saw, or plane. To the inexperienced the square may be merely a tool for use in drawing lines at right angles, or for testing a board to determine whether or not it is straight and true. However, in the hands of a skilled workman who understands how to use the scales and tables on the framing square, it is a highly valuable tool and an essential part of his equipment. Therefore, it is advisable for the mechanic not only to acquaint himself with the fundamental operations performed with the square but also to become familiar with a few of the special layouts where the square is useful for solving common construction problems. The framing square serves the carpenter not only as an efficient tool but also as a handbook and instructor. The use of scales and tables given on the framing square avoids complicated mathematical computations which would consume much of the carpenter's valuable time. Information regarding lines and angles presented by means of scales and tables on the square is simple, practical, and condensed. The laying out of the various cuts is illustrated in a step-by-step method which makes some of the most difficult operations seem easy.

There are many different makes of framing squares and various finishes are applied to different makes. The scales and tables vary with the cost and make. When buying a framing square, it is advisable for a mechanic to spend enough money to secure one with complete tables and scales because they supply information particularly valuable on the job, making the square comparable to an engineer's handbook.

The chief difference in the tables of the various kinds of framing squares is found in the rafter table, as some tables are based upon *unit length* and others upon *total length*. Since space will not permit description of all of the tables, the one most frequently used — the unit length table—is the only one explained in detail in this book. The locations of the various tables and different graduations, or scales, are shown in Fig. 50.

Testing a Framing Square

Smooth up one side of a wide four-foot board. Dress one edge of the board until it is a true straight

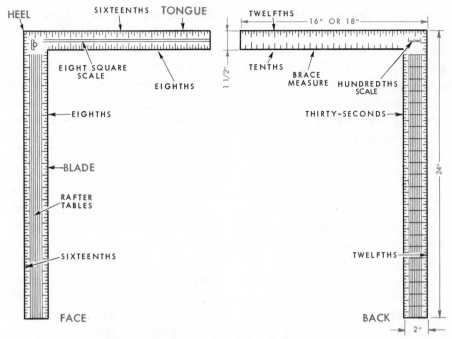

Fig. 50. Locations of scales and tables on framing square.

edge. Then lay the prepared board on the workbench with the straight edge turned toward you and the smoothed face turned upward. Place the square on top of the board with the blade, or body, extending to the left and the tongue at right angles to the straight edge of the board. Hold the square firmly in position with the entire length of the blade aligning perfectly with the straight edge of the board. The tongue will then be extending away from you across the board, as shown at (1), Fig. 51. While still holding the square exactly in line with the edge of the board, take a penknife or a sharp-pointed, hard-lead pencil and draw a mark close against the tongue of the square on the smooth face of the board. Then turn the square over, keeping the heel, indicated as (X), Fig. 51, at exactly the same point but with the blade

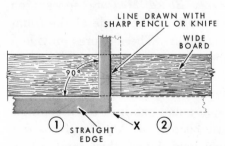

Fig. 51. Testing framing square for accuracy.

57

extending to the right along the straight edge of the board and exactly in line with this edge throughout the entire length of the blade of the square, as shown at (2), Fig. 51. Always hold the square firmly in place along the edge of the board and keep the heel exactly where it was before the square was turned over, then compare the position with the mark which you made across the board. If the edge of the tongue is exactly on the mark, or if a new mark made with the penknife or pencil against the edge of the tongue, in its new position, coincides exactly with the first mark drawn, then the square is truly *square*.

If the angle of the square is found to be less than 90 degrees it can be brought back to the correct position by careful hammering of the metal in the heel. The hammering of the metal stretches it at this point, throwing the end of the tongue outward.

Essex Board Measure

A series of figures known as the *Essex Board Measure* appears on the back of the blade of the framing square. These figures provide a means for the rapid calculation of *board feet*, the unit of measure for lumber. A piece of board one foot square and one inch thick contains one board foot. A piece of board 1 foot long, 1 inch thick, and only 6 inches wide contains ½ foot board measure. Another piece 2 feet long, 1 foot wide, and 1 inch thick contains 2 feet board measure (f.b.m.). We use the term *feet board measure* when referring to quantities of lumber and when determining buying or selling prices of lumber or timber.

You can find the feet board measure for any size of board or timber by arithmetic, but the process can be simplified greatly and much time saved by turning directly to the back of the blade of your framing square. When holding the blade in your right hand and the tongue in your left hand with the heel pointing outward, that is, away from your body, you will be looking at the back of the blade of the square. With the square held in this position, you can observe the inch divisions *1, 2, 3, 4, 5*, and so on, along the outside edge of the square, Fig. 52. These figures show the width in inches of the stick of timber or board to be measured. Under each of these widths seven other figures appear. These figures give directly in feet (to the left of the vertical line) and in twelfths of a foot (to the right of the vertical line) the feet board measure, in boards of that particular width one inch thick, of seven different lengths. These lengths beginning at the top edge of the blade under the *12*-inch mark and reading downward are: *8, 9, 10, 11, 13, 14,* and *15* feet. The Essex board measure gives the num-

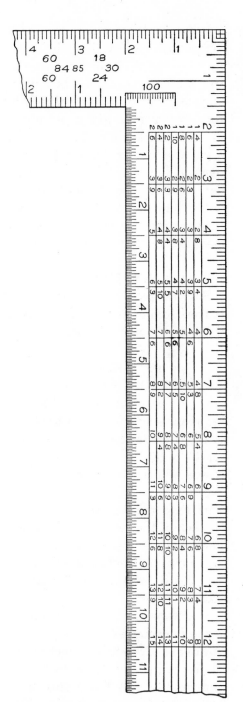

Fig. 52. Essex board measure table.

ber of board feet of practically all the sizes of boards or timber in common use. To find feet board measure the inch graduations, along the outer edge of the back of the blade of the square, are used in combination with the values given along the seven parallel lines.

The figure *12* at the outer edge of the back of the square represents a board 12 inches wide and one inch thick, Fig 52. This is the starting point for all calculations. The numbers in the column directly under the *12*-inch mark indicate the lengths of a piece of board in feet. The regular inch divisions of the square on each side of the *12*-inch mark represent the widths of the boards in inches. The figures under each of these inch division marks represent the number of board feet and the twelfths of a board foot.

When you wish to find the feet board measure of a particular piece of lumber, first find under the *12*-inch mark the figure corresponding to the length (in feet) of your stick of timber. Then follow along the horizontal line under this figure to the left until you come to the point under the inch mark corresponding to the width (in inches) of your stick, and there you will find the figure which gives the contents of your stick of timber in feet board measure. The figure appearing at the left-hand side of the vertical line is full feet board measure and the figure at the right of the vertical line is twelfths of a foot board measure.

EXAMPLE

Find the feet board measure in a board 1 inch thick, 10 feet long, and 9 inches wide.

PROCEDURE

a) First, look in the column of figures underneath the *12*-inch mark on the outside edge of the back of the blade of the square and near the middle of the back of the blade you will find the number *10*.

b) Follow along the horizontal line underneath this number and to the left of it, until you come to the column of figures underneath the 9-inch mark at the edge of the blade. There you will find the numbers 7|6, which stands for seven and six twelfths feet board measure, which is the feet board measure of your board. If the board were more than 1 inch thick, you would find the feet board measure by multiplying the figure just found by the thickness of the timber in inches. If the piece were more than 12 inches wide, you would follow the horizontal line underneath the figure *10* in the *12*-inch column to the right instead of to the left.

A length of 15 feet is the longest timber indicated in the column of figures underneath the *12*-inch mark on the outer edge of the back of the blade of the square. If the feet board measure is required for a stick longer than 15 feet, it can be found by following the directions given in the preceding example, but using only one half of the actual length, then doubling the results, since it is evident that doubling the length of a piece of timber doubles the contents in feet board measure. In order to show how to deal with a larger and longer piece of timber than provided for in the Essex board measure, another example follows.

EXAMPLE

Find the feet board measure in a timber 10 inches wide, 16 inches thick, and 23 feet in length.

PROCEDURE

a) Divide the length of 23 feet into two parts of 10 and 13 feet. Let the 10-inch dimension be taken as the width and consider the timber to be made up of 16 separate boards each one inch thick and 10 inches wide.

b) Find the feet board measure for each of the two pieces of board. Then add the results and multiply the sum by 16 feet to find the entire feet board measure of the whole stick of timber.

c) Following the procedure used in the foregoing example and referring to Fig. 52, we find a 1-inch board 10 feet long and 10 inches wide contains $8\frac{4}{12}$ feet board measure.

d) Following the same procedure

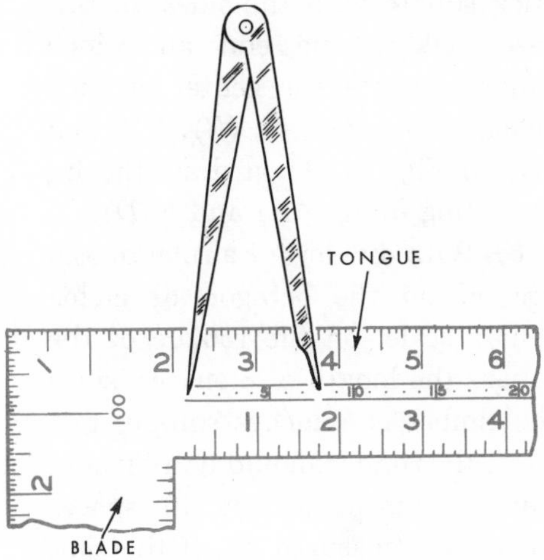

Fig. 53. Octagon scale on face of tongue of framing square.

for finding the number of board feet in a board 13 feet long, 10 inches wide, and 1 inch thick, we find this board would contain $10\frac{10}{12}$ feet board measure. Adding the contents of the two boards together gives $19\frac{2}{12}$ feet board measure. Multiplying this sum by 16 gives $306\frac{8}{12}$ feet board measure, the entire contents in board feet of the 23-foot stick of timber.

Using the Octagon Scale

You will find the octagon scale on the face of the tongue of the framing square, Fig. 53. This scale, sometimes known as the *eight-square scale*, consists of a series of divisions in the shape of dots marked off along the middle of the tongue of the square. Starting nearly under the 2-inch mark on the outside edge near the heel, the dots continue al-

most to the other end of the tongue. There are 65 of these dots on a square having a 16-inch tongue. Every fifth dot is numbered, thus you find on the square: *5, 10, 15, 20* and so on up to *65*. The octagon scale is used for laying out figures with 8 equal sides.

Sometimes it becomes necessary for a carpenter to transform a square stick of timber into an eight-sided stick, for example, an octagonal newel post for a stairway. To do this, it is necessary to lay out an eight-square or octagon on the end of a square stick of timber. The method for doing this follows.

PROCEDURE

a) In laying out an octagon it is necessary first to square the stick to the desired size, for example, 8 inches. Then cut the end of the stick square with the sides, in this case making the end an 8-inch square. Locate the center of each side as shown at (A), (B), (C), and (D) in Fig. 54. Then draw the intersecting lines (AB) and (CD).

b) With dividers or a ruler, measure off on the octagon or eight-square scale, on the tongue of the square the length of 8 spaces, since the timber is 8 inches square, Fig. 53. If the timber should be 10 inches square, the length of 10 spaces should be measured off, if the timber should be 12 inches square, the length of 12 spaces should be measured off, and so on.

c) After measuring off the length of 8 spaces on the octagon scale apply this measurement to each side of the square timber on both sides of the center points, (A), (B), (C), and (D), as (Aa), (Ab), (Bf), (Be), (Ch), (Cg), (Dc), (Dd), Fig. 54. Joining the points (ah), (bc),

(de), and (fg), will outline on the end of the stick a figure having 8 equal sides. Then with this as a guide the entire stick can be shaped to this form by cutting off the solid triangular pieces from each of the four corners.

Converting a Timber from Square to Octagon

Any square stick, or timber, can be laid out also for an octagon timber with the framing square by using the following method.

PROCEDURE

a) Lay the framing square on the face of the timber to be cut, with the heel of the square on one side of the timber and the tip of the blade, that is, the 24-inch mark, on the other edge of the timber as shown at Fig. 55, left.

b) Holding the square firmly in this position, mark points on the timber at the inch divisions 7 and 17. Through each of these points draw a line parallel to the edges of the timber.

c) Proceeding in the same manner, draw corresponding lines on

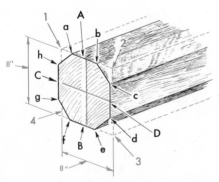

Fig. 54. Method of laying out an octagon on end of square stick.

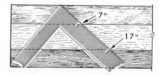

Fig. 55. Laying out an octagon on square stick of timber.

the other three sides of the timber. These lines are used as cutting lines and indicate the amount of wood that must be removed to change the timber from a square to an octagon. The end of the octagon timber is shown at Fig. 55, right.

Calculating Proportions with Framing Square

1. Proportions. The inside edge of the back of the tongue on a framing square can be used to figure many problems involving costs, wages, etc., where a definite rate is established. The method is shown in the following example.

EXAMPLE

1. If clay soil, to be used as a fill, costs $9.00 for an 8 cubic yard load, how much would 3¼ cubic yards cost?

PROCEDURE

a) Lay the square on a board with a straight and smooth edge as shown in position (*1*), Fig. 56. Hold the square to the proper figures so that these figures are over the edge of the board as shown in Fig. 56. In this case, the figure *8* (cu. yds.) on the inside of the blade and the figure *9* ($9.00 for 8 yards) on the inside of the tongue. Draw a line with a sharp pencil along the edge of the blade. Then slide the square to the right, along this line, until the figure *3¼* on the inside of the blade touches the edge of the board,

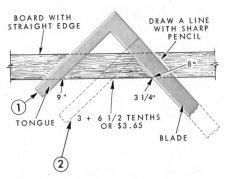

Fig. 56. Calculating costs with framing square.

as shown in position (2), Fig. 56. Read the figure on the inside of the tongue and you will find it to be *3* and *6½/10ths*, or $3.65, the cost of 3¼ yards.

2. Reductions or Enlargements. The framing square can be used for calculating proportions for finding reductions or enlargements. For example, correct proportions in reducing or enlarging a rectangular figure can be quickly obtained by means of sliding the framing square. The need for such calculations may arise when paneling a wall to keep small panels to the same proportions as larger panels. A similar need arises when making enlargements in photography. The following example gives the method of procedure when making reductions or enlargements.

EXAMPLE

2. What should be the width of a small panel 6 feet in length in order

to retain the same proportions as a larger panel measuring 4′0″ x 7′0″?

PROCEDURE

a) Lay the framing square (with the 12th scale upward) to *4″* on the tongue and *7″* on the blade as in position (*1*), Fig. 57.

b) Draw a line with a sharp pencil along the blade of the square.

c) Slide the square to the right, along this line, to the position shown at (*2*), Fig. 57, with the figure *6* on the blade touching the edge of the board. The figure on the

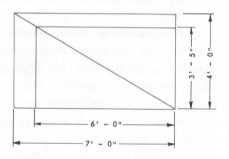

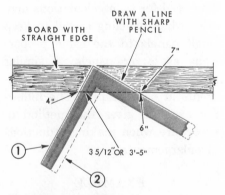

Fig. 57. Calculating proportions with framing square.

tongue will then be *3⁵⁄₁₂ths*, or 3 feet and 5 inches, the correct width of the rectangle that has a length of 6 feet.

Use of Framing Square with Circles

The framing square is especially useful when finding the circumferences of circles and also when finding the centers of circles. Likewise, the framing square can be used to advantage to find the capacity of pipes, to find the center of arcs, and the size of an elliptical hole in a pitched roof through which a pipe is to be passed. Read carefully the following instructions for finding:

1. Circumference of a circle.
2. Capacities of round pipes.
3. Center of a circle.
4. Center of an arc.
5. Layout of an ellipse.

1. Finding the Circumference of a Circle. The circumference of a circle can be found with the framing square by the following method.

PROCEDURE

a) Lay the square along the edge of a straight smooth board, as shown at (*1*), Fig. 58, to the figures *12″* on the blade and *3⅝″* on the tongue.

b) Draw a line along the blade with a sharp pencil.

c) Slide the square to the left to position (*2*), Fig. 58, holding the blade along this line to the figure which is equal to three times the diameter of the circle. Make a check

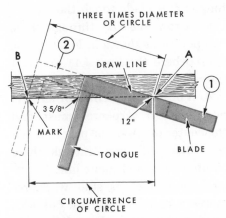

Fig. 58. Finding circumference of circle with framing square.

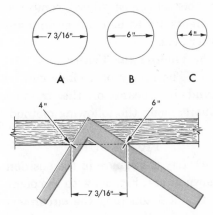

Fig. 59. Pipe *A* has same capacity as pipe *B* plus pipe *C*.

mark on the tongue as at (*B*), Fig. 58.

d) Measure the bridge, or distance, between the points (*A*) and (*B*), Fig. 58; this figure is the approximate circumference of the circle.

2. Finding the Capacities of Round Pipes. The size of a round pipe, required to carry the capacity of two or more other round pipes, can be found with the framing square, using the following method.

PROCEDURE

a) Lay the framing square along the edge of a straight stick, as shown in Fig. 59, with the size of one pipe (its diameter) on the tongue and the size of the other pipe on the blade.

b) Mark with a sharp pencil along the tongue and the blade.

c) Measure the bridge, or distance, between the two points at the edge of the board. This distance is the diameter of a pipe which will be large enough to carry the capacity of the two smaller pipes.

When three pipes are to be joined and their contents emptied into a fourth pipe the capacity of this pipe is found by the following method. First find the diameter required for a pipe to carry the capacity of two of the smaller pipes as in the foregoing paragraphs. Take this figure on one side of the square and the diameter of the third pipe on the other side of the square. The bridge, or distance, between these two points will be the diameter required for a round pipe which is to carry the capacity of the other three pipes. This same procedure can be followed for joining any desired

65

number of pipes whose combined contents are to be emptied into another pipe.

3. Finding the Center of a Circle. The center of a circle can be found by means of the framing square, using the following method.

PROCEDURE

a) Lay the square in the position shown at *(1)*, Fig. 60, with the point of the heel touching the circumference, using the same figure on both the tongue and blade of the square.

b) Make check marks at the points where the tongue and blade touch the circumference.

c) Draw line *(A)* through these points, as shown in Fig. 60.

d) Move the square to the position *(2)*, Fig. 60, and hold the square in the same position as in position *(1)*, Fig. 60.

e) Make check marks on the circumference at the points where the

tongue and blade touch the circle.

f) Draw line *(B)* through these two points, as shown in Fig. 60. The point where the lines *(A)* and *(B)* intersect is the center of the circle.

4. Finding the Center of an Arc. Sometimes a carpenter must find the center of an arc or part of a circle which will pass through three points not in a straight line. Circular layout, such as stair work, requires a carpenter to lay out arcs which must pass through certain points.

PROCEDURE

The center of an arc, which must pass through three points not in a straight line, can be found with the framing square by connecting the three points with straight lines, as shown at *(A-B)* and *(B-C)*, Fig. 61.

a) Find the centers *(a and b)* of the lines *(A-B)* and *(B-C)*.

b) Lay the square to these lines with the heel at the point *(a)*, posi-

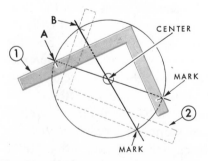

Fig. 60. Finding center of a circle with framing square.

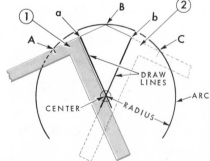

Fig. 61. Locating center of arc with framing square.

tion (*1*), Fig. 61; and at the point (*b*), *position* (*2*), Fig. 61.

c) Draw lines along the blade of the square through the points (*a*) and (*b*), as shown in Fig. 61. The point where these two lines intersect is the *center* of the arc.

5. Layout of an Ellipse for Pipe Passing through Pitched Roof. Passing a pipe through a pitched roof, as shown in Fig. 62, requires the cutting of an elliptical hole for the pipe. The length of the required ellipse, for any given pipe size, and the layout of the elliptical hole on the roof can be found by the following methods.

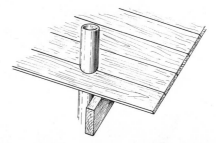

Fig. 62. Round pipe passing through pitched roof.

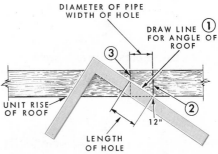

Fig. 63. Finding length of elliptical hole for pipe.

PROCEDURE

a) Lay the framing square on a board with a straight edge, taking the unit run (12 inches) on the blade and the unit rise of the roof on the tongue, as shown in Fig. 63.

b) Draw a line, shown as (*1*) in Fig. 63, along the blade. This gives the angle of the roof.

c) Lay out and draw, at right angles to the edge of the board, lines (2) and (3), as shown in Fig. 63. The distance between these two lines should be the same as the diameter, or width, of the pipe; that is, the width of the hole to be cut.

d) Measure the distance between the points where the lines (2) and (3) cut line (1). This gives the length of the ellipse, hence the length of the elliptical hole required

for passing the pipe through the roof. After finding the size required for the elliptical hole, it must be laid out on the roof.

e) The elliptical hole for the pipe, shown in Fig. 62, can be laid out on the roof by locating the center of the pipe (*0*), Fig. 64. Draw the center lines; (*AB*) major axis, length of hole, and (*CD*) minor axis, width of hole, of the ellipse, shown at Fig. 64, top.

f) With (*C*) as a center and (*AO*) as a radius, draw an arc cut-

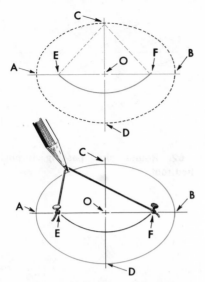

Fig. 64. Laying out ellipse with string.

Miter and Butt Joints on Polygons

Laying Out Miter and Butt Joints. The framing square is useful when laying out the angle for cuts in joining the pieces which form the sides of objects, such as boxes, plates on buildings, in cabinet construction, and columns which have many sides.

The two joints commonly used are the miter and the butt joints, shown in Fig. 65. In framing plates of a building, nails are commonly used to hold the joints together. In cabinet construction the joints frequently are made secure by using a spline on miter joints and the tongue and groove for butt joints as shown in Fig. 65.

ting the line (*AB*) at the points (*E*) and (*F*).

g) Drive a nail at each of the points (*C*), (*E*), and (*F*). Then tie an inelastic cord or string tightly around these three nails.

h) Remove the nail at (*C*) and holding a pencil in its place proceed to draw the ellipse, keeping the string taut, as shown at Fig. 64, bottom[1].

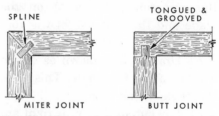

SPLINE   TONGUED & GROOVED

MITER JOINT   BUTT JOINT

Fig. 65. Miter and butt joints commonly used.

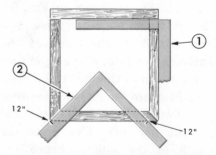

Fig. 66. Layout of joints for square objects.

[1]When laying out the ellipse, extra space should be allowed around the pipe if it is to be the outlet for smoke from a heating plant, or stove. In such a case, the ellipse should be drawn so as to allow a 2-inch air space around the pipe. This precaution is necessary in order to avoid danger from fire.

On square objects the butt joint is an angle of 90 degrees. Such a joint can easily be laid out by holding the framing square as at (*1*), Fig. 66. The miter joint is laid out by taking any figure such as 12 on both the tongue and blade of the square. Lay the square so that these figures are on the edge of the stick, or board, as shown at (*2*), Fig. 66.

The layout of miter and butt joints for three common polygons is shown in Fig. 67. Note that the figure on the blade for all of these joints is always 12″ while the figure on the tongue will vary, depending upon the shape of the figure and the joint. By always using the figure 12 on the blade as a constant, then there will be only one figure to remember when laying out the joint. This is an important fact to remember as it will simplify the operation.

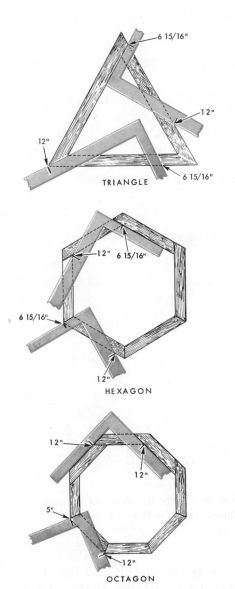

Fig. 67. Layout of miter and butt joints for three types of polygons.

Hopper Joints

Laying Out Hopper Joints.
When making a square or rectangular box the four corners form an angle of 90 degrees and the miter joints to 45 degrees. However, the hopper is wider at the top than at the bottom, as shown at Fig. 68, left. This type of jointing requires a butt joint of more than 90 degrees and a miter cut of more than 45 degrees.

Since the hopper is like a roof turned upside down the principles of roof framing are applied in laying out the cuts. The run, Fig. 68, left, is the distance the top extends over the bottom, this is the same as the

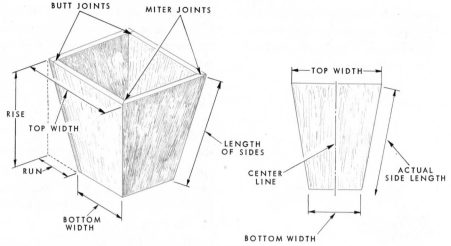

Fig. 68. Layout of miter and butt joints for hopper.

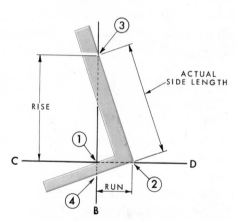

Fig. 69. Method used to obtain figures for miter and butt joints on hopper.

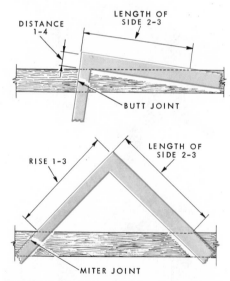

Fig. 70. Layout for obtaining the angle of the miter and butt joints on hopper.

run of the common rafter on a roof. The rise is the distance vertically between the top and the bottom of the hopper. The length of the side is the same as the length of a common rafter. The butt joint is the same as the backing of a hip rafter and the miter joint is the reverse of the roof sheathing cut.

70

The method of laying out the side of a hopper from a center line to get true lengths of the joints is shown at Fig. 68, right. When miter joints are used on square hoppers, all sides will be the same. When butt joints are used, two sides are smaller by the thickness of the material of the other two sides. The layout in Fig. 69 will give all necessary figures, which are to be used on the framing square, as shown in Fig. 70, for obtaining the angle of the butt and miter joints.

Framing Square: Advanced Work

Advanced work on the use of the framing square will be found in *Appendix B* of this text and in *Fundamentals of Carpentry, Vol. II*.

Checking on Your Knowledge

The following questions give you the opportunity to check up on yourself. If you have read the chapter carefully, you should be able to answer the questions. If you have any difficulty, read the chapter over once more so that you have the information well in mind before you go on with your reading.

DO YOU KNOW

1. What tools the apprentice carpenter should have in his tool kit, and what tools he should add as he advances to more complicated construction work?

2. How carpentry tools are classified?

3. How the framing square can help you in the solution of various difficult problems of construction?

4. What are some of the important hammering and percussion tools?

5. What are the important measuring tools?

6. Why contractors furnish much of the larger and more expensive equipment?

7. Into how many groups tools may be classified?

8. What useful tables are found on the face and back of a standard steel framing square?

9. In addition to the framing square, what are some of the other important layout and measuring tools?

10. What are some of the power-driven tools?

11. What source of power they use?

12. Why work should be held firmly?

13. When a plumb line is used? Why?

14. What a straightedge is and when it is used?

15. How to describe a chalk line and its use?

16. What types of hammers are used in carpentry?

17. Some substitutes for hammers?

Tools: Part II
Cutting Tools: Saws, Borers, Planers and Sanders

Chapter

4

The modern carpenter does most of his work with cutting tools—tools that remove part of the wood to provide proper length, good joints, smooth surfaces.

To accomplish this the carpenter must know the various kinds of cutting tools, their correct use, and their necessary care so that top-quality work can be performed. He must know why a rip saw differs from a cross-cut, why there are many styles of planes, when to use one style of tool instead of another, how to use tools to obtain best results.

The field of cutting tools has been one where many striking advances have been made in the application of portable power to the tasks that take repetitious movements of the hands and arms. The push and pull, push and pull, push and pull, time after time, to drive a saw through a plank, smooth down a rough surface or drill a hole can often be done rapidly and effortlessly with proper portable tools. While these tools take much of the plain hard work out of the job they do not replace the need for careful use of hand tools—they have merely replaced some of the rougher, more monotonous aspects of the work.

While saving hours of time these power tools have made new demands on the workman. He must be alert, sure of what he is doing, and trained to handle the tool. He should be safety conscious every minute. The high speed and sharp edges on these power tools can cause injuries of the most serious nature—injuries that can not occur with slower hand methods. The electricity which powers these tools may add hazards to the careless workman.

Today the carpenter must not only know his hand tools but he must know power tools as well. He must be able to use either kind with ease and skill. While portable power tools may have lightened some of the laborious work, they have also increased the knowledge, skill and judgment required of the carpenter.

Saws

Both manually operated saws and power saws are used by the carpenter. The principal manually operated saws used in the carpentry trade are: *handsaws* (both *ripsaw* and *crosscut*); the *compass saw*, *coping saw*, *backsaw*, and *hack saw*. Tools not commonly used by the carpenter include other types of saws, such as the turning saw and tenon saw. Most manufacturers make saws in various grades, of either hard or soft steel, and as either regular or lightweight models to suit individual needs.

Various *power saws* are also used on the job or in the shop. Power saws are either portable or stationary. The common portable power saws are the *electric hand saw*, *sabre saw* and *reciprocating saw*. The *circular table saw*, *radial saw* and *band saw* are usually stationary, although the radial saw, and sometimes the circular table saw, is often moved to the job site. Power saws are furnished by the contractor.

Hand Operated Saws

Handsaws. Handsaws are available with either a curved or a straight back. (Fig. 1). The straight edge, which may be used for drawing lines before sawing, is an advantage of the straight-back saw. The better grades of handsaws are taper ground; that is, the blade is thinner along the back than it is along the cutting or toothed edge; such saws need little *set*. Usually prices are governed by quality. The greatest satisfaction ordinarily is obtained from the use of a relatively high-priced tool of superior quality.

Crosscut Saw. This saw is de-

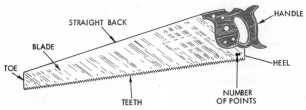

Fig. 1. Straight back hand saw.

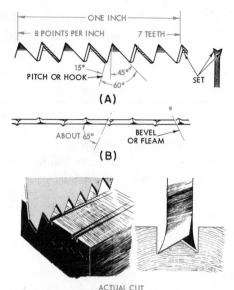

Fig. 2. Crosscut saw teeth which cut like two rows of knife points.

signed to cut across the grain of the wood. Therefore, its teeth must be sharpened like a knife so they will cut the fibers of the wood on each side of the saw cut, or kerf, Fig. 2. The blade is commonly from 20 to 26 inches long and has from 7 to 11 points to the inch. The more teeth that there are to the inch the finer the cut will be. The 8 point saw is most commonly used in rough construction, and the 10 and 11 point saw for finished carpentry work. The shape of the teeth of the crosscut saw depends upon the nature of the work the saw is intended to perform and also upon the hardness of the wood which is to be cut. For general work, the front face of the

tooth should have a *pitch*, commonly called *hook*, of 15 degrees, see (A), Fig. 2; and a *bevel* of about 65 degrees, see (B), Fig. 2; each tooth should be sharpened with the file held in a horizontal position. For hardwood the tooth is filed with the same pitch and bevel, but the file is not held in a horizontal position; the handle must be held lower than the tip of the file. This will produce a bevel on the front of the tooth while the back of the tooth will remain straight. To produce a smooth cut in softwood, the pitch of the tooth should be about 20 to 25 degrees and the bevel about 45 degrees, with the handle of the file held lower than the tip. The point of the tooth will then be long and sharp and will be more apt to cut the soft fibers instead of tearing them.

A dull saw will not cut rapidly. It will tear the fibers of the wood instead of cutting them; these torn fibers will hang into the saw cut and cause the saw to bind. Dull teeth will reflect light and will appear as bright spots, whereas the tip of a sharp tooth will not be visible. The tip of the tooth is *set*. That is, it is *bent* toward the side of the point of the tooth to give it the clearance which is essential in wet or green wood.

Ripsaw. The ripsaw is used to cut wood with the grain and has a 26 inch blade and, in most cases,

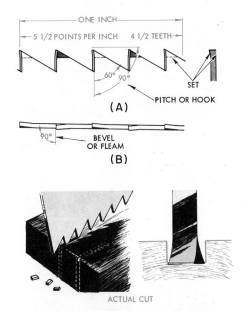

(A)

(B)

ACTUAL CUT

Fig. 3. Ripsaw teeth which cut like a gang of chisels in a row.

A carpenter should have no less than three handsaws: a 7- or 8-point 26-inch crosscut saw for rough work, a 10- or 11-point 26-inch crosscut saw for finish work, and a 5½- or 6-point 26-inch ripsaw. An old 7- or 8-point crosscut saw which has been worn down makes a useful extra tool, as it is convenient for sawing into tight places and can be used where there is danger of cutting into nails.

SAFETY: HANDSAWS

1. Keep your attention focused on the work area.

2. Keep saw blades sharp and properly set.

3. Use the right saw for the job. A coarse saw is best for fast, rough work; a fine saw is best for smooth, accurate work.

4. Make sure that the material being cut is free from nails and other obstructions.

5. Be sure that the material being cut is well supported.

6. Use saws properly. Start cut by drawing saw backward. Steady saw with thumb held high on the blade. Do *not* place thumb on the material being cut. Fig. 4 illustrates the proper method of using a crosscut saw. Fig. 5 illustrates the proper method of using a ripsaw.

7. After using saw, wipe on a thin film of oil to prevent rust.

8. Store saws in a designated place in the toolbox to protect the teeth or hang in a designated location.

5½ or less points per inch. The teeth of this saw must be filed chisel-like to cut the wood fibers in the bottom of the saw cut instead of at the side, Fig. 3. The front of the tooth is at right angles, or 90 degrees, to the line of the teeth, see (A), Fig. 3. That is, the front of the tooth has no bevel, see (B), Fig. 3. Some mechanics prefer to file the ripsaw with a slight bevel. This makes it possible, when desirable, to use the ripsaw as a crosscut saw for cutting heavy timbers. The teeth of the ripsaw must have *set*. That is, the teeth must be *bent* to give them proper clearance. It will be observed that only the tip of the tooth is set, not the whole tooth.

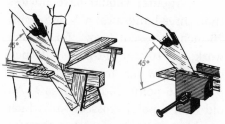

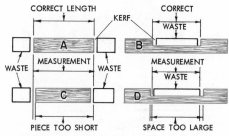

ABOUT 45° IS THE CORRECT ANGLE BETWEEN THE SAW AND THE WORK FOR CROSSCUT SAWING.

BE SURE TO SAW CAREFULLY ON THE WASTE SIDE OF THE LINE AS AT A AND B. SAWING ON THE LINE OR ON THE WRONG SIDE OF THE LINE MAKES THE STOCK TOO SHORT AS AT C OR THE OPENING TOO LARGE AS SHOWN AT D.

Fig. 4. Proper use of the crosscut saw. (Stanley Works)

ABOUT 60° IS THE CORRECT ANGLE BETWEEN THE SAW AND THE WORK FOR RIP SAWING.

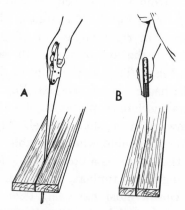

START THE SAW CUT BY DRAWING THE SAW BACKWARD. HOLD THE BLADE SQUARE TO THE STOCK. STEADY IT AT THE LINE WITH THE THUMB.

A. IF THE SAW LEAVES THE LINE TWIST THE HANDLE SLIGHTLY AND DRAW IT BACK TO THE LINE.

B. IF THE SAW IS NOT SQUARE TO THE STOCK, BEND IT A LITTLE AND GRADUALLY STRAIGHTEN IT. BE CAREFUL NOT TO PERMANENTLY BEND OR KINK THE BLADE.

Fig. 5. Proper use of the ripsaw. (Stanley Works)

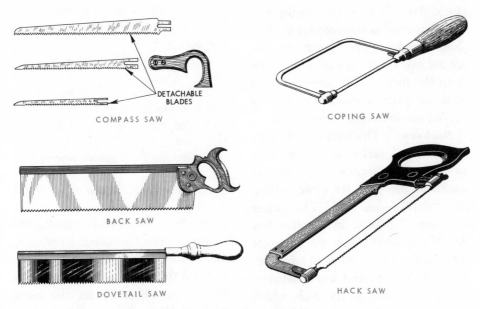

Fig. 6. Selection of saws commonly used by the carpenter.

Compass Saw. This saw (Fig. 6) is 10, 12, or 14 inches long with 10 points to the inch. Its main application is cutting holes and openings, such as for electrical outlets, where a power tool would be too large and for starting the cut in tight places where the ordinary hand saw will not fit. The compass saw may be equipped with a blade for cutting nails (with 13 points to the inch). The compass saw is very similar to the keyhole saw. The keyhole saw, however, is smaller than the compass saw and has smaller blades. The keyhole saw is used for making small holes, such as for keyholes in doors, although modern practice employs a lock or latch jig and a brace and bit.

Coping Saw. This saw is used for coping joints and has a 6⅜ inch long blade which is ⅛ inch wide. See Fig. 6. When it is necessary to join two intricate moldings at right angles, the joint is usually coped. This entails first cutting one piece of stock away to receive the molded surface of the other piece, at an angle of 45 degrees to the stock. The blade of the coping saw can be turned as desired, for cutting sharp angles. The teeth of the coping saw blade should point away from the handle. The coping saw is also sometimes used for cutting curved surfaces and circles.

Backsaw. The backsaw (Fig. 6) has a metal strip along the back to stiffen the blade. The shorter backsaws are used for close cutting and for precision work. The longer backsaws are used in a miter box which guides the saw for accurate cutting. Backsaws range in size from 10 to 28 inches and have between 11 and 14 points to the inch, which makes a very fine and finished cut.

Dovetail Saw. This saw (Fig. 6) is similar to a backsaw but has smaller teeth and a different shaped handle. It is used for fine finish work, etc.

Hack Saw. The hack saw blade is between 10 inches and 12 inches long, and has 14 to 32 points to the inch. See Fig. 6. It is used to cut metal such as nails and bolts. It is finding increasing use with the growing popularity of metal trim. The hack saw may also be used to cut nails at the joint between two boards. Hammer the boards apart to get room to insert the blade. The hack saw should not be used to cut wood. Do not use the hack saw with heavy pressure for a long period; stop and let the blade cool. If the blade gets too hot it will snap.

SAFETY: HACK SAWS

1. Keep your attention focused on the work.
2. Make a file cut to start the hack saw.
3. Be sure that the material to be cut is firmly secured or clamped.
4. Use both hands to control the hack saw.
5. Reduce the pressure when finishing a cut.
6. Store the hack saw in its proper place in the toolbox.

Saw Set. This is a tool used in the maintenance of crosscut hand saws and ripsaws. See Fig. 7. It is used to bend the teeth to alternate sides, to provide clearance for the blade while cutting. The teeth are bent alternately to the right and to the left, to an angle determined by the setting of the saw set.

Fig. 7. Saw set.

Portable Power Saws

Electrical Hand Saw. This saw, (Fig. 8) is a very powerful portable

Fig. 8. Electric hand saw. (Skil Corp.)

tool, which finds its main use on construction jobs and in maintenance work. These hand held saws are available in sizes to accommodate saw blades from about 6 inches to 12 inches in diameter. The 6½ and 7¼ inch blades are most commonly used. The diameter of the saw blade controls the maximum depth of cut that may be made with the saw. Electric hand saws are primarily used for crosscutting and ripping and, accordingly, standard models are usually equipped with a combination rip and crosscut blade, although special blades are available.

Fig. 9A illustrates the parts and terminology associated with the electric hand saw. Learn these and be familiar with the operation of the saw before using.

The base of the saw may be raised or lowered on a calibrated scale to control the depth of the cut, see the *depth scale* and *depth lock knob,*

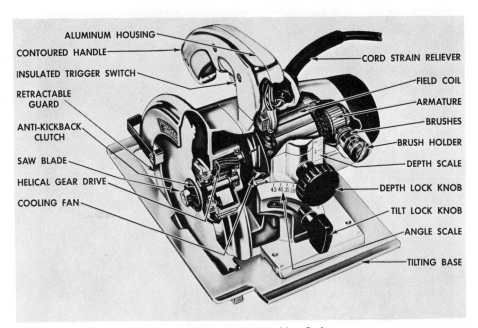

Fig. 9A. Portable power saw parts. (Porter-Cable Machine Co.)

Fig. 9A. Most electric hand saws will make a bevel cut of up to 45 degrees, the angle of the cut being indicated on a calibrated quadrant, see *angle scale* and *tilt lock knob*, Fig. 9A.

The blade, and the operator, are protected by a safety blade guard which is pushed back by the work piece and returns automatically when the saw is removed from the work. See the *retractable guard*, Fig. 9A. This feature is also called a *telescoping blade guard*. This safety device is of vital importance and should not be taken off or jammed back.

Two of the accessories available for the portable power saw are the *ripping fence* or *guide*, Fig. 9B, which permits the ripping of lumber to a pre-determined width, and the *saw protractor* which enables the operator to make rapid, accurate cuts at any angle up to 90 degrees. The protractor is placed on the board, with the desired angle set, and the saw shoe is advanced along the straight edge in making the cut.

In construction work, sub-floor and roof boards may be trimmed with the electric hand saw, all at one time, after laying, rather than cutting each length individually before laying. This method results in a better and faster job.

Fig. 9B. Ripping fence used with a portable power saw. (Millers Falls Co.)

SAFETY: PORTABLE POWER SAW

Do not use this tool unless you understand its operation and know the safety rules.

1. Be sure that the saw is properly grounded.

2. Remove tie, rings, wristwatch, and roll up sleeves.

3. With saw off and disconnected from power source, make sure that the blade is in good shape and is the proper type for the work to be done. Check to see that the blade is tight.

4. Check to see that the retractable blade guard is functioning properly before connecting saw to power source. Never tie back the blade guard.

5. Make all adjustments with power off and with saw disconnected from power supply.

6. Always make certain switch is in OFF position before connecting into power source. Keep electrical cord clear of operation.

7. Make sure that material to be cut is firmly supported and free of obstructions.

8. Bring the saw blade up to the desired point of cut, back up slightly, and start the motor. When full speed is reached, advance the saw through the work. Do not force the saw.

9. *Never* reach underneath the material being cut.

10. Stand to one side of the cut.

11. When through the cut, release the switch. Apply brake or wait until blade stops before setting saw down.

12. Disconnect saw from power.

13. To remove saw blade stand in operating position and turn the arbor nut towards you.

Sabre Saw. The sabre saw or bayonet saw (Fig. 10) is a versatile saw with many applications. It is usually an orbital blade saw with a stroke of $\frac{7}{16}$ to 1 inch. (With an orbital blade cutting action, the blade cuts on the upward stroke only and moves slightly away from the work on the downward stroke.) The tip of the blade is pointed and sharp, by which means the saw is able to start its own hole.

The base or shoe is adjustable so that either left-hand or right-hand bevel cuts may be made. Sharp angles and curves may easily be cut, and a guide fence is available as an accessory.

Many special saw blades may be obtained for cutting wood, metal sheets, rods, tubes, plastics, fiberglass, masonite, leather, and many other materials. Some models have variable speeds to suit the toughness of the material being sawed.

Reciprocating Saw. This is a general all-purpose saw, Fig. 11, and has, as its name implies, a reciprocating or up-and-down cutting action, although some models are equipped with dual-action cutting which allows them to cut with either a reciprocating or orbital action. The cutting stroke of the reciprocating saw is about 1 inch. This saw may be equipped with a wide selection of blades and is used to cut anything from soft woods to plastics and hard metals. The blade, of

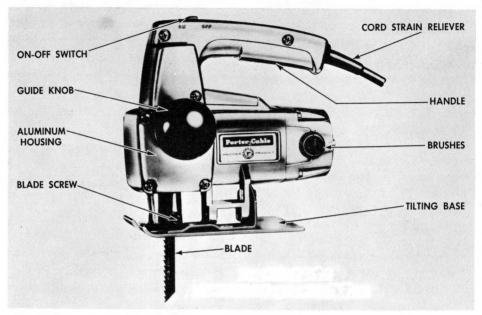

ON-OFF SWITCH

GUIDE KNOB

ALUMINUM HOUSING

BLADE SCREW

CORD STRAIN RELIEVER

HANDLE

BRUSHES

TILTING BASE

BLADE

Fig. 10. Heavy duty sabre saw and parts. (Porter-Cable Machine Co.)

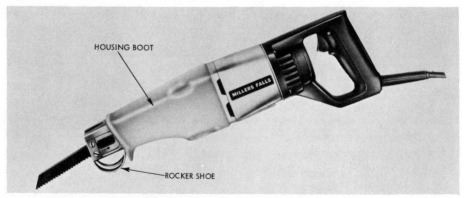

HOUSING BOOT

ROCKER SHOE

Fig. 11. Heavy duty reciprocating saw. (Miller Falls Co.)

course, should be chosen to fit the specific job. Most models have variable cutting speeds. The pointed blade allows the saw to start its own hole. Some reciprocating saws have a front guide, others (see Fig. 11) are guided by grasping the housing boot or nose piece.

SAFETY: SABRE SAWS AND RECIPROCATING SAWS

Do not use this tool unless you understand its operation and know the safety rules.

1. Be sure that the saw is properly grounded.

2. Remove tie, rings, wristwatch, and roll up sleeves.

3. Use the proper saw blade for the work to be done; be sure the blade is securely locked in place.

4. Clamp the material to be cut, using bench vise or clamps.

5. Be sure that the material to be cut is free of obstructions.

6. Keep your full attention focused on the work.

7. Always make sure that switch is in OFF position before connecting to power source.

8. Grip handle firmly with right hand and control forward and turning movements with left hand on front guide. (In some types of reciprocating saws, the saw is guided by grasping the housing boot. See Fig. 11.)

9. *Sabre saw.* To start cut, place forward edge of saw base on edge of material, start motor, and move blade into work.

Reciprocating saw. To start cut, place saw blade near material to be cut, start motor, and move blade into work.

10. Keep cutting pressure constant. Do not overload the saw.

11. *Never* reach underneath the material being cut.

12. When through cutting, turn off switch. Do not put saw down until motor stops.

13. When work is completed, disconnect saw from power source and remove saw blade.

Stationary Power Saws

Circular Table Saw. This saw, Fig. 12A, is one of the most frequently used power tools. This tool employs a circular saw blade, up to 16 or more inches in diameter, and is equipped with many accessories and safety devices. The axis of the saw can usually be tilted from the vertical. This feature is known as a tilting arbor and is adjusted by a graduated handwheel on the side, or on the front of some models, of the machine. (See the *saw tilt handwheel*, Fig. 12A.) Another handwheel located on the side (on the front of some models) of the machine raises or lowers the saw blade to give a cut of different depth, or for cutting wood of varying thickness. (See the *saw raising handwheel*, Fig. 12A.)

The saw blade is protected by a safety blade guard which also incorporates anti kick-back fingers to prevent the work being thrown back at the operator, causing him bodily harm. (See *splitter*, Fig. 12A.) Although this guard can be flipped back or even taken off for making adjustments to the saw, it should always be in place when the saw is in actual operation. The controls of the ripping fence are all located forward, near the operator, as a safety

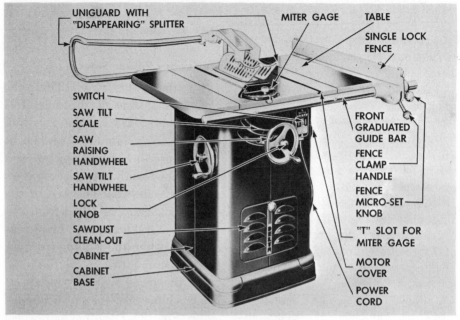

Fig. 12A. Circular table saw and parts. (Rockwell Mfg. Co.)

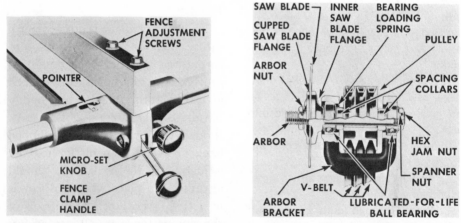

Fig. 12B. Fence control assembly *(left)* and arbor assembly *(right)* for circular table saw. (Rockwell Mfg. Co.)

precaution. The ripping fence locks to two guide bars located at the front and back of the machine and allows for minute adjustments in position. (See Fig. 12B, *fence control assembly* detail.) The arbor assembly, Fig. 12B, shows how the saw blade is attached.

There are various *circular saw blades* available for the table saw. The ones commonly used are the crosscut, rip, combination, and hollow ground. These blades should be frequently inspected for damage and sharpened when necessary. Fig. 13 illustrates some of the common circular saw blades.

Another accessory for the table saw is the dado head, Fig. 13, which will cut grooves from ⅛ of an inch to $^{13}/_{16}$ of an inch wide in $^1/_{16}$ of an inch steps. The blades and chippers are matched in sets to assure clean, even cuts with or against the grain. A set consists of two outside blades and four inside cutters, Fig. 13.

When using the dado or molding cutter heads, a cast insert must be used in the table top to reduce the size of the saw aperture. There are many different styles of knives available in sets, fitting the molding cutter head, for making moldings of various configurations.

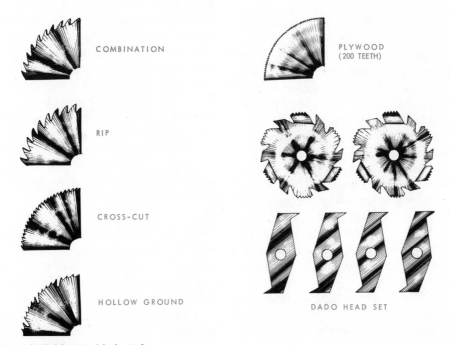

COMBINATION

PLYWOOD
(200 TEETH)

RIP

CROSS-CUT

HOLLOW GROUND

DADO HEAD SET

Fig. 13. Table saw blade styles.

Fundamentals of Carpentry

SAFETY: CIRCULAR TABLE SAWS

Do not use this tool unless you understand its operation and know the safety rules.

1. Be sure that the saw is properly grounded.

2. Remove tie, rings, wristwatch, and roll up sleeves.

3. With power off and cable disconnected, make sure that all safety devices are functioning properly. Always use the safety devices and guards. Check the blade to see that it is right type for the work to be done and that it is in good condition. (See safety rules for circular saw blades.) Be sure that the blade fits perfectly and that there is no play. Be sure that the blade will clear both sides.

4. Make all adjustments before connecting to power supply.

5. Make sure that the work to be cut is free of nails and obstructions. Care must be taken if warped or twisted boards that do not lie flat on the table must be cut—they may kick back.

6. The wearing of goggles is recommended.

7. Be sure that the work area is cleared of loose material that might cause tripping or falling. Be sure that the saw table is clear of scraps. (The saw table is cleaned with a brush when the saw is *not* running. The power controls must be locked in an OFF position when brushing.)

8. Slide material against fence or hold it solidly against miter gage. Thus the possibility of twisting the material while it is in the saw is eliminated. Never attempt to saw without these devices.

9. Make certain that the material to be cut is solidly against the fence. Use the ripping fence for ripping and the crosscutting fence for crosscutting.

10. No free hand cutting should be done under any circumstances. Always use a guide.

11. Use the splitter attachment (safety blade guard) when cutting.

12. The saw should project only ⅛ to ¼ inch above the stock when cutting.

13. Turn on power and allow blade to come to full speed before starting cut.

14. Never reach over or lift stock over the saw when it is running.

15. Do not place your hands in front of or over running blade. Keep the hands a safe distance from the blade. The left hand can be used to hold the stock against the fence and the bed of the saw when *ripping*. However, it should be kept a good distance from the blade. The right hand is used to feed the stock into the saw. Put the thumb on the end of the board and place the fingers on top, keeping them close to the fence. It is good practice to hook the little finger over the top of the fence to guide the hand. The thumbs can be hooked over the miter gage when *crosscutting*.

16. Rip stock before crosscutting to avoid the unsafe practice of ripping short lengths.

17. When feeding stock through the saw, arch the hand. Do not lay the hand flat on the stock.

18. Stand to one side when turning on power. Do not stand in line with the revolving circular saw. Stand either to

the left or to the right, whichever is more convenient.

19. Stand to one side when running saw. The stock may be thrown back from the machine (this is called *kickback*). Saws should be equipped with an anti-kickback device; however, always assume that kickback is possible.

20. Do not force the saw. Crowding the saw is dangerous and may result in breaking the saw.

21. Never attempt to cut more than one piece at a time.

22. Use a pusher stick for cutting small pieces (12″ or less in length) or ripping narrow stock (4″ or less wide).

23. Get help when cutting long pieces. When ripping long pieces, get someone to hold up the piece while you *push* it through. Never pull a board through a saw, always feed.

24. Fasten a block to ripping fence when it is used as stop for crosscutting.

25. The dado head must be taken off the saw arbor after use.

26. Do not brush off the bed or remove small pieces from the saw table with the hand when the saw is running.

27. Turn off power if blade overheats. Overheating is usually caused by a dull saw. When a saw becomes overheated, it loses its set and the material binds on the saw. It must be filed and set before being used again.

28. When through cutting, shut off power and disconnect from power source. Do not leave until the blade has come to a complete stop. Never leave a running saw unattended.

29. Store saw blades in a safe, designated place where there is no likelihood of accidental contact with teeth.

SAFETY: CIRCULAR SAW BLADES*

A saw in good condition will cut easily and clear itself. It will not kick back, and it will not twist or burn or snake. More than half of all saw accidents can be prevented simply by keeping saws in good condition.

Every circular saw should be inspected and sharpened at regular intervals. If used continuously, it should be sharpened two to four times a day.

Don't attempt to file or sharpen a saw unless you are qualified and authorized to do such work.

CHECK FOR THESE:

1. *Proper Jointing*—All the teeth should be even in length.

2. *Straight Blade*—The blade should not be lumpy or warped.

3. *Correct Gumming*—The depth, size, and shape of the gullets should be such as to let all sawdust discharge freely. The bottom of the gullet should be round, see Fig. 14.

4. *Proper Set*—The cut in the wood should be a trifle wider than the thickness of the saw blade.

5. *Sharpness*—A sharp saw sings—a dull saw grunts.

6. *Cracks*—A saw must be discarded if it has a crack longer than 5 per cent of the diameter. Fig. 14 "D" illustrates a type of crack that commonly occurs.

*State of California: Department of Industrial Relations, Division of Industrial Safety, Bulletin 108 (Rev).

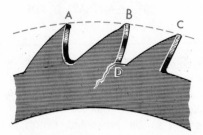

Fig. 14. Properly and improperly shaped power ripsaw teeth. "A" illustrates a properly shaped ripsaw tooth: the point is sharp, the gullet well rounded and the tooth is filed straight across, not rounded. Teeth "B" and "C" are improperly shaped with dull points and square gullets. "D" illustrates a typical break in the blade.

BLADE MAINTENANCE:

1. Inspect a saw to see that it is sharp and free from cracks.

2. Use the right saw for the right job. Don't use a ripsaw for crosscutting or a crosscut saw for ripsawing.

3. When sharpening or gumming circular saws with an emery wheel, use a free cutting wheel.

4. Discard saw if teeth become case hardened, blued or glazed. Teeth are then likely to crack or break.

5. When setting a circular saw, make sure that the set is in the point of the tooth and not below the root of the tooth.

6. Make sure there is no end play or lateral motion in the arbor.

7. See that the collar and stem of the arbor fit perfectly.

8. Store circular saw blades in a place where there is no likelihood of accidental contact with the teeth.

Radial Saw. A radial saw, Fig. 15, is a very versatile power tool which is used in all types of construction, including house construction, form construction, and timber construction. It is used both on the construction job or in the shop. It may weigh more than 200 pounds, but it is balanced so that it can easily be carried by two men—it is narrow enough to pass through an ordinary door.

The radial saw has many of the characteristics of a table saw but differs in one important respect. The material being cut always remains in the same place, while it is the saw itself that moves.

The turret arm to which the saw head is attached allows the saw head to swing in a full circle about the horizontal plane, while keeping the saw over the table. The motor unit, of which the saw is a part, also tilts to any desired angle. This flexibility allows practically any type of cut or dado to be made, including left-hand mitering. The position of the fence is variable and, in the interests of safety, the fence controls are in the front of the machine out of the way of the saw blade. During the making of complicated cuts, an advantage is realized with the radial saw by being able to see the cut at all times, particularly when making dados. (The blades for a dado head set are illustrated in Fig. 13.)

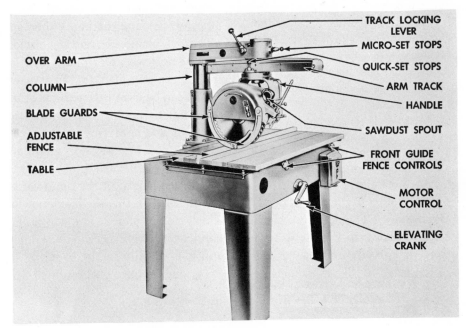

Fig. 15A. Radial saw and parts. (Rockwell Mfg. Co.)

SAFETY: RADIAL SAW

Do not use this tool unless you understand its operation and know the safety rules.

1. Be sure that the saw is properly grounded.

2. Remove tie, rings, wristwatch, and roll up sleeves.

3. With power off and cable disconnected, make sure that all safety devices are functioning properly. Check blade to see that it is the right type for the work to be done, is in good condition, and is tight on the arbor.

4. Make all adjustments before connecting to power supply.

5. Make sure that work to be cut is free of nails and obstructions. Be sure

that the work area is cleared of loose material or scraps that might cause tripping or falling. Be sure that the saw blade is clear and that the table is cleared of scraps.

6. (The table is cleaned with a brush when the saw is *not* running. Power must be turned OFF.)

7. Make certain that the material to be cut is solidly against the fence.

8. Be sure the blade guard is adjusted to the thickness of the material to be cut.

9. Cut only one piece at a time.

10. Keep your full attention focused on the work.

11. Wear goggles if necessary.

12. Turn on power and allow blade to

come to full speed before starting cut.

13. Always pull the blade, rather than pushing it through the material to be cut. Have a firm grip on the handle.

14. Do not force the saw. Crowding the saw is dangerous and may result in breaking the saw.

15. Keep hands away from the direction of travel of the saw.

16. When through, shut off power, and disconnect from power source. Do not leave until blade has come to a complete stop.

Band Saw.   The main use of the band saw, shown in Fig. 16A, is the cutting of curved surfaces, or contour cutting as it is sometimes called, although it is equally suitable for straight cutting. Other applications include: trimming circles, cutting notches, and ripping. Special blades are supplied for most saws which can be used with various other building materials, such as plastic, bakelite, and nonferrous metals.

Since band saws are manufactured in a great variety of sizes and styles, the length of the band varies to fit the particular machine for which it is intended. The width of a band very rarely exceeds one inch, and it is usually in the order of $\frac{1}{8}$ to $\frac{1}{4}$ inch wide. The pitch of the

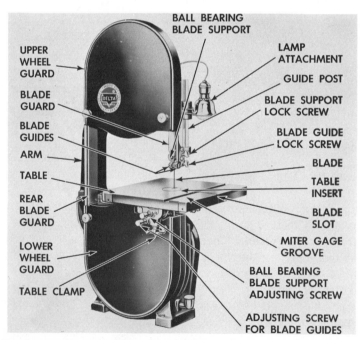

Fig. 16A. Band saw and parts. (Rockwell Mfg. Co.)

teeth and the cutting speed are largely determined by the material being cut.

The sawing table can be tilted on most machines to the exact angle, with respect to the vertical, at which the cut is desired, Fig. 16B, left.

The upper and lower guides for the band saw blade are illustrated in Fig. 16B. The saw blade guides are adjustable.

The fence (Fig. 17) is supported on two guide bars and may be adjusted over a wide range, its exact position with respect to the saw being indicated on a scale calibrated in inches. The guide bar (Fig. 17) and the pivoting work support body are equipped with a scale and pointer, reading through about 120 degrees. There are usually adjustable positive stops at the 45 degree and the 90 degree positions.

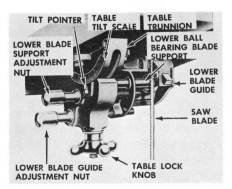
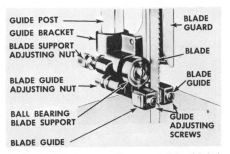

Fig. 16B. Lower guide and table assembly (left) and upper guide assembly (right). (Rockwell Mfg. Co.)

Fig. 17. Fence, guide bar and miter gage for band saw.

Fundamentals of Carpentry

SAFETY: BAND SAWS

Do not use this tool unless you understand its operation and know the safety rules.

1. Be sure that the saw is properly grounded.
2. Remove tie, rings, wristwatch, and roll up sleeves.
3. With power off and cable disconnected, make sure that the wheel guards are securely in place. Check the blade to see that it is the right type and width for the work to be done and that it is in good condition.
4. Make all adjustments before connecting to power supply.
5. Make sure that the work to be cut is free of nails and obstructions.
6. The wearing of goggles is recommended.
7. Be sure that the work area is cleared of loose material that might cause tripping or falling. Be sure that the saw table is clear of scraps. (The saw table is cleaned with a brush when the saw is *not* running. The power controls must be locked in an OFF position when brushing.)
8. Be sure that the work is within the capacity of the saw. No cutting radius should be too small for the blade.
9. Be sure that the upper guide is as close (roughly ⅛ to ¼ inch) to the work as possible.
10. The ripping fence or other attachments should be in place before starting cut.
11. The work should be planned to avoid damaging the blade. Make "release" cuts before cutting long curves.

12. Secure a helper if long pieces of wood are to be sawed. The helper supports the work—he does not guide or pull it.
13. Stand clear when turning on power. When band saws break, as they occasionally do, it happens when the saw is in operation. Never turn on the power when anyone is standing in line with the wheels—and never stand in line with the wheels yourself.
14. Keep your full attention on the work. Do not allow minor disturbances to distract your attention when band saw is in operation. It is highly unsafe to look around or to attempt to speak to another person.
15. Keep fingers at least 2 inches from blade when cutting. Never place your hands in front of cutting edge of saw blade. Extreme caution should be exercised when sawing curves. The material cuts more easily with the grain than across the grain. Because of this, the work is not carried through the saw at an even speed, and your hands are likely to be carried in front of the saw and into the moving blade. Never attempt to hold material in a way that your thumbs or fingers are in line with the saw blade.
16. Do not reach around blade. Never attempt to reach around the moving blade. If it is necessary to remove small pieces, clean the saw, or make adjustments, *turn off the power*. The blade might break, and your hand and arm would be in a dangerous position.
17. Do not crowd the saw. Feed wood into the band saw only as fast as the teeth of the blade are removing the wood. Unnecessary pressure forces the

blade against the roller guides, which may cause the blade to overheat and break.

18. Round material may be cut on band saw only when it has been mounted in a holding device. It is very dangerous to attempt to hold cylindrical stock with the hands when it is being cut because the material has a tendency to spin and crowd the blade. When it is mounted securely in a jig and the setup has been approved, it is safe to cut round stock on a band saw.

19. Shut off power if anything goes

wrong or if any adjustments must be made. Small pieces of wood often become wedged in the table insert. Never attempt to correct this situation while the saw is running. If the saw kerf closes and the wood cannot be removed, stop the machine. If the blade should break, and it is not convenient to push the switch on the saw, pull the plug or shut off the power at the main switch.

20. When finished cutting, shut off power and disconnect from power source. Do not leave until the blade has come to a complete stop. Never leave a running saw unattended.

Boring Tools

All wood-boring augers and drill bits, held by the brace and hand drill, are known to the trade as *boring tools*. These tools include a variety of instruments used in one way or another in connection with boring holes in wood.

Brace and Bits

The common bit brace, the auger bits, as well as a number of special tools belong in this classification.

Ratchet-Bit Brace. This brace (Fig. 18) usually has a 10-inch sweep which is large enough for average work. (The *sweep* refers to the diameter of the circle or half circle made in turning the handle.) With the ratchet-bit brace, the handle does not turn a full circle. Rather, a half circle is made by the

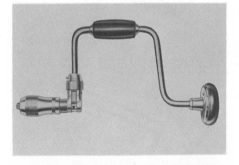

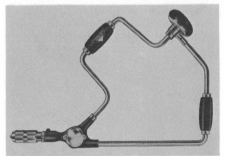

Fig. 18. Braces used by the carpenter: ratchet brace (top) and corner brace (bottom). (Miller Falls Co.)

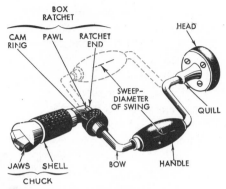

Fig. 19. Ratchet brace and parts.

handle turn. This allows the ratchet-bit brace to work close in corners or close to walls. A good ratchet-bit brace may be adjusted to turn either left or right. Various sizes and kinds of bits may be used in the brace. They are inserted and tightened in the brace jaws. Fig. 19 illustrates the parts and terminology associated with the ratchet brace.

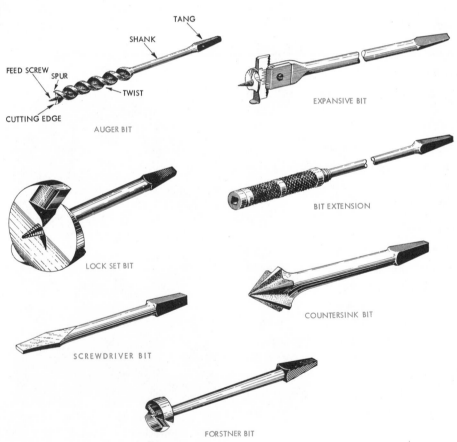

Fig. 20. Bits used by the carpenter.

Corner Brace. This brace is used for ease in boring in corners and against walls (Fig. 18). The handle turns a full revolution.

Auger Bits. These (Fig. 20) are used to bore holes in wood. They commonly come in sizes from ¼ of an inch to 1 inch. Larger sizes are available. The number on the tang indicates the size in $\frac{1}{16}$ths, ranging from ¼ inch on up. A number 12 bit is illustrated in Fig. 20, which means that it is a $\frac{12}{16}$th, or ¾ths, of an inch. The fineness or coarseness of the *feed screw* determines the speed of the bit. Three screw threads are available: fine, medium, and coarse. A fine thread is recommended for slow, precision work. A coarse thread is recommended for fast, rough work. The selection of auger bits usually carried by the carpenter runs from ¼ inch to 1 inch and is called a *set*. A set of bits is often kept in a plastic roll which has an individual pocket for each bit. See Fig. 21. Larger holes are made with an *expansive bit* (Fig. 20). These bits are available with a choice of two adjustable cutters, the smaller of which is used for holes between ⅞ of an inch and 1½ inches. The larger cutter is used for holes up to 3⅛ inches. *Lock bits* or *large hole bits* (Fig. 20) are used with a lock jig to make holes for the installation of cylindrical locks.

Bit Extensions. These add to

Fig. 21. Plastic roll and set of bits. (Stanley Works)

the length of the standard bit (Fig. 20). They are commonly obtainable in 18 to 24 inch lengths. The bit extension is used in form construction where two holes have to be lined up at a distance to receive the wall tie and also when a hole is needed in a surface which cannot be reached with the standard bit. It is also used to bore a hole in stock, such as a timber, which is thicker than the length of a standard bit.

Screwdriver Bits. These (Fig. 20) are useful for driving large screws in heavy hardware and are also used in a brace for removing old screws that refuse to budge with a regular screwdriver. A Phillips bit is also available.

Countersink Bit. This (Fig. 20) is not actually a drill but is used to increase the diameter of the top of a drilled hole to receive the head of a screw. The countersink is conical in shape. Therefore, the deeper the countersink is allowed to penetrate, the greater will be the diameter of the hole. Counter sink bits are available up to a maximum of ¾ of an inch.

Forstner Bit. This bit (Fig. 20) has no screw to center it and pull it into the wood. Cutting is done by two lips and the circular rim. The hole, therefore, has a flat bottom as there are no spurs or screw to cut below the lips. This bit is used where a shallow hole is needed part way

through the stock without marring the opposite side.

For other bits, or bits for a particular job, consult manufacturer's catalogs. Always choose a bit to fit the specific job.

SAFETY: BRACE AND BITS

1. Keep your full attention focused on the work.
2. Keep bits sharp.
3. Select the right type and size of bit for the job.
4. Be sure that the bit is securely tightened in the brace.
5. Make a hole with an awl to start the bit and to assure that the bit will be well centered.
6. Learn how to use a brace properly (see Fig. 22). Keep the brace straight and at a right angle to the hole being drilled. Do not twist the brace to one side. Apply firm, steady pressure.
7. Do not bore all the way through a board. Complete the hole by boring from the other side. See Fig. 22.
8. Do not drive a bit any deeper than the twist. If the shank is driven into the wood, clogging and over-heating may result.
9. Remove a bit from a hole by reversing the direction of the bit turn.
10. Clean bits with an oily rag.
11. Oil brace periodically.
12. Store brace and bits in a designated place in the toolbox. Store bits separately. Bits are often kept in a plastic roll which has an individual pocket for each kit. See Fig. 21.

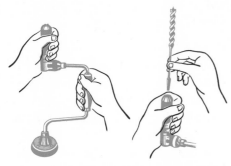

TO PLACE THE BIT IN THE CHUCK, GRASP THE CHUCK SHELL AND TURN THE HANDLE TO THE LEFT UNTIL THE JAWS ARE WIDE OPEN. INSERT THE BIT SHANK IN THE SQUARE SOCKET AT THE BOTTOM OF THE CHUCK AND TURN THE HANDLE TO THE RIGHT UNTIL THE BIT IS HELD FIRMLY IN THE JAWS.

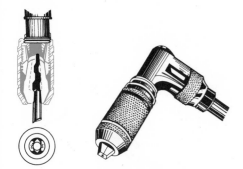

TO OPERATE THE RATCHET TURN THE CAM RING. TURNING THE CAM RING TO THE RIGHT WILL ALLOW THE BIT TO TURN RIGHT AND GIVE RATCHET ACTION WHEN THE HANDLE IS TURNED LEFT. TURN THE CAM RING LEFT TO REVERSE THE ACTION.
THE RATCHET IS INDISPENSABLE WHEN BORING A HOLE IN A CORNER OR WHERE SOME OBJECT PREVENTS MAKING A FULL TURN WITH THE HANDLE.

BIT BRACE CHUCKS OF THE ABOVE DESIGN WITHOUT A SQUARE SOCKET ARE OPERATED IN LIKE MANNER. THE CORNERS OF THE TAPER SHANK OF THE BIT SHOULD BE CAREFULLY SEATED AND CENTERED IN THE V GROOVES OF THE JAWS.

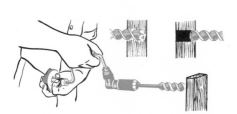

TO BORE A HORIZONTAL HOLE, HOLD THE HEAD OF THE BRACE CUPPED IN THE LEFT HAND AGAINST THE STOMACH AND WITH THE THUMB AND FOREFINGER AROUND THE QUILL. TO BORE THRU WITHOUT SPLINTERING THE SECOND FACE, STOP WHEN THE SCREW POINT IS THRU AND FINISH FROM THE SECOND FACE. WHEN BORING THRU WITH AN EXPANSIVE BIT IT IS BEST TO CLAMP A PIECE OF WOOD TO THE SECOND FACE AND BORE STRAIGHT THRU.

TO BORE A VERTICAL HOLE, HOLD THE BRACE AND BIT PERPENDICULAR TO THE SURFACE OF THE WORK. TEST BY SIGHT. COMPARE THE DIRECTION OF THE BIT TO THE NEAREST STRAIGHT EDGE OR TO SIDES OF THE VISE. A TRY SQUARE MAY BE HELD NEAR THE BIT.

Fig. 22. Brace and bit operation. (Stanley Works)

Fig. 23. Bit gage.

Bit Gage. The gage is an attachment to a drill bit, to make a hole of a specific depth. See Fig. 23. It acts as a stop, and when the required depth is reached, prevents the drill from penetrating the material any further. Other types of bit gages are also available.

Hand Drills

Hand Drill. This tool is used to make holes from ¼ inch to ⅜ of an inch in diameter (Fig. 24). It is operated by the turning of a handle which is geared to the chuck. For ease in operation, the drill holes should be started with an awl or punch.

Breast Drill. Similar in appearance to the hand drill, except that it is a heavier tool and is used for making larger holes (Fig. 24).

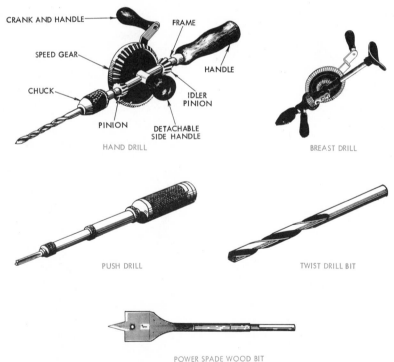

Fig. 24. Drills and bits.

Greater pressure can be applied while drilling than with the hand drill by applying the chest or shoulder to the breast plate.

Push Drill. A very useful tool for the installation of small builder's hardware (Fig. 24). It operates semi-automatically and can be used in one hand, so that the work piece may be held in place with the other hand. As the handle is pushed in, it rotates the drill, and a spring in the handle causes it to return to its original position when the pressure is released. A set of *drill points* (bits) ranging form $\frac{1}{16}$ inch to $\frac{11}{64}$ of an inch is stored in the handle.

Twist Drill. A bit used to make holes in wood, metal, fiber, plastic, and other materials (Fig. 24). Twist drills are used both in hand drills and in power drills. Depending upon the use, whether metal or wood, the drill point will have different point angles and different cutting edge angles. A carbon steel twist drill, which is used for boring wood, should not be used to drill holes in hard metals. Twist drills which are used on hard metals will have HS (high speed) or HSS (high speed steel) stamped on the shank. If the shank has no letter markings, it is carbon steel and should be used for drilling wood.

Power Auger Bit. This bit is used in electric power drills for drilling into wood, plastic, composition, wallboard, etc. (Fig. 24). Sizes

range from $\frac{3}{8}$ to $1\frac{1}{4}$ inch. The size of the bit is given on the cutting blade.

Portable Power Drills

Portable Electric Drill. The electric drill (Fig. 25) is an important and frequently used item in the carpenter's tool kit since, apart from precision, it adds speed to his

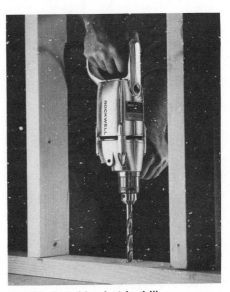

Fig. 25. Portable electric drill.

work. Fig. 26 illustrates the parts and terminology associated with the portable electric drill. Note that two types of handles are available: the *D-handle* (Fig. 25) and the *pistol grip handle* (Fig. 26). Heavier drills will have a *spade handle*. In addition, some models have an auxiliary handle for better control, Fig. 25.

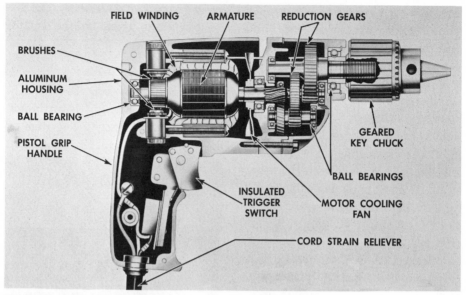

BRUSHES

ALUMINUM HOUSING

BALL BEARING

PISTOL GRIP HANDLE

FIELD WINDING   ARMATURE   REDUCTION GEARS

GEARED KEY CHUCK

INSULATED TRIGGER SWITCH

BALL BEARINGS

MOTOR COOLING FAN

CORD STRAIN RELIEVER

Fig. 26. Portable electric drill and parts. (Rockwell Mfg. Co.)

Portable drills are available in the size range of ¼ inch to about 1¼ inches, this dimension being the maximum size of drill that the particular model will accommodate. This, however, is not the final limitation, for some large drill bits and auger bits are available with reduction shanks. The largest portable drill used by the carpenter is probably the ¾ inch drill, and he uses this size for making holes for carriage and machine bolts in truss construction. This size of drill is also used with a special cutting tool for making grooves for split rings used in large trusses. Drill speeds may be varied for driving in harder materials, such as ceramic tile, brick, etc. Screwdriver attachments

may be used for driving or removing screws.

Battery operated drills may also be obtained. These run off a portable battery which may be recharged from any 115 volt outlet. Some drills are cordless and have the battery located in the handle of the drill. These are also rechargeable.

SAFETY: PORTABLE POWER DRILLS

Do not use this tool unless you understand its operation and know the safety rules.

1. Be sure that the drill is properly grounded.

2. Remove tie, rings, and wristwatch, and roll up sleeves.

3. Be sure that the material to be drilled is securely clamped.

4. Drill should be turned off and disconnected from power source while removing or installing drill bit.

5. Before connecting to power source, make certain switch is in OFF position.

6. Use the proper drill for the job. Be sure that the drill is not faulty or dull.

7. Before starting drill, make certain drill bit is securely gripped in the chuck.

8. Check to see that key has been removed from chuck before starting drill.

9. Locate the exact point where the hole is desired and indent with center punch or awl.

10. Keep your full attention focused on the work.

11. Drill with even, steady pressure, and let the drill do the work.

12. When work is completed, disconnect drill from power source and remove drill bit.

Stationary Power Drills

Drill Press. The drill press is a commonly encountered shop tool and, although it suffers from a certain immobility from the carpenter's point of view, it compensates for this characteristic by being adaptable for the jobs of routing, mortising, jointing, shaping, sanding, and plug cutting. See Fig. 27. It is, of course, the ideal tool for drilling on a production basis.

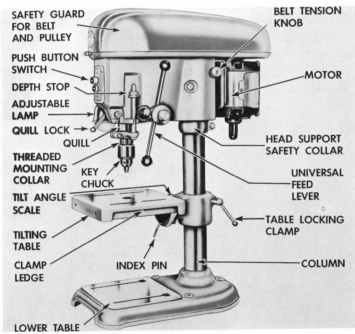

Fig. 27. Drill press and parts. (Rockwell Mfg. Co.)

The drilling table can be raised or lowered and locked in position and, in some models, it can also be tilted in any direction. The speed of the drill may be changed by means of a series of pulleys and belts located in the head of the machine, where the driving motor is usually located. Various drilling speeds must be used according to the nature of the material being drilled and the drill in use.

The drill itself is lowered to the work by means of a feed lever which returns the drill automatically when released. The drill may also be locked in a specific position, or for a specific limit, which is particularly desirable for precision depth and repeat drilling, and for mortising and shaping. In using the drill press, the work should be firmly clamped to the table rather than being held in place by hand. Otherwise, it is likely to break loose and start spinning freely, causing possible harm to both the operator and the press.

SAFETY: DRILL PRESSES

Do not use this tool unless you understand its operation and know the safety rules.

1. Be sure that the drill is properly grounded.

2. Remove tie, rings, and wristwatch, and roll up sleeves. Do not wear gloves or loose clothing.

3. Keep the floor clean around the drill press and if you spill oil put sawdust over it. Use a brush to clean table; be sure that the drill is OFF when cleaning table.

4. Be sure that the material to be drilled is securely clamped.

5. Turn drill off and disconnect from power source before installing drill bit.

6. Watch that the hand feed lever does not fly into your face when you are adjusting the column.

7. Use the proper drill for the job. Use drills that are sharp and properly ground. Always check to be sure that they are the correct size. *(Never* use a regular manual auger bit on a drill press.)

8. Check to be sure that the correct drill speed has been selected.

9. Check to make sure that the belt guard has been replaced.

10. Before connecting to power source, make certain switch is in OFF position.

11. Before starting drill, make certain drill bit is securely gripped in the chuck.

12. Check to see that the chuck key has been removed before starting drill.

13. Locate the exact point where the hole is desired and indent with center punch or awl.

14. Hammering on the drill press table is not allowed except with soft hammers to adjust the work.

15. Keep your full attention focused on the work. Do not talk to persons while either you or they are operating a machine.

16. Wear headgear to prevent the possibility of loose hair being caught in the revolving spindle.

17. Keep waste and rags away from revolving drill and chips.

18. Use the side ledges and table slots for clamping the work to the table.

19. Drill with even, steady pressure, and let the drill do the work.

20. Keep fingers away from chips and moving parts. Turn the drill off and remove chips with brush or piece of wood.

21. Never try to remove material that has become jammed while the spindle is revolving. If the work becomes loose, stop the machine.

22. Do not overtax the drill. Broken, overheated, or dull drills will slow up production. On deep holes, back out frequently, and allow the drill to cool.

23. Ease up on feeding when the drill breaks through work.

24. Watch that you do not drill into the table or into any clamps used to hold the work.

25. Back your drill out as soon as you stop feeding the drill. The drill will become dull if left in the work and will drag.

26. Turn off the power before making *any* adjustments.

27. When work is completed, turn off power, disconnect drill from power source and remove drill bit. (Hold drill bit when removing to avoid dropping.) Clean machine and return drill bits to their designated storage area.

Paring and Shaving Tools

The paring and shaving tools include those which have knife edges, such as the plane and the chisel, the two most important of the group.

Hand Operated Planes

Together with the hammer, saw, square, and chisel, the *plane* is one of the principal tools used by the carpenter. The preparation of wood surfaces consists in smoothing or planing, which can be carried to any extent and may include sandpapering or even polishing. The instrument used for the rougher part of this work is called a *plane*, which consists of a sharp blade, or knife, in the form of a chisel held in place in a large block of wood or iron by means of clamps, so that the knife can be kept steady and guided easily. There are a great many different kinds of planes, but the principle of all of them is the same. The knife projects at the bottom through a slot and takes off a shaving which is relatively thick or thin according to the distance which the knife projects below the body of the plane. Any imperfection in the edge of the knife will be repeated on the surface of the wood. The plane family consists of various members, with each plane designed for a particular purpose, although some planes will perform a number of different operations. The following list is suggested in the order in which they should normally be bought. Actual job conditions, however, may cause the order to vary.

1. Jack plane
2. Block plane
3. Rabbet plane
4. Jointer plane
5. Smooth plane
6. Spokeshave
7. Router plane
8. Bullnose plane

The various parts of the Stanley smooth plane, a development of the original Bailey plane, are shown in Fig. 28. However, this plane is only one of several different makes available to the mechanic today. To de-

scribe in detail all the different planes on the market would require more space than is available for that purpose in this book. Hence, only a few types are given special mention: the jack plane; the smooth plane; the jointer plane; and the fore plane.

Jack Plane. A plane for all-around work is the jack plane shown in Fig. 29. This plane is used for rough work and to give preliminary smoothing to lumber coming directly from the mill. Although the jack plane is manufactured in various sizes, the 14-inch length with a 2-inch *cutter* or *blade* is most commonly used. The craftsman who uses the 14-inch length jack plane is

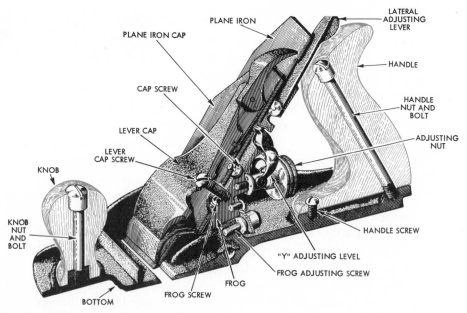

Fig. 28. The Stanley smooth plane.

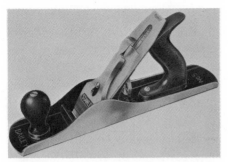

Fig. 29. Jack plane for rough work and preliminary smoothing. (Stanley Works)

Fig. 31. Smooth plane, usually smaller than jack plane. (Stanley Works)

able not only to smooth and join a board but, also, to do other all-around work with this tool.

Block Plane. The *low-angled steel block plane*, Fig. 30, which can be operated with one hand, is a desirable plane for fitting. One hand operates the plane while the other holds the material to be worked.

Fig. 30. Low-angled steel block plane; operated with one hand. (Stanley Works)

Smooth, or Smoothing, Plane. The smooth plane, Fig. 31, though similar in construction to the jack plane, is usually much shorter. Since

it is not expected to take off as much material as the jack plane, it does not require as great a force to operate the smoothing plane. This is a short, finely set plane, and it may be made of either iron or wood. Being light in weight, it is easy to operate and will produce a smooth (though not true) surface quickly. A smoothing plane 8 inches long with a 1¾-inch cutter is recommended.

Jointer Plane. The largest of the planes is the jointer, Fig. 32. The jointer planes vary in size from 20 to 24 inches in length. When it is necessary to smooth a large surface,

Fig. 32. Jointer plane. Largest of the carpenter's planes, is intended for use on the work bench. (Stanley Works)

or to make the edge of a board absolutely true so that two such surfaces, when finished, will fit together closely, this plane is used following the preliminary smoothing by the jack plane. The jointer plane is made long and heavy because it is intended for use on long boards and for obtaining a true surface when joining two boards. The carpenter finds the jointer plane indispensable in fitting doors and making the edges straight and true.

Fore Plane. Between the jack plane and the jointer is a tool called the fore plane. Some carpenters prefer an 18-inch fore plane to a 22-inch jointer since the smaller plane reduces the weight of the tools a carpenter must carry around with him. However, the long length of the jointer usually insures a truer-planed surface than is obtained with the fore plane which is shorter in length.

Other Planes and Shaving Tools. A few of the other planes which might prove desirable to own are illustrated and explained in Figs. 33 to 40. A desirable plane for planing into corners or against perpendicular surfaces is the *duplex rabbet plane*, Fig. 33, with its ½ inch cutter. This plane is also convenient in size as it measures only 8 inches in length. The *router plane*, Fig. 34, is used for surfacing the bottom of grooves or other depressions parallel with the surface of

the wood. The *bull-nose plane*, Fig. 35, will work close into corners or other places hard to reach. The *fiberboard grooving plane*, Fig. 36 is used for cutting grooves and bevels in fiberboard. The *fiberboard bevel plane*, Fig. 37, with its razor sharp blade, is used for cutting bevels on fiberboard and other soft materials.

The *forming plane*, Fig. 38, with a serrated bottom, is used on plywoods, end grain, plastics, leather, fiber composition board, soft metals, etc. Holes by the serrations allow the waste material to pass upward.

The *spokeshave*, Fig. 39, is used to smooth curved surfaces, either concave or convex. The *drawknife* or *drawshave*, Fig. 40, is used for cutting off large quantities of material and for smoothing curved surfaces. It is pulled toward the operator in cutting. Tool catalogs should be consulted when special work demands the use of additional planes.

Fig. 33. Duplex rabbet plane for planing into corners. (Stanley Works)

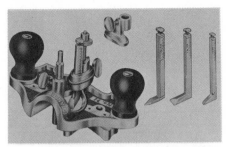

Fig. 34. Router plane used for surfacing grooves. (Stanley Works)

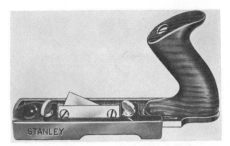

Fig. 37. Fiberboard bevel plane. (Stanley Works)

Fig. 35. Bull-nose rabbet plane for working close into corners. (Stanley Works)

Fig. 38. Forming plane used on wood, plastics, leather, soft metals, fiber composition boards. (Stanley Works)

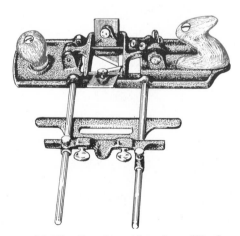

Fig. 36. Fiberboard grooving plane. (Stanley Works)

Fig. 39. Spokeshave for curved surfaces.

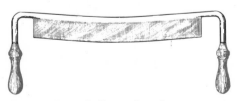

Fig. 40. Draw knife or drawshave.

TO START PLANING TAKE AN EASY BUT FIRM POSITION DIRECTLY BACK OF THE WORK.

AT THE END OF THE STROKE THE WEIGHT OF THE BODY SHOULD BE CARRIED EASILY ON THE LEFT FOOT.

HOLD THE PLANE SQUARE WITH THE WORK FACE OF THE WORK.

PLANE END GRAIN HALF WAY FROM EACH EDGE.

IF THE PLANE IS PUSHED ALL THE WAY THE CORNERS WILL BREAK.

IT IS EASIER TO PLANE A LONG EDGE STRAIGHT WITH A LONG PLANE THAN WITH A SHORT ONE. A LONG PLANE BRIDGES THE LOW PARTS AND DOES NOT CUT THEM UNTIL THE HIGH SPOTS ARE REMOVED.

Fig. 41. How to use a plane. (Adapted from Stanley Works)

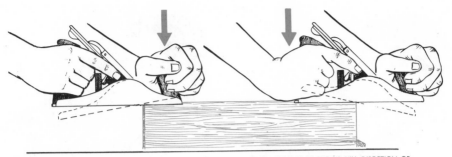

TO CUT A SMOOTH STRAIGHT EDGE THE PLANE IS PUSHED WITH THE GRAIN, THAT IS IN THE UP HILL DIRECTION OF THE FIBRES.
TO KEEP THE PLANE STRAIGHT PRESS DOWN ON THE KNOB AT THE BEGINNING OF THE STROKE AND ON THE HANDLE AT THE END OF THE STROKE. AVOID DROPPING (LOWERING) THE PLANE AS SHOWN BY THE BROKEN LINES. IT ROUNDS THE CORNERS.

TO OBTAIN A SMOOTH SURFACE PLANE WITH THE GRAIN. IF THE GRAIN IS TORN OR ROUGH AFTER THE FIRST STROKE REVERSE THE WORK.
IF THE GRAIN IS CROSS OR CURLY, SHARPEN THE PLANE IRON CAREFULLY, SET THE PLANE IRON CAP AS NEAR THE CUTTING EDGE AS POSSIBLE AND ADJUST THE PLANE IRON TO TAKE A VERY THIN EVEN SHAVING.

Fig. 41. Cont'd.

SAFETY: HAND PLANES

1. Keep your full attention focused on the work.

2. Be familiar with how to properly use a plane. See Figs. 41 and 42.

3. Keep cutting blades sharp. Check to make sure that the edge has no nicks.

4. Be sure that the material to be planed has no nails or obstructions.

5. Use a piece of paper to check a plane iron for sharpness. Do *not* use your fingers—they could be cut.

6. Sight along the bottom of the plane to check blade alignment. Do *not* feel with your fingers.

7. Keep all five fingers around the knob of the plane. If your fingers extend over the front or edge of the plane, they may be injured by slivers on the return stroke.

8. Use the proper plane for the job.

9. Store planes in a designated place in the toolbox.

TO ADJUST THE PLANE IRON VERTICALLY, FOR THE THICKNESS OF THE SHAVINGS, SIGHT ALONG THE PLANE BOTTOM AND TURN THE ADJUSTING SCREW FORWARD TO PUSH THE PLANE IRON OUT, OR TURN IT BACK TO PULL THE PLANE IRON IN.

TO ADJUST THE PLANE IRON LATERALLY FOR EVENNESS OF SHAVINGS, LOOSEN THE LEVER CAP SCREW, SIGHT ALONG THE PLANE BOTTOM, PRESS THE PLANE IRON TO THE RIGHT OR TO THE LEFT AND TIGHTEN THE LEVER CAP SCREW.

THE BLOCK PLANE IS A TOOL USED IN ONE HAND. THIS MAKES IT EASY TO USE WHEN THE WORK CANNOT BE TAKEN TO A VISE.

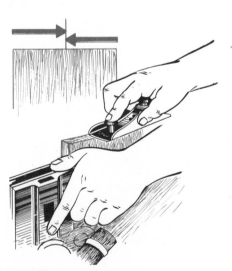

THE BLOCK PLANE IS USED TO PLANE SMALL PIECES AND TO PLANE THE ENDS OF MOULDINGS. TRIM AND SIDING.

THE BLOCK PLANE IS THE HANDIEST TOOL FOR PLANING CORNERS AND CHAMFERS ON SMALL PIECES OF WOOD.

Fig. 42. How to use a block plane. (Stanley Works)

Portable Power Planes

Portable Power Plane. These planes provide fast, accurate edging on all types of cabinet work and in the fitting of doors, drawers, window sash, storm sash, screens, shutters, transoms, and inside trim. See Fig. 43. It is in speed, particularly, that the power planes outdistance the hand planes since they will do a planing job many times faster than a hand plane. Most power planes are equipped with a spiral cutter, which results in a fine, smooth finish regardless of the grain direction.

Planes are available which will finish surfaces up to about 2½ inches wide, depending on the width of the cutter supplied. A graduated dial on the front of the machine adjusts the front shoe for depth of cut, which may on some models be a maximum of $\frac{3}{16}$ of an inch. This adjustment may also be made during the planing operation. The angle fence will tilt up to about 15 degrees outboard and about 45 degrees inboard.

Power Block Plane. This plane is used for lighter work than the larger power plane. See Fig. 44. Its smaller size and one-handed operation allows it to work in smaller places and to work more easily on smaller surfaces. It is used to rough plane flat surfaces prior to finish sanding and to work on edges and such things as cabinet doors. It may be used for trimming rabbet cuts, for cutting V-grooves, or, when equipped with a bevel planing fence, for accurately cutting bevels. The power block plane may be used on wood, plastic, composition, and aluminum.

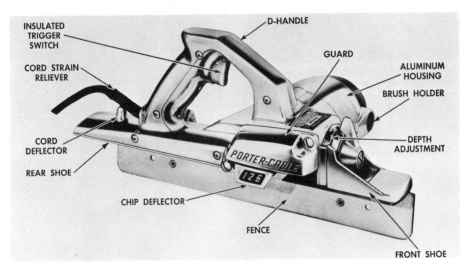

Fig. 43. Portable power plane and parts. (Porter-Cable Machine Co.)

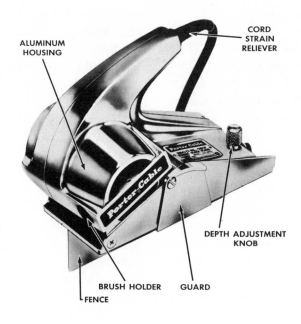

ALUMINUM
HOUSING

CORD
STRAIN
RELIEVER

DEPTH ADJUSTMENT
KNOB

BRUSH HOLDER   GUARD

FENCE

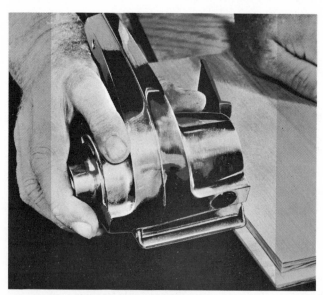

Fig. 44. Power block plane. (Porter-Cable Machine Co.)

SAFETY: PORTABLE POWER PLANES

Do not use this tool unless you understand its operation and know the safety rules.

1. Be sure that the plane is properly grounded.

2. Remove tie, rings, and wristwatch, and roll up sleeves.

3. Be sure that the material to be worked is free of obstructions and securely clamped.

4. To make adjustments, turn power off, and disconnect plane from the power source.

5. To start cut, place front shoe on edge of work. Start motor and move plane along the work.

6. Keep your full attention on the work.

7. Keep cutting pressure constant. Do not overload the plane.

8. It is a bad practice to attempt to plane stocks of varying thicknesses at the same time.

9. When through the cut, turn off motor. Do not set plane down until motor stops.

10. When work is completed, disconnect plane from the power source.

Portable Router. This router is extensively used in the shop and in construction work for fine joinery, inlay work, or decorative wood finishing. See Fig. 45. Many varieties of cutters and accessories are available for this tool. With the proper choice of cutter and jig (tool guide), the router will do such diverse jobs as beading, grooving, fluting, rounding, mortising, and dovetailing. Fig. 46A illustrates some of the common cuts made by a router. By using two

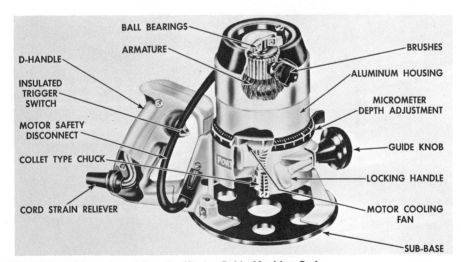

Fig. 45. Portable router and parts. (Porter-Cable Machine Co.)

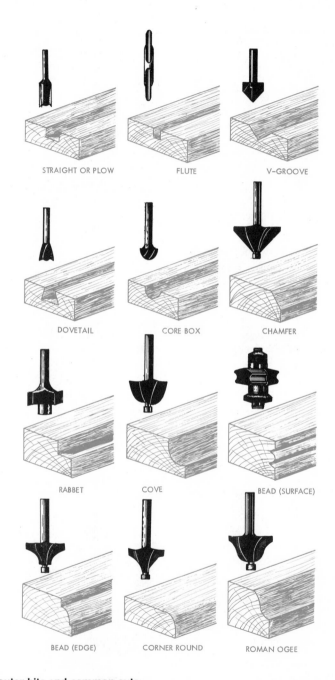

Fig. 46A. Router bits and common cuts.

Fig. 46B. Portable router equipped with hinge butt template kit. (Black & Decker Mfg. Co.)

special template jigs, butt mortising (Fig. 46B) and lock mortising may be accomplished on a production basis at production speed. In fact, these two operations can be done fast enough by one man to keep several carpenters busy installing the butts and locks.

Standard equipment for the portable router usually includes, among others, a combination straight and circular guide, slot and circle cutting attachments, template guides, dovetail joint fixture, and the hinge mortising template. Fig. 46B illustrates a router with a hinge butt template kit. This attachment quickly cuts slots for hinges on door frames.

SAFETY: PORTABLE ROUTERS

Do not use this tool unless you understand its operation and know the safety rules.

1. Be sure that the router is properly grounded.

2. Remove tie, rings, and wristwatch, and roll up sleeves.

3. When inserting router bits, making adjustments, and when router is not in actual use, *disconnect* from power source.

4. Select proper router bit for work to be done. Insert shank in collet chuck and tighten collet nut.

5. Make sure that work piece is rigidly held in desired position and is free of obstructions.

6. Hold router firmly and against the work, using both hands.

7. Keep your attention focused on the work.

8. Make a trial cut on a piece of scrap lumber.

9. Keep cutting pressure constant. Do not overload the router.

10. When work is completed, release trigger switch, disconnect the router from the power source and remove router bit.

Stationary Power Planes

Jointer. A jointer is designed for straightening wood by planing the surfaces. See Fig. 47. The operation of straightening the face of the board is called *facing*. The operation of straightening the edge is called *jointing*. Jointing usually implies that the edge is to be surfaced (jointed) at right angles to the face side. Other operations that may be performed on the jointer include beveling, chamfering, tapering, and rabbeting. (Fig. 46A illustrates some

115

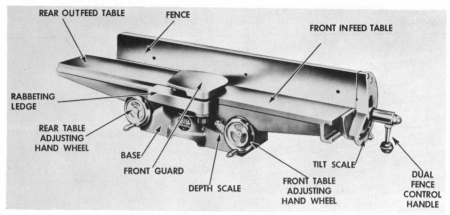

Fig. 47. Long bed jointer and parts. (Rockwell Mfg. Co.)

of these cuts.) Hollow glue joints can also be made.

This power tool usually has a three-knife cutter head of a cylindrical shape with the knives set in it longitudinally and, in a typical operation, gives many thousand knife cuts a minute. See Fig. 48. The

Fib. 48. Jointer cutter head. (Rockwell Mfg. Co.)

length of each knife varies from 4 inches to 36 inches. The common size is the 6-inch jointer, Fig. 48.

The fence, may usually be tilted to a maximum of 45 degrees in either direction (from the horizontal plane), with the actual degree of tilt shown on a gage. (See the *tilt scale*, Fig. 47.) Many jointer fences have positive stops at 90 degrees and at 45 degrees for making chamfer and bevel cuts. A lock with single lever control locks the fence at any position across the work table. Both front and rear tables, on the machine illustrated, may be raised or lowered, and locked in position on inclined dovetailed ways. The cutter head guard affords maximum coverage of the cutter knives at all times. The stock is fed by hand over tables, while knives, attached to a revolving cylinder, remove the wood. The length of these knives determines the size of the jointer. The cutter knives are usually made of properly tempered, high-speed tool steel and should give good service, but they should, nevertheless, be inspected frequently and sharpened when necessary.

Jointers commonly rest on a specially designed steel stand.

SAFETY: JOINTERS

Do not use this tool unless you understand its operation and know the safety rules.

1. Be sure that the jointer is properly grounded.

2. Remove tie, rings, and wristwatch, and roll up sleeves.

3. Make all adjustments with switch locked in OFF position.

4. Only make adjustments for thickness of cut and position of fence. If you discover any part other than the fence or tables to be loose or out of adjustment, report it at once.

5. Adjust jointer for minimum cut. If more than ⅜ inch of stock is to be removed, in reducing it to width, time will be saved by sawing the stock to within ⅛ inch of the finished size. Because hardwood taxes the machine more than soft woods, always take thinner cuts when surfacing such wood as maple, birch, and oak. Since wide surfaces also tax the machine, cuts more than 1/16 inch should not be attempted on wide surfaces. The jointer is usually set for 1/32 inch to make the final cut so that the smoothest surface may be secured.

6. Make sure that the work to be cut is free of nails and obstructions. Examine the stock for knots and splits before running it over jointer. Use only new stock. Never attempt to surface end grain free hand.

7. The wearing of goggles is recommended.

8. Be sure that the work area is cleared of loose material that might cause tripping or falling. Be sure that the table is clear of scraps. (The table is cleaned with a brush when the saw is *not* running. The power controls must be locked in an OFF position when brushing.)

9. Make certain that the material to be cut is solidly against the fence and that the fence is locked.

10. Make sure that the guards are in place over the knives before turning power on.

11. Never attempt to surface more than one piece at a time.

12. Be sure that the direction of the grain is determined and marked on the wood, and the stock is arranged so that the knives will not cut against the grain.

13. Get help with long pieces. The helper holds the stock up—he does *not* pull.

14. Stand clear when turning on switch. A jointer runs at a very high speed and, if a breakdown should occur, it would likely happen when the jointer is started. When you stand to one side, you are out of the way if something does go wrong.

15. Never stand directly back of stock. Form the habit of standing to one side to avoid an injury if the stock should be thrown from the machine.

There is always a chance that stock may be caught by the revolving knives and cause a kickback.

16. Always keep your hands away from cutterhead. When jointing an edge, the left hand is used to hold the stock against the table and fence. The right hand is then free to feed the stock into the cutterhead slowly and evenly. In surface planing, a push block is always placed against the end of the board to *finish the cut.* Always have the push block placed so that you can reach it to finish the cut.

17. Keep your full attention on the job. Never talk to anyone while operating the jointer. When the material you are working on is on the jointer, it is not safe to look around or attempt to speak to another person.

18. Do not plane short pieces. When a number of short pieces are to be made, it is a good practice to plane the edges and surfaces of a longer piece and then cut the pieces to length. Stock that is less than 10 to 12 inches long cannot be properly supported on the rear table. Short pieces of stock have been the cause of serious accidents on the jointer, so avoid planing short pieces.

19. Do not joint narrow strips less than 1 inch wide.

20. Do not brush off the bed or remove small pieces from the joiner table with the hand when the saw is running. Turn the motor off before cleaning or brushing.

21. Use pusher stick when planing narrow or flat pieces of stock.

22. Take a light cut when facing.

23. Do not let the fingers project over stock or pass near the knives.

24. Operations involving stop-cuts must be held in place by a stop.

25. Turn off power if you leave jointer before finishing a job. Never allow the jointer to run unattended. A person not realizing that the jointer is running might be seriously injured.

26. Never lean stock against jointer or pile it on the table.

27. When through cutting, shut off power. Do not leave until the blade has come to a complete stop. *Never* leave a running jointer unattended.

Other Paring and Shaving Tools

Wood Chisels. Chisels, Fig. 49, are used to cut away wood to receive hardware or to accept another piece of wood. They are available in widths from $\frac{1}{8}$ of an inch to 2 inches. Blade length may vary from 3 to 6 inches.

The *socket wood chisel* or *firming chisel* (Fig. 49) is used in framing and other rough work and is designed to withstand a great deal of pounding. A cutting edge ranging from $1\frac{1}{2}$ to 2 inches is recommended. For finer work, such as fitting locks, putting on hinges, and for cabinet work, a more delicate *lightweight wood chisel* or *finish chisel* is needed (Fig. 49).

Although much of a carpenter's work can be accomplished satisfactorily with three sizes of chisels— $\frac{3}{8}$ inch, $\frac{3}{4}$ inch, and $1\frac{1}{2}$ inch—

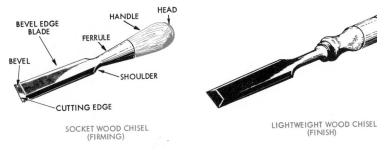

SOCKET WOOD CHISEL
(FIRMING)

LIGHTWEIGHT WOOD CHISEL
(FINISH)

Fig. 49. Wood chisels.

nevertheless, it would be ideal for him to own a kit of tools including a full set of chisels ranging in size from ⅛ inch to 1¾ inches in width, plus a butt chisel for hanging doors.

Wood chisels are commonly made with two different handles. With the *socket* type of handle (Fig. 49, left) the handle fits into the hollow socket (ferrule) of the chisel. With the *tang* type of handle (Fig. 49, right) the chisel tang fits into the handle, usually plastic.

SAFETY: WOOD CHISELS

1. Focus your attention on the area being cut and, if using a mallet, on hitting the head of the chisel.

2. Keep cutting edge sharp and free of nicks.

3. Do not use wood chisels with loose or defective handles.

4. Use a wood chisel for the job it was designed for. Do not use as a pry or wedge.

5. Learn how to use a chisel properly. See Figs. 50A and 50B.

6. Be sure that the material to be cut has no nails or other obstructions.

7. Be sure that the material to be cut is securely clamped.

8. Use a mallet for striking a wood chisel.

9. When cutting, always keep hands back of the cutting edge. Cut away from the body.

10. Carry a wood chisel with its cutting edge downward. Carry at the side, close to your body.

11. Store wood chisels in a designated place in the toolbox.

Flooring Chisel. An all-metal chisel that is designed for hard usage, and when there is a possibility that the wood contains nails and other obstructions (Fig. 51). Since it is also used as a tool for framing work, it must be designed to withstand a great deal of hard pounding.

Cold Chisels. These, Fig. 51, are available with blades from ¼ inch to

TO CUT, HORIZONTALLY, WITH THE GRAIN: THE CHISEL IS HELD SLIGHTLY TURNED TO ONE SIDE AND THEN PUSHED FROM THE WORKER. IT IS HELD WITH THE BEVEL DOWN FOR A ROUGHING CUT AND WITH THE BEVEL UP FOR A PARING CUT.

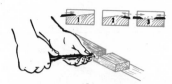

TO CUT, HORIZONTALLY, ACROSS THE GRAIN WITH THE WORK HELD IN THE VISE: PRESS THE FOREFINGER AND THUMB TOGETHER ON THE CHISEL TO ACT AS A BRAKE.
TO AVOID SPLINTERING THE CORNERS, CUT HALF WAY FROM EACH EDGE TOWARD THE CENTER. REMOVE THE CENTER STOCK LAST.

TO CUT ACROSS THE GRAIN WITH THE WORK HELD AGAINST THE BENCH HOOK, THE HEEL OF THE LEFT HAND STEADIES THE WORK WHILE THE FINGERS PRESS THE CHISEL FIRMLY AGAINST THE WOOD.

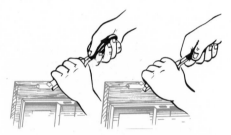

TO CUT A CHAMFER: HOLD THE CHISEL INCLINED TO ONE SIDE PARALLEL TO THE SLOPE OF THE CHAMFER AND CUT AS IN CHISELING HORIZONTALLY WITH THE GRAIN.

IF THE WORK IS WIDE THE CHISEL IS HELD BEVEL DOWN, SO THE HANDLE WILL CLEAR THE WORK AND THE BLADE WILL NOT DIG IN TOO DEEP, AS IT IS PUSHED FORWARD.

TO CUT A STRAIGHT, SLANTING, CORNER IS THE SAME AS HORIZONTAL CHISELING. THE WORK IS HELD IN THE VISE WITH THE GUIDE LINE HORIZONTAL.

TO CUT A ROUND CORNER, THE CHISEL IS MOVED SIDEWAYS ACROSS THE WORK MAKING A SERIES OF CUTS CLOSE TOGETHER EACH ONE TANGENT TO THE CURVE.

TO CUT A CHAMFER ON END GRAIN, THE CHISEL IS MOVED SIDEWAYS ACROSS THE CORNER OF THE WORK, HELD SO THAT THE CHISEL MAKES A SLIDING HORIZONTAL CUT.

AT ALL TIMES KEEP BOTH HANDS BACK OF THE CUTTING EDGE.
THE CHISEL IS CONTROLLED WITH THE LEFT HAND, PRESSING FIRMLY ON THE CHISEL AND THE WOOD. THE POWER IS APPLIED WITH THE RIGHT HAND. THE CHISEL IS HELD SLIGHTLY TURNED SO THE EDGE SLIDES ACROSS THE WORK OR THE CHISEL IS MOVED TO THE RIGHT AND LEFT AS IT IS ADVANCED, TO GIVE A SLIDING ACTION TO THE CUTTING EDGE. THIS IS EASIER THAN A STRAIGHT THRUST AND LEAVES A SMOOTHER SURFACE ON THE WORK.

Fig. 50A. How to make horizontal cuts with a wood chisel. (Stanley Works)

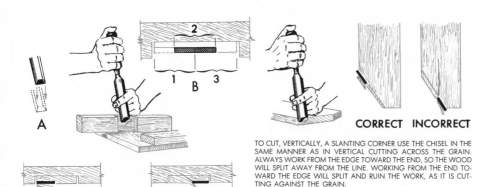

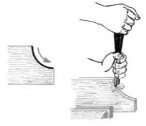

TO CUT, VERTICALLY, A SLANTING CORNER USE THE CHISEL IN THE SAME MANNER AS IN VERTICAL CUTTING ACROSS THE GRAIN. ALWAYS WORK FROM THE EDGE TOWARD THE END, SO THE WOOD WILL SPLIT AWAY FROM THE LINE. WORKING FROM THE END TOWARD THE EDGE WILL SPLIT AND RUIN THE WORK, AS IT IS CUTTING AGAINST THE GRAIN.

TO CUT, VERTICALLY, ACROSS THE GRAIN (A) THE CHISEL SHOULD BE SLIGHTLY TILTED TO ONE SIDE TO GIVE A SLIDING ACTION TO THE CUTTING EDGE, OR IT MAY BE HELD STRAIGHT AND MOVED TO ONE SIDE AS IT IS ADVANCED. (B) IF THE SURFACE IS WIDER THAN THE CHISEL, PART OF THE CHISEL PRESSED AGAINST THE PORTION JUST CUT, HELPS TO GUIDE AND KEEP IN LINE THE PART OF THE CHISEL CUTTING A NEW PORTION OF THE SURFACE. (C) CUT WITH THE GRAIN, SO THE WASTE WOOD WILL SPLIT AWAY FROM THE GUIDE LINE.

TO CUT A CONCAVE CURVED CORNER: HOLD THE BEVEL SIDE OF THE CHISEL AGAINST THE WORK WITH THE LEFT HAND; WITH THE RIGHT HAND PRESS DOWN AND DRAW BACK AT THE SAME TIME, GIVING A SWEEPING CURVED DIRECTION TO THE CUT.
ALWAYS WORK WITH THE GRAIN FROM THE EDGE TOWARD THE END.

TO CLEAN THE CORNERS OF A TENON, NOTCH, DADO OR RABBET GRASP THE CHISEL BY THE BLADE, NEAR THE EDGE; RAISE ONE CORNER OF THE CUTTING EDGE BY TILTING THE HANDLE AWAY AND DRAW THE CHISEL TOWARD YOU. THE WORK IS HELD BY THE LEFT HAND WHILE THE CHISEL EDGE AND ONE CORNER, GUIDED BY THE RIGHT HAND, ACT LIKE A KNIFE.

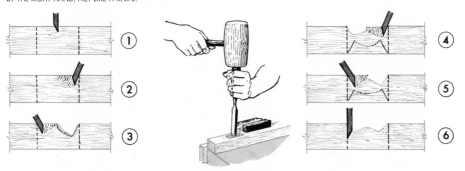

THE MALLET MAY BE SAFELY USED ON THE CHISEL WHEN THE CUTTING EDGE IS ACROSS THE GRAIN. WHEN THE EDGE IS WITH THE GRAIN, THE USE OF THE MALLET IS VERY LIKELY TO SPLIT THE WOOD. THE MALLET MAY BE USED ON THE CHISEL TO BEAT OUT A MORTISE, TO CUT THE ENDS OF A MORTISE (WHEN THE BULK OF THE MATERIAL HAS BEEN BORED OUT), WHEN THE WOOD IS HARD AND IN ROUGHING OUT (WHEN THERE IS A LARGE AMOUNT OF MATERIAL TO BE REMOVED).

Fig. 50B. How to make vertical cuts with a wood chisel. (Stanley Works)

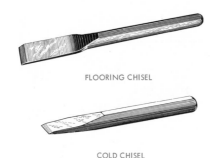

FLOORING CHISEL

COLD CHISEL

Fig. 51. Chisels.

1¼ inches wide and from 5 inches to 18 inches in length. They are made to cut metal, such as nails.

Wood Rasps and Wood Files. These are also used for dressing down and smoothing wood surfaces. See Fig. 52. A rasp is used for the coarser, rough work, and wood files are used for the smoother, finish work. Both rasps and wood files come in several shapes and many different degrees of coarseness. The degree of coarseness or fineness of the teeth indicates the use. The finer the teeth, the finer the work produced. A rasp or wood file, when in use, should always be equipped with a handle (Fig. 52). The handle fits over the tang.

SAFETY: COLD CHISELS

1. Keep your attention focused on the work.
2. Keep the cutting edge ground free of burrs. Be sure that the edge has no oil on it.
3. If the head mushrooms, dress flat before using.
4. Use a ball peen hammer for striking a cold chisel. *Never* use a claw hammer.
5. Hold the cold chisel so that your hand will not be injured if the hammer misses. Grip near the head with a loose grip so that the hand can give.
6. Wear goggles when chipping with a cold chisel. Chip away from the body.
7. The material should be securely held in a vise.
8. Store cold chisels in a designated place in the toolbox.

SAFETY: WOOD RASPS AND FILES

1. Keep your attention focused on the work.
2. Never use a rasp or file without a handle. Handles come in various sizes. Be sure that the rasp or file has the proper handle and is well balanced.
3. Use rasps and files for the job they were designed for. Do not use as a pry or wedge.
4. Use the full surface of the rasp or file by employing a long, firm, even stroke. Cut only on the forward stroke. Use both hands. Do not jerk back and forth or let the rasp or file slide over the work.
5. Be sure that the material to be worked on is securely clamped.
6. Avoid filing against vise jaws— they will ruin the teeth.
7. Do not blow filings where they

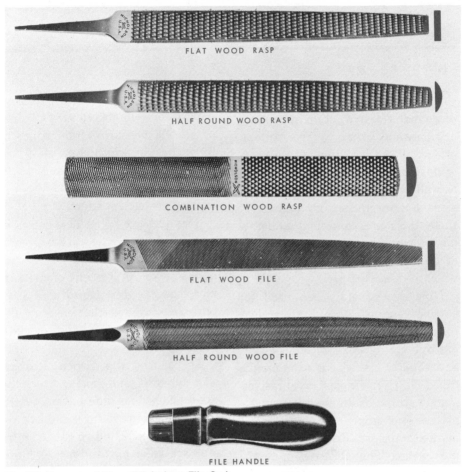

FLAT WOOD RASP

HALF ROUND WOOD RASP

COMBINATION WOOD RASP

FLAT WOOD FILE

HALF ROUND WOOD FILE

FILE HANDLE

Fig. 52. Rasps and files. (Nicholson File Co.)

can fly into your own or someone else's face.

8. Never hit a rasp or file with a hammer.

9. Tap gently to clear rasp or file teeth of material. Never hit a rasp or file against a hard surface.

10. Do not run your hand over rasp or file teeth or over the work surface being filed. Oily perspiration will cause rasps and files to slip.

11. Use chalk or charcoal on new rasps and files to keep chips from sticking and also to remove oil.

12. Remove resinous deposits by soaking in turpentine.

13. Never throw rasps or files on top of each other, as this dulls the teeth.

14. Store in a designated place, keep separated, and protect against moisture.

Abrading Tools

All implements used for wearing down material by friction or rubbing are known as *abrading tools*. Among others, these include whetstones, grindstones and files for sharpening, as well as the abrasive papers, such as sandpaper and emery papers. If these tools are examined under a microscope it will be found that all of them have sharp edges or teeth which do the cutting.

Different minerals are used as cutting agents for making abrasive tools. Three of these used in their natural state are: *garnet*, *emery*, and *quartz* which is commonly called *flint*. Examples of abrasives manufactured by an electric-furnace process are *silicon carbide*, trademarked *Carborundum*, and *aluminum oxide*. The abrasive minerals are shaped and bonded to form abrasive tools, such as whetstones and grindstones.

Abrasive Papers

The abrasive minerals are crushed and graded for making abrasive papers. To make sandpaper or the emery papers, a paper backing is coated with some kind of adhesive substance, such as glue. Then the crushed mineral is powdered over the paper. The same method is used in making abrasive cloth. Abrasive papers come in sheets 9 x 11 inches or in rolls measuring from 1 inch to 27 inches in width and up to 50 yards in length. The 27-inch width is used principally on machines and on belt or drum sanders.

The abrasive paper also comes in *open coat* where the abrasive particles are separated and cover only about 50 to 70 per cent of the surface. The *closed coat* has the abrasive particles close together covering the entire surface of the paper or cloth backing.

As used by the carpenter, abrasive papers (sandpapers) or cloths are made of four different materials. Two of them are natural and two are manufactured. The two natural minerals are called *flint* and *garnet*. Flint, which was originally used for sandpaper, is still in use today. It makes a softer abrasive which will crumble quickly. This quality makes it more suitable for sanding painted surfaces as the abrasive will crumble off the surface and will not gum up the sandpaper. Garnet does not crumble as easily as flint. Since it is also sharper, it will stand up better for sanding wood surfaces. Though more expensive than flint, garnet is more economical in the long run.

Silicon carbide, an artificial abrasive, is made of silicon and coke, a product of an electric furnace operated at extremely high temperature. This abrasive is used for sanding floors. Another artificial abrasive, *aluminum oxide*, is also the result of fusing in an electric furnace. It has as its base *bauxite*, a natural mineral. This abrasive is used for hand sanding of wood.

The comparative grit numbers for various abrasive papers are shown in Table I. To remove tool marks, by hand sanding on bare wood, use garnet paper ranging from *medium*, No. ½ and 0 to *fine*, No. ³⁄₀ or ⁴⁄₀, for the finished surface.

The coarseness of sandpaper originally was designated as #3 for very coarse to 7/0 for very fine. This designation of abrasives is still in practice today. However, the more modern method is to designate the coarseness by the size of the screen through which the abrasive must

TABLE I. APPROXIMATE COMPARISON OF GRIT NUMBERS

ARTIFICIAL*	GARNET	FLINT	GRADE
400–10/0	——	——	
360	——		
320–9/0	——	7/0	
280–8/0	8/0	6/0	Very fine
240–7/0	7/0	5/0	
220–6/0	6/0	4/0	
——	——	3/0	
180–5/0	5/0	——	
150–4/0	4/0		
——	——	2/0	Fine
120–3/0	3/0	——	
——	——	0	
100–2/0	2/0	——	
——	——	½	
80–0	0	——	
——	——	1	Medium
60–½	½	——	
50–1	1	1½	
——	——	2	
40–1½	1½	——	
——	——	2½	Coarse
36–2	2	——	
30–2½	2½	3	
24–3	3	——	
20–3½	3½	——	
16–4	——	——	Very Coarse
12–4½	——	——	

* Includes *silicon carbide* and *aluminum oxide*.

125

pass in the manufacturing process. When a screen with 280 openings per square inch is used, the paper is designated as 280.

Due to difference in hardness of some of the abrasives, it will be noted that a coarser grade of flint paper is used to bring about the same result as with garnet or artificial papers. For example, an 8/0 garnet paper is the same in coarseness as 280-8/0 artificial paper, but it would require a 6/0 flint paper to give the same results.

Portable Power Sanders

Three types of *portable sanders* are manufactured. They are the belt sander, the orbital sander, and the disc sander.

Belt Sander.   This sander is used for large flat areas, in production

Fig. 53. Portable belt sander. (Porter-Cable Machine Co.)

work, and in maintenance work such as the removal of old paint and varnish prior to refinishing (Fig. 53). Belts are available in three grades, the choice of which is dictated by the nature of the job. The direction the belt should face is indicated on the inside of the belt. Some models of this type of sander are equipped with their own integral dust bags to

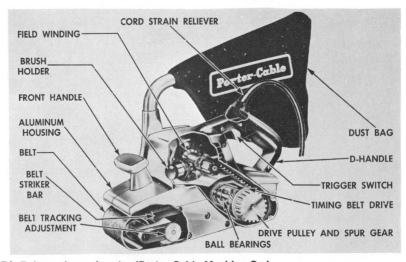

Fig. 54. Belt sander and parts. (Porter-Cable Machine Co.)

collect the dust produced by the sanding operation (Fig. 54). Usually, the trigger has a locking device for continuous operation. Fig. 54 gives the terminology and parts associated with the belt sander.

SAFETY: BELT SANDERS

Do not use this tool unless you understand its operation and know the safety rules.

1. Be sure that the sander is properly grounded.

2. Remove tie, rings, and wrist-watch, and roll up sleeves.

3. Check to see that the sanding belt is in good condition, of the proper grit size for the work to be done, and that it is properly installed.

4. Before connecting to the power source, be sure that the switch is in the OFF position.

5. Start sander above the work. Let rear of the belt touch first. Level the machine as it is moved forward.

6. Keep your attention focused on the work.

7. Sand in the same direction as the wood grain, moving the sander back and forth over a wide area. Do not pause in any one spot.

8. Use successively finer grit until finish is obtained.

9. Stop sander to make adjustments.

10. Lift sander off the work before stopping motor.

11. After turning off, wait until belt is completely stopped before setting down.

12. When work is completed, disconnect from power source and remove belt.

Fig. 55. Portable orbital or finish sander. (Porter-Cable Machine Co.)

Orbital Sander. An orbital sander or finish sander, Fig. 55, is used in smaller and less accessible areas than the belt sander and for finer work. It is not restricted to a limited number of abrasive surfaces since it uses standard sheet abrasive paper and cloth. The abrasive paper is cut to size and applied to the sander by means of clamps at each end of the base-plate. As implied by its name, the base of the sander oscillates in an orbital pattern. So that even pressure can be applied to the work surface, a rubber or felt pad is used between the oscillating base-plate and the abrasive paper. This pad extends beyond the base-plate, permitting the sanding of corners and sanding in other close quarters such as right up to the riser of a stair tread. Orbital sanders usually have a trigger-locking device. Fig. 56 gives the terminology and parts associated with the orbital sander.

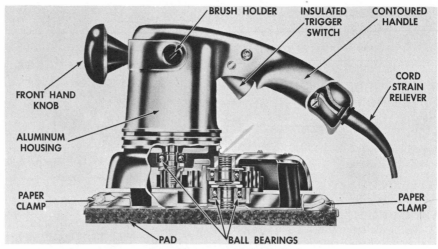

Fig. 56. Orbital sander and parts. (Porter-Cable Machine Co.)

SAFETY: ORBITAL OR FINISH SANDERS

Do not use this tool unless you understand its operation and know the safety rules.

1. Be sure that the sander is properly grounded.

2. Remove tie, rings, and wristwatch, and roll up sleeves.

3. Check to see that the sanding sheet is in good condition, of the proper grit size for the work to be done, and that it is properly installed.

4. Before connecting to the power source, be sure that the switch is in the OFF position.

5. Start sander above the work. Set sander on the work evenly and move slowly back and forth in a wide, overlapping pattern. Do not pause in any one spot.

6. Keep your attention focused on the work.

7. Use successively finer grit until the finish is obtained.

8. Stop sander to make adjustments.

9. Lift sander off the work before stopping motor.

10. After turning off, wait until motor stops before setting down.

11. When work is completed, disconnect from power source, and remove sanding sheet.

Disc Sander. Although the disc sander (Fig. 57) is used for some of the same purposes as the belt sander and the orbital sander, its main asset is that it can be used to sand uneven and curved surfaces. This sander is not used to sand raw (untreated) wood, as it tends to break up the wood fibers. The disc sander is also slightly more versatile than the other two types of portable sanders in that it can be used with a number of accessories in place of the sanding disc. With the use of a

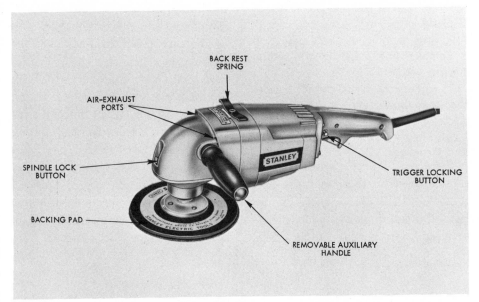

BACK REST
SPRING

AIR-EXHAUST
PORTS

SPINDLE LOCK
BUTTON

STANLEY

TRIGGER LOCKING
BUTTON

BACKING PAD

REMOVABLE AUXILIARY
HANDLE

Fig. 57. Portable disc sander. (Stanley Works)

wire torque brush, the disc sander can be used for cleaning cracked paint and other deposits. A felt pad used in place of the sanding disc results in a portable buffer for rubbing down lacquered surfaces. Used with a rubber pad and a polishing bonnet, the disc sander makes a versatile portable polisher.

SAFETY: PORTABLE DISC SANDERS

Do not use this tool unless you understand its operation and know the safety rules.

1. Be sure that the sander is properly grounded.

2. Remove tie, rings, and wristwatch, and roll up sleeves.

3. Check to see that the sanding disc is in good condition, of the proper grit size for the work to be done, and is properly secured.

4. Before connecting to power source, be sure that the switch is in the OFF position.

5. Wear goggles and a dust mask if conditions warrant.

6. Start sander above the work. Allow sander to come to full speed before placing on the work surface.

7. Keep your attention focused on the work.

8. Do not lay the whole disc flat on the work—tilt to one side. Sand on downward side of the disc.

9. Set sander on work evenly and move slowly back and forth in a wide, overlapping pattern. Do not pause in any one spot.

10. Stop sander to make adjustments.

129

11. Lift sander off the work before stopping motor.

12. After turning off, wait until disc is completely stopped before setting down.

13. When work is completed, disconnect from power source, and remove disc.

Stationary Power Sanders and Grinders

Sanders. There are two kinds of sanders used in the shop: the belt sander and the disc sander. Fig. 58 gives the terminology and parts associated with a *belt sander*. This model uses a 6 inch belt. The terminology and parts for the *disc sander* are given in Fig. 59. This model uses a 12 inch disc.

Either type of sander is usually equipped with an adjustable, tilting table, which, from its normal position at right angles to the sanding surface, may be tilted to a maximum of 45 degrees away from the abrasive surface, or 35 degrees toward the abrasive surface. The table is equipped with a slot parallel to the sanding surface for a miter gage

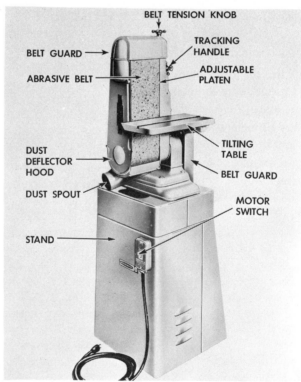

Fig. 58. Belt sander and parts. (Rockwell Mfg. Co.)

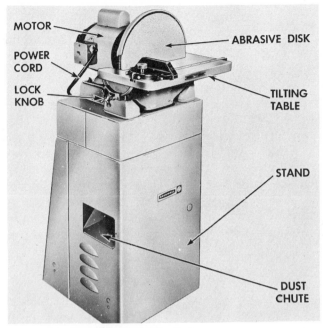

MOTOR

POWER CORD

LOCK KNOB

ABRASIVE DISK

TILTING TABLE

STAND

DUST CHUTE

Fig. 59. Disc sander and parts. (Rockwell Mfg. Co.)

which assures accuracy in all sanding operations. If the table is entirely removable, this is an advantage, since it allows long pieces of material to be sanded more conveniently.

The belt sander in particular gives a uniform cutting speed across the entire surface of the belt which results in a smooth, even cut. Both types of sander can be operated on curved, straight, or angular surfaces, and the unsupported side of the belt sander may be used for sanding irregular surfaces.

The abrasive belts are changed by releasing the belt tensioner, slipping the belt off and replacing it with a new one. Abrasive discs are held to the backing plate by means of an adhesive compound.

Some models have a combined belt and disc sander in one machine. See Fig. 60. A common drive motor is used. These combined machines can usually be employed in either a horizontal or a vertical position.

SAFETY: STATIONARY BELT SANDERS

Do not use this tool unless you understand its operation and know the safety rules.

1. Be sure that the sander is properly grounded.

2. Remove tie, rings, and wristwatch, and roll up sleeves.

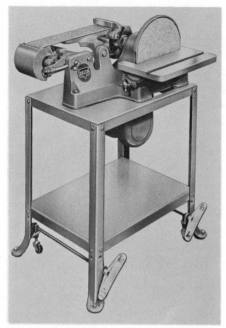

Fig. 60. Combination belt and disc sander. (Rockwell Mfg. Co.)

3. Check to see that the sanding belt is in good condition, of the proper grit size for the work to be done, and is properly installed.

4. Before connecting to the power source, be sure that the switch is in the OFF position.

5. Wear goggles.

6. Wear a dust mask if necessary.

7. Make all adjustments with the power OFF.

8. Make certain that the stock being sanded is resting firmly against back stop on the bed of the machine. (A back stop is commonly attached to the belt sander when finishing flat work.)

9. Be sure that the belt guards are securely attached before turning on power.

10. Check to see that the floor around sander is cleared of loose material and free of oil spots.

11. Keep hands away from the belt when sander is running.

12. Keep your full attention focused on the work. Thinking about something else or looking away from your work may lead to painful injury.

13. Small pieces of stock should not be held in the hands. Because stock has a tendency to rotate, the fingers may be pulled against the abrasive. If you have many small pieces of stock to be sanded, perhaps a fixture or holding device can be made.

14. On thin stock use a push block. Both hands should be placed on the push block which is designed to hold thin stock against the abrasive. It is easy for a person to be injured if he attempts to sand thin stock on this machine without the push block.

15. Sander should not be adjusted while in motion. Stop sander to make adjustments.

16. Sand in the same direction as the wood grain. Sand the material back and forth over a wide area. Do not pause in any one spot.

17. Use successively finer grit until finish is obtained.

18. When work is completed, turn off power, disconnect from power source, and remove belt.

SAFETY: STATIONARY DISC SANDERS

Do not use this tool unless you understand its operation and know the safety rules.

1. Be sure that the sander is properly grounded.

2. Remove tie, rings, and wristwatch, and roll up sleeves.

3. Check to see that the sanding disc is in good condition, of the proper grit size for the work to be done, and is properly secured.

4. Before connecting to power source, be sure that the switch is in the OFF position.

5. Wear goggles.

6. Wear a dust mask if necessary.

7. Make all adjustments with the power OFF.

8. Set up the sander to take as small a cut as possible.

9. Check to see that the floor around sander is cleared of loose material and free of oil spots.

10. Check to see that the clearance between the sanding disc and table or rest is not more than 1/16".

11. Small pieces of stock should not be held in the hands. The stock has a tendency to rotate when it is sanded. Small pieces of stock may slip away from your fingers and pull against the revolving disc. If many small pieces need to be sanded, a jig can perhaps be made to hold them. If only a few pieces are to be sanded, it is safer to do the work by hand rather than by machine.

12. Sand on the downstroke side of disc. *Never* sand on the upstroke. If you try to sand on the upstroke, the stock has a tendency to be lifted from the table. On the downstroke, the stock is pushed against the table.

13. Keep your full attention on the work. It is not safe to look around or at-tempt to speak to another person. The operator of any power tool should always give his full attention to the work being done.

14. Turn off the power if you leave the sander before you have finished the job.

15. Stop the sander to make adjustments.

16. If a piece of stock gets caught on the edge of the bed of the machine, do not try to save the stock. Stop the machine.

17. Use successively finer grit until the desired finish is obtained.

18. Never touch a moving sanding disc. This may couse a painful and probably a serious injury. Be sure the disc has completely stopped before touching it with your hands. After shutting off power, sander may be stopped by sanding a scrap piece of wood.

19. When work is completed, turn off power, disconnect from power source, and remove disc.

Grinders. Models are available as either single or double purpose units. However, the double purpose units (Fig. 61) are now more or less standard. The primary use of the grinder is the maintenance of various cutting and drilling tools used by the carpenter. Many accessories are available for grinders considerably extending their usefulness. Other uses made possible by the application of accessories include polishing and cleaning of various materials and even sanding. The

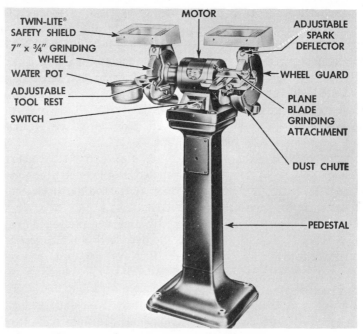

TWIN-LITE®
SAFETY SHIELD

7" x ¾" GRINDING
WHEEL

WATER POT

ADJUSTABLE
TOOL REST

SWITCH

MOTOR

ADJUSTABLE
SPARK
DEFLECTOR

WHEEL GUARD

PLANE
BLADE
GRINDING
ATTACHMENT

DUST CHUTE

PEDESTAL

Fig. 61. Double-purpose bench grinder and parts. (Rockwell Mfg. Co.)

double purpose grinder is usually directly driven by an electric motor, although some are designed to be belt driven. Twin arbors allow for the mounting of the grinding wheels which are made in various grades and of various materials depending on or dictated by their intended use. The two commonest abrasive materials for this application are vitrified aluminum oxide and silicon carbide. (The latter, being harder and more durable, is more expensive.) For grinding very hard materials, or for a very fine cut to close tolerances, diamond wheels are occasionally used. Accessories which are mounted

in the place of the abrasive wheels include cloth or fiber wheels for buffing and polishing and wire wheels of various types, sometimes known as scratch wheels, which are used for cleaning and finishing work.

The wheels themselves are always guarded so that only the working area is exposed. The shields are sometimes equipped with exhaust ducts so that the waste may be collected and disposed of conveniently. Also commonly attached to the shield is a device known as a spark deflector, which is adjustable and also gives further protection against flying particles, but this is not necessary if an eye shield is used.

An important accessory designed to further protect the operator is an *eye shield* (see Fig. 61) which mounts over the working area and is equipped with shatterproof glass. Eye shields are sometimes combined with a lamp, which floods the working area with almost shadowless light. The eye shield is such an important safety measure that it is now standard equipment on many models. In its absence goggles should always be worn; even when an eye shield is present it is wise to wear goggles.

Apart from a tilting support table, often with a groove for mounting jigs and fixtures, two additional devices are available for use with grinders. They are a plane grinding attachment (Fig. 61) and a drill grinding attachment. A wheel dresser, often diamond, is used as a maintenance tool to even the surface of abrasive wheels which have become worn or damaged by chipping.

SAFETY: GRINDERS

Do not use this tool unless you understand its operation and know the safety rules.

1. Be sure that the grinder is properly grounded.

2. Remove tie, rings, and wristwatch, and roll up sleeves.

3. Check to see that the grinding wheel is in good condition, of the proper type for the work to be done, and is properly and securely installed.

4. Before connecting to the power source, be sure that the switch is in the OFF position.

5. Always wear goggles. (Some grinders have safety shields which prevent most but not all of the sharp pieces of steel and grit from getting into your eyes. Only goggles give complete protection.)

6. Wear a dust mask if necessary.

7. Wear close-fitting garments. Loose or ragged clothing is hazardous. Do not wear gloves.

8. Check to see that the floor around the grinder is cleared of loose material or oil spots.

9. Use a grinder only when wheel guards are in place. Wheel guards protect you if a wheel breaks when grinding. Wheel guards also protect others who might accidentally bump into the grinder while it is running. It is not safe to use the grinder when the wheel guards are removed.

10. Set work rest at or above center and 1/16" away from wheel. Accidents have happened because of too much space between the rest and the wheel, for tools may become wedged in this space, causing the grinding wheel to break and fly apart. The flying pieces could easily cause a serious injury. After dressing the wheel, stop the grinder, and set the work rest above center and 1/16" away from the wheel. Tighten the work rest so that it will not move when you are using it.

11. Stand to one side when turning

on grinder. During the starting period, the motor increases in speed so rapidly that a great strain is placed upon the wheel. If the emery wheel has defects, it may fly apart during the starting period, so it is good practice to stand to one side when starting the grinder.

12. Never touch a grinding wheel with your hands. When the grinder is turned off, the weight of the wheels might keep it running for a long time. Because it looks as though it were stopped, you might carelessly touch the wheel with your hand. This could cause a painful and probably a serious injury.

13. Hold the work firmly on the tool rest.

14. Do not hold tool with a cloth, and do not wear gloves. Keep the tool cool by dipping it in water; then you will not have to protect your hands from the hot metal. The use of gloves or a cloth is not safe because the fabric might be caught and pull the hand into the revolving wheel.

15. Grind on face of wheel. Most grinding wheels were made for face grinding only. Grinding on the side of the wheel may wear a groove, weaken the wheel, and finally cause it to break.

16. Small pieces should not be ground on the emery wheel without a proper holder.

17. Do not grind thin stock; this is a dangerous practice. The thin edge may turn down and drag the operator's hand into the machine.

18. Keep fingers clear of the abrasive wheel.

19. Stop grinder to make adjustments. Never put work on the table or remove it without stopping the wheel.

20. Never remove guard when grinding.

21. Grinding work for a long time in the same spot on your wheel will wear a groove in the wheel.

22. Avoid grinding round corners on grinding wheel.

23. Two people should never use the machine at the same time.

24. Keep hands away from your eyes. It is easy to rub fine particles from hands or face into them. Wash your hands thoroughly after using grinder.

25. Never leave any particle from an emery wheel in your eye overnight or wipe anything out of your eye with cotton waste, match, pencil, or toothpick. See a doctor if eye causes trouble.

26. Get prompt first aid if you are injured on the stone (grinder wheel).

27. Keep your full attention focused on the work. Horseplay should never be engaged in around grinding wheels.

28. When work is completed, turn off power, and disconnect from power source. Never leave the grinder unattended while the wheel is still turning.

Other Abrading Tools

In order to do satisfactory work, a carpenter must keep his tools sharp. The sharpening is done with a tool grinder and a whetstone. Contractors usually furnish the grinder, but each mechanic is expected to provide his own whetstone. A combination whetstone, with both a medium and fine surface, takes care of the usual tool-sharpening job. Size 2 x 6 x 1 inch is recommended.

Tapered files and mill files are used for sharpening such things as saws, auger bits, knives, etc. On the job, however, most tools are sharpened by an outside contractor.

Goggles

Although goggles are not exactly tools, they should be found in every carpenter's tool kit and should be used to protect the eyes whenever there is a danger of getting flying particles of metal, dust, and dirt in the eyes. Goggles are particularly necessary when working with scraping and abrading tools, and that is why they are emphasized in connection with this section on abrading tools.

Checking On Your Knowledge

The following questions give you the opportunity to check up on yourself. If you have read the chapter carefully, you should be able to answer the questions. If you have any difficulty, read the chapter over once more so that you have the information well in mind before you go on with your reading.

DO YOU KNOW

1. The two kinds of handsaws and the difference between them?
2. The important portable power saws?
3. What additional accessory must be used on a table saw when a dado head is used?
4. What different types of circular saw blades are available for the table saw?
5. What the main use of the band saw is considered to be?
6. In what important respect the radial saw differs from the table saw?
7. What advantage is realized by the use of the radial saw over the table saw in making complicated cuts?
8. How a ratchet brace works?
9. Three types of hand drills?
10. The different types of power drills?
11. What types of hand planes are listed in this chapter?
12. How the power plane differs from the hand plane as far as the grain of the wood is concerned?
13. Two uses of the portable router?
14. The term used to describe the operation of straightening the edge of a board?
15. What the term facing means?
16. The number of knives usually found on the cutting head of a jointer?
17. How many types of portable sanders are available, what they are called and what their respective uses are?
18. Which type of portable electric sander is used for the sanding of corners not otherwise easily accessible?
19. The names of the two commonest abrasive materials used for making grinding wheels?
20. Three minerals used as abrasive agents?

Construction Lumber

Chapter

5

Wood to most people is just a commodity; a material that is purchased at a lumberyard and used for making shelves, cabinets, and other small items. Others realize that virtually every building constructed depends on wood for some part of its structure. Small buildings, like homes and garages, may be almost entirely of wood, brick veneer homes have a frame, and even brick houses depend on wood to provide floors, roofs, partitions, windows, doors, cabinets, and ornamental trim.

Only the carpenter, and others working with wood, realize that many kinds of wood are used: fir, pine, hemlock, larch, spruce, oak, birch, cedar, maple, redwood, to mention the more common. Each has certain qualities that give it

value for certain uses. Some take a fine finish, others have great strength, a few have weather resistance; ease of working, availability, and stability are other factors that must be considered along with price.

Many of the "why's" of wood are covered in this chapter. Why is some wood better than others for some uses? What are the problems that each presents? What is the relation between wood and the growing tree? What are the terms that the carpenter must know to communicate with the architect, the lumberman, and the contractor? This chapter will answer those questions and many more, and will give you an insight into how wood grows and finally becomes lumber.

Growth of Wood

Wood is composed essentially of cellulose in minute elongated cells, called *fibers*, firmly cemented together by lignin. The fibers are tapered at the end and run vertically in standing trees. In softwoods the length of the fibers is about ⅛th of an inch and in hardwoods about ¹⁄₂₄th of an inch. The central diameter of a fiber is about ¹⁄₁₀₀th of the length.

The appearance of different woods varies with the arrangement of the cells or fibers. In addition to the fibers running with the grain there are bands of cells extending radially from the pith or center of the tree across the grain toward the bark. These so-called *wood rays* or *medullary rays* are responsible for the prominent flaky figure in some woods when quartersawed. In most woods these rays are small and inconspicuous.

The weight and strength of wood depends upon the thickness of the cell walls. The shape, size, and arrangement of the fibers, the presence of the wood rays, and the layer effect of the springwood and summerwood, Fig. 1, account for the large difference in the properties

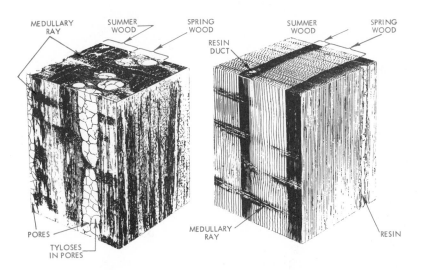

Fig. 1. Magnified blocks of white oak *(left)* and shortleaf pine *(right)*. The top of each block represents the end—cross, or transverse section. The left side shows a quarter-sawed section (hardwood) and vertical grain or radial section (softwood). The right side illustrates flatgrain, plain-sawed, or tangential section.

along and across the grain of different types of wood.

Hardwoods and Softwoods

Trees commonly cut into lumber and timber products are divided into two broad groups: *hardwood* and *softwood*.

The term *softwood* as used in the lumber trade does not necessarily mean a tree whose wood is soft, nor does *hardwood* always indicate one whose wood is hard. In fact, no definite degree of hardness divides the two groups. The custom has developed of calling the coniferous trees *softwood*, and the broad-leaved trees *hardwood*. Coniferous trees are those with needles or scale-like leaves, popularly called *evergreens*. Broad-leaved trees are often termed *deciduous* because most of those in the United States shed their leaves each year.

In general, the woods in the *hardwood* group are harder than those in the *softwood* group. However, a few of the softwoods are harder than many hardwoods. Southern or yellow pine, especially the long leaf variety, is an example of a hard *softwood*. Some *hardwoods*, on the other hand, are among our softest woods, an example being basswood.

Hardwoods have large cells which conduct the sap from the roots to the leaves. Such cells are not found in the softwoods. When the cells in hardwood are split in the process

of lumber manufacturing they show as pores in the wood; as a result the hardwoods are also known as *porous woods*. Because of this peculiar cell structure, greater care must be exercised in seasoning and drying of hardwoods to prevent warping, twisting, and general distortion of the lumber.

The commercial softwoods and hardwoods of the United States are:

SOFTWOODS

Cedars and	Larch
junipers	Pines
Cypress	Redwood
Douglas fir	Spruce
White fir	Tamarack
Hemlocks	Yew

HARDWOODS

Alder	Gums
Ashes	Hackberry
Aspen	Hickories
Basswood	Locust
Beech	Magnolia
Birches	Maples
Buckeye	Oaks
Butternut	Sycamore
Cherry	Walnut
Chestnut	Willow
Cottonwood	Yellow
Elms	poplar

Lumber suitable for structural purposes may be obtained from other groups; but for some reason these groups have not been utilized extensively as yet except in the immediate vicinity where they grow. This is especially true of bamboo which grows in abundance in China and the Philippine Islands and is used there extensively for building purposes. Although the wood has certain characteristics which might make it suitable for use in other locations, it has not been introduced into other countries. Of another group, not used for structural purposes, the palms are the best-known representatives.

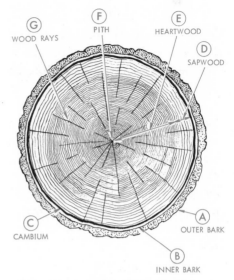

Fig. 2. Cross section of tree trunk.

Heartwood and Sapwood

The cross section of a log cut from a tree trunk shows distinct zones of wood. First, there is the *bark* placed like a sheath around the outside of the log; then, a light-colored zone next to it called *sapwood;* and an inner zone, usually darker in the center, called *heartwood*. In the structural center of the log and usually of the heartwood is the *pith*, sometimes termed in the lumber trade as *heart center*. When a piece of lumber contains the pith, it is called *boxed pith*; when it does not, it is termed *sidecut* (pithless). A cross section of a tree trunk is shown in Fig. 2. The outer bark, or corky layer, shown at (*A*), is composed of dry dead tissue which gives the tree protection against external injuries. The inner bark (*B*) is moist and soft. It carries prepared food from the leaves to all growing parts of the tree. The wood and bark cells are formed in the microscopic cambium layer shown at (*C*) just inside the inner bark. Immediately beneath the bark is the light-colored wood (*D*) known as *sapwood*. The sapwood carries sap from the roots to the leaves. The inactive heartwood is shown at (*E*). This part of a tree is formed by a gradual change in the sapwood and gives the tree strength. The pith (*F*) is the soft tissue about which the first wood growth takes place in the newly formed twigs. The various layers of the tree are connected by wood rays (*G*) which extend from the pith to the bark and provide for the storage and transference of food.

A tree grows by forming new layers of wood at the point where the bark and sapwood meet. *Cambium* is the technical name for this layer of soft cellular tissue from which new bark and new wood originate. The cambium is supplied with nourishment by a fluid known as *sap* which circulates through the wood cells located immediately underneath the bark. These wood cells make up the living, active portion of the tree. These cells also carry water from the roots to the uppermost parts of the tree. Various salts obtained from the soil and dissolved in the water are carried by the ascending current from the most minute rootlet to the topmost branches and leaves. Food for the plant is also stored in the wood cells, to be used when needed.

A young tree is composed entirely of sapwood. The heartwood is formed in the central portion as the tree grows older. As the cells mature and become inactive, the heartwood usually turns darker in color. The thickness of the sapwood varies in different kinds of trees, and depends to some extent upon the age of the tree. The conditions under which growth takes place may also affect the thickness of the sapwood.

All heartwood was once sapwood. During the transition period of growth, the changes which take place have no effect upon the mechanical properties of the wood.

Hence, so far as strength is concerned, there is no difference between sapwood and heartwood. However, when in contact with the soil and under conditions conducive to decay, heartwood is more durable than sapwood. Therefore, it is better to use heartwood if the material is not to be treated with preservatives and conditions are conducive to decay. But it is better to use sapwood if preservatives are to be used, because heartwood does not absorb preservatives readily.

Rings of Annual Growth

There is a marked difference in the manner of growth in different kinds of trees. The trees with which this study is especially concerned show annual growth rings and include both the broad-leaved trees and the evergreens. These are known as *exogens* because they grow from without. However, there are certain exogenous trees which show no distinct annual growth rings, for example some species of evergreen tropical trees. The palms and bamboos do not show annual growth rings. These are known as *endogens* because they grow from within.

In cool temperate climates, examination of the cross section of a freshly cut tree shows a number of concentric rings starting at the center of the pith and continuing outward to the bark. Each of these rings represents the growth the tree makes during one year; that is, from the time active growth begins in the spring to the time the tree becomes dormant in the fall. Therefore, the approximate age of the tree can be determined by counting the rings of annual growth on a cross section cut as closely as possible to the ground, because the oldest part of a tree trunk is its base. The annual rings of a cross section taken fifteen feet above the ground would perhaps show fewer rings because that section would be of a more recent growth than the lower section. These annual rings vary in width according to conditions under which growth takes place. Narrow rings being formed during years when there is a short dry season and wider rings during years when conditions are more favorable for growth. The annual growth rings appear in the cross section of lumber as concentric circles or portions of circles.

Springwood and Summerwood. In many woods each ring of annual growth is made up of two parts: (*a*) an inner light-colored portion known as *springwood*, and (*b*) an outer darker portion of later growth known as *summerwood*, also sometimes called *autumnwood*.

Springwood is made up of relatively large, thin-walled cells formed during the early part of each growing season. Summerwood is formed later in the year and is made up of cells having thicker walls and smaller openings. Therefore, summerwood or autumnwood contains more solid wood substances and appears to be darker in color than springwood. In both softwoods and hardwoods growing in regions having climatic seasons this phenomenon appears although it is less noticeable in hardwoods.

The proportion of springwood and summerwood present in pieces of softwood lumber has an important effect upon its strength properties and physical characteristics. In some species there is a gradual change from springwood to summerwood. In other softwoods the change from springwood to summerwood is more or less abrupt, thus resulting in well-marked bands of darker, more solid wood substance, and usually in a large proportion of summerwood and correspondingly stronger material.

Rate of Growth and Density. The rate at which trees grow and form wood substance has an important effect upon their strength properties. It has been shown by experiments that, in the softwoods commonly used for structural purposes, an accurate measure of this strength is provided by the relative width and the character of wood in each annual growth ring. In these woods, pieces having medium to narrow growth rings have been found to have generally higher strength properties than those having wide growth rings.

In addition, in certain woods, pieces with a considerable proportion of each annual ring made up of the dense, darker summerwood have still higher strength properties. Therefore, in grading structural material for use under known loads, a part of the specification is consideration of the number of rings per inch radially and the density, or proportion of summerwood.

Material having a specific minimum number of annual rings per inch is termed *close grained* and that having in addition 33 per cent or more summerwood is termed *dense*. Examples are given in the illustrations, Figs. 3, 4, and 5. In Fig. 3, the section of structural tim-

ber shown has 7 annual growth rings per inch and 35 per cent summerwood, therefore, it is close grained and dense. In Fig. 4, the section of the structural joist shown has 5 annual growth rings per inch and 25

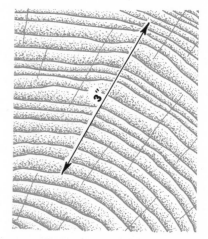

Fig. 4. Section of end of structural joist which is neither close grained nor dense.

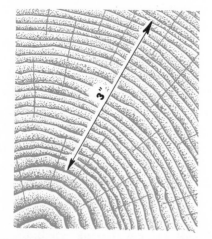

Fig. 3. Section of structural timber showing wood grain which is both close grained and dense.

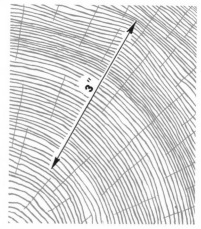

Fig. 5. Section of end of structural joist which is close grained but not dense.

per cent summerwood, hence is considered neither close grained nor dense. In Fig. 5, the section of structural joist illustrated has 15 annual growth rings per inch and 30 per cent summerwood, therefore, it is considered close grained but *not* dense.

Grain and Texture

The terms *grain* and *texture* are used in various ways to describe certain characteristics of wood. The wood from slow-growing trees in which the annual growth rings are narrow is sometimes described as *close grained;* that from rapidly growing trees with wide rings as *coarse grained.* This is another way of describing the number of rings per inch and is important in strength grading.

Wood in which the direction of the fibers (*not* the annual rings) are parallel to the sides of the piece is called *straight grain;* while *cross grain* is used to describe wood in which the fibers are at an angle with the sides of the piece. *Cross grain* also includes *spiral grain* in which the fibers wind around the trunk of the tree. The expression *slope of grain* is employed in the grading of structural material to describe the extent of coarse grain permitted, since slope of grain has an important influence on strength.

However, *grain* and *texture* usually refer to the physical properties of appearance rather than properties of strength. For example, *fine grain* is used to describe woods in which the cells are small and thick walled, making a compact wood with smooth surface, as in maple, birch, and pine. The *coarse-grain* woods, such as oak, walnut, and chestnut, are those in which the cells are large and open, producing a slightly roughened surface due to the large cells being cut where they intersect the surface.

When sawed in such a manner that the annual rings (grain) form an angle of 45 degrees or more with the wide faces, lumber is described as *edge grain, vertical grain,* or *rift-sawed* in softwoods, and *quarter-sawed* or *comb-grained* in hardwoods. The term *flat-grain* or *flat-sawed* in softwoods and *plain-sawed* in hardwoods describes lumber in which the annual growth rings are at an angle of 45 degrees or less with the wide faces of the piece. Flat-grain is also known as *tangential section. Bastard-sawed* in hardwoods is material midway between true *quarter-sawed* and true *plain-sawed,* Fig. 6. The appearance of edge grain in softwoods and quartersawed in hardwoods is shown at (*A*), Fig. 6. The illustration at (*B*), Fig. 6, shows a piece of lumber described as *flat-grain* or *flat-sawed* in softwoods and *plain-sawed* in hardwoods.

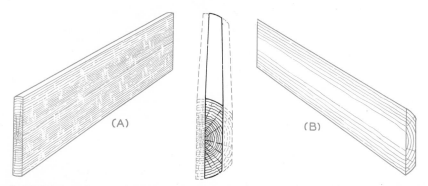

Fig. 6. *(A)* Edge grain in softwood and quartersawed in hardwoods; *(B)* flat-sawed in softwoods and plain-sawed in hardwoods. (U.S. Forest Products Laboratory)

Moisture in Wood

Wood in standing trees contains moisture in two forms: as free water held in the cell cavities; and as imbibed hydroscopic moisture held in the cell walls. When green wood begins to lose its moisture, the cell walls remain saturated until all free water has been evaporated. The point at which all the free water has been evaporated and the walls of the fibers or cells begin to lose their moisture is called the *fiber saturation point*. Although varying somewhat between species, the fiber saturation point is about 25 per cent of most woods.

The moisture in wood is expressed as a percentage of the oven-dried weight. This percentage is determined as follows: a representative sample of wood is weighed; then the same piece of wood is dried in an oven, at a temperature of slightly more than 212 degrees, until no fur-

ther loss of weight takes place. The wood is weighed again and the difference between the original weight and final weight is found. This difference divided by the final (oven-dry) weight (times 100) gives the percentage of the oven-dried weight.

For example, if a 10 ounce test sample weighed 8 ounces after oven drying:

$$\frac{10 \text{ oz.} - 8 \text{ oz.}}{8 \text{ oz.}} \times 100 =$$

$$\frac{2 \text{ oz.}}{8 \text{ oz.}} \times 100 = 25\%$$

moisture content

The original green test sample had a moisture content of 25 percent.

The moisture-content requirements are more exacting for lumber or wood products to be used for the interior finish of buildings than for lumber or wood products that are to be used out of doors. Requirements of moisture content in wood intended for outdoor purposes do not need to be so exacting as for interior-finish lumber because, under ordinary atmospheric conditions, lumber used outdoors does not reach so low a moisture content. Then, too, a higher character of service is required of the interior-finish lumber. In most cases, lumber for both exterior and interior use should be dried to approximately the value of moisture content to which it will come when in service. The moisture-content values for various regions in the United States are shown in Table I. The values given here are the recommendations of the United States Department of Agriculture for moisture content for various wood items at the time of installation.

When the moisture content of wood falls below the fiber saturation point, the wood changes in size. However, in seasoning, the surface of green wood dries more rapidly than the interior and reaches the fiber saturation point first. In such a case shrinkage may start while the average moisture content is considerably above the fiber saturation point. Wood shrinks most in the direction of the annual growth rings (tangentially), about one-half to two-thirds as much across these rings (radially), and very little, as a rule, along the grain (longitudinally).

The fact that wood changes in size with change in moisture content is an important consideration to be remembered when constructing the frame for a building. For example, a stud in a wall will not shrink appreciably in length, whereas it will shrink somewhat in both the 2-inch and the 4-inch dimensions. Therefore, it is well to avoid as much as possible the use of cross-section material in wall construction. If a joist is green when put in place it will

TABLE I. MOISTURE CONTENT VALUES FOR VARIOUS WOOD ITEMS

Use of Lumber	Moisture Content (Percentage of Weight of Oven-Dry Wood) for—					
	Dry Southwestern States		Damp Southern Coastal States		Remainder of the United States	
	Average	Individual pieces	Average	Individual pieces	Average	Individual pieces
	Per Cent	Per Cent	Per Cent	Per Cent	Per Cent	Per Cent
Interior finish woodwork and softwood flooring..	6	4–9	11	8–13	8	5–10
Hardwood flooring......	6	5–8	10	9–12	7	6–9
Siding, exterior trim, sheathing, and framing	9	7–12	12	9–14	12	9–14

shrink in depth as it seasons in the building. The combined effects of radial and tangential shrinkage on the shape of various sections in drying from the green condition are illustrated in Fig. 7. In this diagram are shown the characteristic shrinkage and distortion of flats, squares, and rounds as affected by the direction of the annual rings. Tangential shrinkage is about twice as much as radial shrinkage.

When wood is drying, shrinkage is proportional to the moisture lost below the fiber saturation point. Approximately one-half of the total shrinkage possible has occurred in wood seasoned to an air-dry condition (12 to 15 per cent moisture content) and about three-fourths in lumber kiln-dried to a moisture content of about 7 per cent. Hence, if

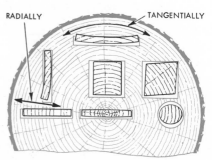

Fig. 7. Cross section of tree trunk showing characteristics shrinkage and distortion of flats, squares, and rounds as affected by the direction of the annual rings.

wood is properly seasoned, manufactured, and installed at a moisture content in accordance with its service conditions there will be excellent possibilities of satisfactory service without any serious changes in size or distortion of the cross section.

Defects and Blemishes In Wood

Timber is not a manufactured material like iron or cement but is a natural product developed through many years of growth in the open air and exposed continually to varying conditions of wind and weather. Since wood is a natural product it is peculiarly liable to contain defects of different kinds. Most of these defects cannot be corrected. Therefore, they render much of the wood unsuitable for use in construction work. Moreover, it cannot be assumed safely that several different pieces of timber, even though cut from the same log, will have similar characteristics or will give exactly the same service under the same conditions. In addition to injuries incurred during growth there are other injuries due to improper handling or to preparatory processes, such as sawing. In view of these injuries, regardless of the cause, each piece of timber must be judged separately and subjected to careful inspection to insure satisfactory results when the piece is used in an important position. Oftentimes, such careful inspection will reveal some hidden weakness, defect, or blemish which will warrant the rejection of this particular timber as inferior and not suitable for the service for which it was intended.

As the term is used in the trade, a *defect* is an irregularity occurring in or on wood that will tend to impair its strength, durability, or utility value. Though not classified as a defect, a *blemish* is any imperfection which mars the appearance of wood. Some of the commonly recognized defects and blemishes in yard lumber are discussed in the following paragraphs.

Bark Pockets. A patch of bark nearly, or wholly, enclosed in the wood is known as a *bark pocket.*

Checks. A lengthwise separation of wood tissues is known as a *check.* Checks usually occur across the rings of annual growth and are due to shrinkage. In any log of wood there is always the possibility of shrinkage in two directions— along the radial lines following the direction of the medullary rays, and around the circumference of the log following the direction of the annual rings. If the wood shrinks in both directions at the same rate, the result will be only a decrease in the

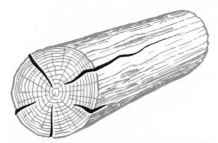

Fig. 8. Checks caused by wood shrinking more rapidly around the circumference of a log than along the radial lines.

volume of the log, but if it shrinks more rapidly around the circumference of the log than along the radial lines, the log will develop cracks, or checks, along the outside, as shown in Fig. 8.

Cross Grain. When the cells, or fibers, of wood do not run parallel with the axis or sides of a piece of timber, the result is a twisting and interweaving of the wood fibers known as *cross grain.*

Decay. A disintegration of the wood substance due to the action of wood-destroying fungi is called *decay.* Incipient decay is the early stage of deterioration in which the disintegration has not proceeded far enough to soften or to otherwise perceptibly impair the hardness of the wood. In typical or advanced decay the disintegration is readily recognized because the wood has become punky, soft, spongy, stringy, pitted, or crumbly. Table II gives the decay resistance for some of the common woods.

TABLE II. WOODS: CLASSIFICATION FOR DECAY RESISTANCE*

Heartwood durable even when used under conditions that favor decay	Cedar, Alaska Cedar, eastern red Cedar, northern white Cedar, Port Orford Cedar, southern white Cedar, western red Chestnut Cypress, southern Locust, black Osage-orange Redwood Walnut, black Yew, Pacific
Heartwood of intermediate durability but nearly as durable as some of the species named in the high-durability group	Douglas fir (dense) Honey locust Oak, white Pine, southern yellow (dense)
Heartwood of intermediate durability	Douglas fir (unselected) Gum, red Larch, western Pine, southern yellow (unselected) Tamarack
Heartwood between the intermediate and the nondurable group	Ash, commercial white Beech Birch, sweet Birch, yellow Hemlock, eastern Hemlock, western Hickory Maple, sugar Oak, red Spruce, black Spruce, Engelmann Spruce, red Spruce, Sitka Spruce, white
Heartwood low in durability when used under conditions that favor decay	Aspen Basswood Cottonwood Fir, commercial white Willow, black

Practically all native species of wood will be free from decay, indefinitely, if kept either constantly dry or continuously submerged in water. The principal factors affecting the rate of decay are moisture and temperature. The heartwood of all species is more resistant to decay than the untreated sapwood. The rate of decay varies in each species and even in each tree. The decay-resistant grouping of common native species made by the United States Department of Agriculture (Table II.) is based upon estimates made from service records and general experience with the heartwood.

*Source: United States Wood Handbook

Holes. A piece of wood may be defective because of *holes* extending partially or entirely through the piece. Such holes may be due to many different causes, such as injury through improper handling, or from wood-boring insects or worms. Whatever the cause, holes in wood make it unfit for use in construction work.

Imperfections Occurring at the Mills. Many defects or blemishes occur during the process of milling lumber. These include such imperfections as: chipped, loosened, raised or torn grain; skips in dressing; variations in sawing; miscut lumber; machine burns; gouges; mismatching; and insufficient depth in tongue and groove.

Knots. At the juncture of the branches with the main trunk of a tree, some fibers of the wood turn aside to follow along the limb. When a branch is broken off near the trunk leaving a small piece attached to the tree, the tree continues to grow, but the broken piece of limb dies. As the tree increases in size the piece of dead limb becomes embedded in the trunk. In the course of time the dead wood is buried and entirely covered over by living woody tissue. These bits of wood, known as *knots*, have no connection with the living wood but occupy a place within the body of the tree with sound wood all about them. When a section of a tree, containing knots, is sawed into lumber and the knots are cut through, they will loosen eventually and fall out, leaving round or irregular *knot holes* in the boards. Knots are more or less common in all lumber. So long as they remain in place, the presence of a limited number of knots will not harm a piece of lumber which is subjected to a compressive stress. However, knots tend to weaken greatly a piece of timber subjected to a tension stress or when used as a beam. Knots also affect the appearance of polished woodwork.

Knots are differentiated according to size, form, quality, and occurrence. A *pin knot* is ½ inch in diameter or less; a *small knot* is over ½ inch but not more than ¾ inch in diameter; a *medium knot* is over ¾ inch but not more than 1½ inches in diameter; a *large knot* is one more than 1½ inches in diameter. A *spike knot* occurs where a limb is sawed in a lengthwise direction.

Pitch Pockets. Sometimes between rings of annual growth well-defined openings or cracks occur. These are known as *pitch pockets*, and usually contain or have contained pitch, in either solid or liquid form.

Pith. In the structural center of a log occurs the *pith* which is made up of soft spongy cellular tissue. When cut from a portion of the log containing pith a board is not suitable for first-class structural work.

Shake. A lengthwise split, commonly called a *shake*, in a piece of timber usually causes a separation of the wood between the rings of annual growth. Shakes usually are parallel to the growth rings. Such defects always decrease the value of timber.

Heart Shake. When a defect in the central portion of the trunk shows itself at the heart of a tree and in a cross section the shake appears running in a radial direction the defect is known as a *heart shake*, Fig. 9. First a small cavity caused by decay occurs at the center of the trunk, then later flaws or cracks develop and extend from this cavity outward toward the bark.

In a cross section of the trunk of a tree, when a heart shake assumes the form of a single split across the center, the defect is known as a *simple heart shake*. If such a split is crossed at right angles by another similar split this defect is known as a *double heart shake*. Sometimes a number of splits may radiate from the center of the trunk and produce what is known as a *star shake* which is associated with discoloration and decay.

Wind Shakes. A growing tree is subjected to much racking and wrenching by high winds. Defects believed to be caused by the action of high winds are called *wind shakes*, Fig. 10. However, some people believe these defects are produced by the expansion of the sapwood which causes a separation of the annual rings from each other, thus leaving a hollow space in the body of the trunk. This belief and the cup-shaped appearance of the defect on a cross section of the tree

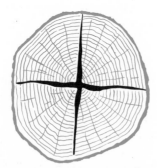

Fig. 9. Heart shake caused by decay beginning at the center of the tree trunk and extending outward.

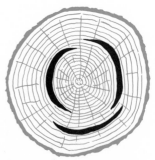

Fig. 10. Wind shake caused by racking and wrenching of a tree by wind.

has suggested the term *cup shakes*, also commonly used.

Split. A lengthwise separation of wood due to the tearing apart of the wood cells is called a *split*. Usually a split occurs across the rings of annual growth, extending from one surface through the piece of timber to the opposite surface, or to an adjoining surface.

Blue Stain. Due to the growth of certain moldlike fungi, a bluish or grayish discoloration, known as *blue stain*, sometimes appears on the surface and in the interior of a piece of unseasoned lumber. Although the appearance of blue stain is objectionable, it does not have any particular effect on the strength of the timber, which can be used in structural work where appearance is not important.

Wane. A defect on the edge or corner of a piece of timber or plank due to a lack of wood or bark, regardless of the cause, is known as a *wane*.

Warping. Any variation from a true or plane surface is called *warping*, Fig. 11. When a piece of timber is permanently distorted or twisted out of shape as by moisture or heat, it is said to be *warped*. Warping is the result of the evaporation or drying out of the water which is held in the cell walls of the wood in its natural state, and the shrinkage which follows. If wood were perfectly regular in structure, so that the shrinkage could be the same in every part, there would be no warping; but wood is made up of a large number of fibers, the walls of which are of different thicknesses in different parts of the tree or log, so that when drying, one part shrinks much more than another part. Since the wood fibers are in close contact with each other and are interlaced making the piece of wood rigid, one part cannot shrink or swell without changing the shape of the whole piece, because the piece as a whole must ad-

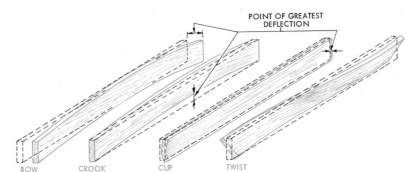

POINT OF GREATEST DEFLECTION

BOW   CROOK   CUP   TWIST

Fig. 11. Various kinds of warp in wood—bow, crook, cup, and twist.

just itself to the new conditions; consequently the timber warps. The distortion due to warping may take different forms, such as a twist, a crook, cupped, or bow-shaped; or any combination of these.

Grading of Lumber

The various defects and blemishes found in lumber necessitate the establishment of certain classification and grading rules. The American Lumber Standards for grading lumber were formulated by the National Bureau of Standards of the United States Department of Commerce. The purpose of setting up such standards was to insure uniform grading throughout the country. Lumber is normally classified in three different ways: by *use*, by method of *manufacture*, and by *size*.

Use Classifications

Use classification is broken down into three principal categories: *structural lumber, factory and shop lumber* and *yard lumber*.

Structural Lumber. Lumber, sometimes termed structural timber, is 5 inches or more in both thickness and width. It is graded according to its strength and to the use which is to be made of an entire piece. Such lumber is used principally for bridge or trestle timbers, for car and ship timbers, for ship decking, and for framing of buildings. (Much of the structural timber used today is formed of glued laminated members. Smaller lumber pieces are glued and laminated together to form larger beams and arches.)

Factory or Shop Lumber. Lumber intended for additional cutting in the process of further manufacturing is known to the trade as factory lumber or shop lumber. Such lumber is used principally in window sashes, doors and door frames, in different types of millwork, and in furniture factories. This lumber is graded on the basis of the percentage of area which will produce a limited number of clear cuttings of a given minimum, or specified, size and quality.

Yard Lumber. The lumber known as *yard lumber* is less than 5 inches in thickness and is intended for general building purposes.

Strips. The yard lumber known to the trade as *strips* is less than 2 inches in thickness and less than 8 inches in width.

Boards. Yard lumber, commonly called *boards*, is less than 2 inches thick and 8 inches or more in width.

Dimension Lumber. When cut to specified sizes yard lumber, of any width and at least 2 inches but not more than 5 inches thick, is called *dimension lumber*.

Manufacturing Classifications

Manufacturing classifications are broken down into three categories: *rough lumber, dressed lumber* and *worked lumber*.

Rough Lumber. Lumber that has *not* been dressed (surfaced) but which has been sawed, edged, and trimmed at least to the extent of showing saw marks in the wood on the four longitudinal surfaces of each piece for its entire length.

Dressed (Surfaced) Lumber. Lumber that has been dressed by a planing machine, for purpose of attaining smoothness of surface and uniformity of sizes, on one side, two sides, one edge, two edges, or a combination of sides and edges.

Worked Lumber. Lumber which in addition to being dressed has been matched, shiplapped, or patterned:

(a) *Matched Lumber.* Lumber that has been worked with a tongue on one edge of each piece and a groove on the opposite edge, to provide a close tongue-and-groove joint by fitting two pieces together; when end-matched, the tongue and groove are worked in the ends also.

(b) *Shiplapped Lumber.* Lumber that has been worked or rabbeted on both edges of each piece to provide a close lapped joint by fitting two pieces together.

(c) *Patterned Lumber.* Lumber that is shaped to a pattern or to a molded form, in addition to being dressed, matched, or shiplapped, or any combination of these workings.

There is a great variety in the shapes and sizes of patterned lumber. The exact dimensions of some of the most common stock lumber patterns are illustrated in Fig. 12. Lumberyard stock of patterned lumber also includes moldings. See Fig. 13. Moldings and other trim members can be obtained in different shapes and sizes, also in a variety of stock designs. When building specifications call for designs not carried in the stock-lumber patterns, a special job of millwork is required to handle this order. Any specification which makes additional work necessarily increases the cost of construction.

In ordering, the particular pattern and the sizes should be specified. In some cases, such as flooring, prefinished worked lumber is available. Manufacturer's catalogs should be consulted for prefinished lumber specifications.

Size Classifications

Lumber is further classified as to size. There are two basic sizes: *nominal* or *rough size* and *actual* or

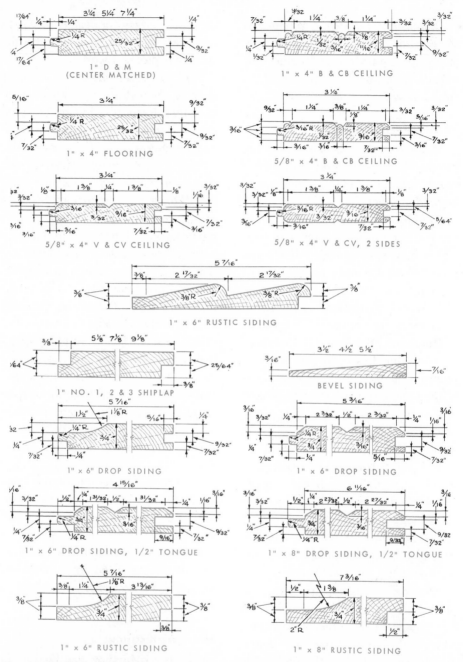

Fig. 12. Typical stock-lumber patterns of dressed and matched flooring, ceiling, and siding (softwood); and lumber patterns of shiplap and other types of siding (softwood). (West Coast Lumbermen's Assoc.)

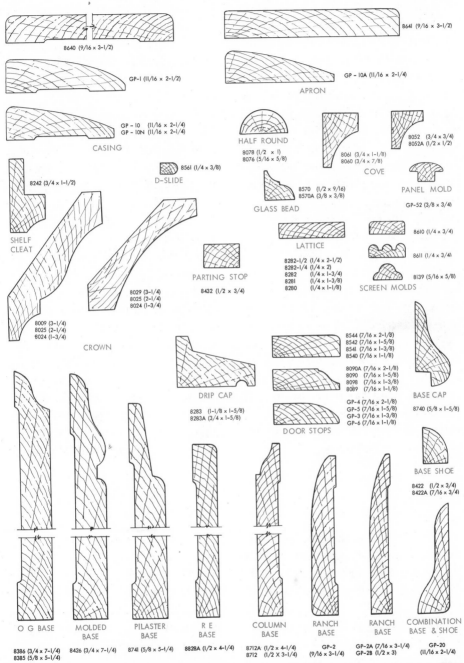

8640 (9/16 × 3-1/2)

8641 (9/16 × 3-1/2)

GP-1 (11/16 × 2-1/2)

GP - 10A (11/16 × 2-1/4)

APRON

GP - 10 (11/16 × 2-1/4)
GP - 10N (11/16 × 2-1/4)

CASING

HALF ROUND
8078 (1/2 × 1)
8076 (5/16 × 5/8)

8561 (1/4 × 3/8)

D-SLIDE

8052 (3/4 × 3/4)
8052A (1/2 × 1/2)

8242 (3/4 × 1-1/2)

8061 (3/4 × 1-1/8)
8060 (3/4 × 7/8)

COVE

PANEL MOLD

8570 (1/2 × 9/16)
8570A (3/8 × 3/8)

GLASS BEAD

GP-52 (3/8 × 3/4)

SHELF
CLEAT

LATTICE

8610 (1/4 × 3/4)

8611 (1/4 × 3/4)

PARTING STOP

8432 (1/2 × 3/4)

8282-1/2 (1/4 × 2-1/2)
8282-1/4 (1/4 × 2)
8282 (1/4 × 1-3/4)
8281 (1/4 × 1-3/8)
8280 (1/4 × 1-1/8)

8139 (5/16 × 5/8)

SCREEN MOLDS

8029 (3-1/4)
8025 (2-1/4)
8024 (1-3/4)

8009 (3-1/4)
8025 (2-1/4)
8024 (1-3/4)

CROWN

8544 (7/16 × 2-1/8)
8542 (7/16 × 1-5/8)
8541 (7/16 × 1-3/8)
8540 (7/16 × 1-1/8)

8090A (7/16 × 2-1/8)
8090 (7/16 × 1-5/8)
8098 (7/16 × 1-3/8)
8089 (7/16 × 1-1/8)

BASE CAP

DRIP CAP

8283 (1-1/8 × 1-5/8)
8283A (3/4 × 1-5/8)

GP-4 (7/16 × 2-1/8)
GP-5 (7/16 × 1-5/8)
GP-3 (7/16 × 1-3/8)
GP-6 (7/16 × 1-1/8)

DOOR STOPS

8740 (5/8 × 1-5/8)

BASE SHOE

8422 (1/2 × 3/4)
8422A (7/16 × 3/4)

O G BASE

8386 (3/4 × 7-1/4)
8385 (5/8 × 5-1/4)

MOLDED
BASE

8426 (3/4 × 7-1/4)

PILASTER
BASE

8741 (5/8 × 5-1/4)

R E
BASE

8828A (1/2 × 4-1/4)

COLUMN
BASE

8712A (1/2 × 4-1/4)
8712 (1/2 × 3-1/4)

RANCH
BASE

GP-2
(9/16 × 3-1/4)

RANCH
BASE

GP-2A (7/16 × 3-1/4)
GP-2B (1/2 × 3)

COMBINATION
BASE & SHOE

GP-20
(11/16 × 2-1/4)

Fig. 13. A typical page from a manufacturer's catalog. Molding patterns are shown. The numbers are the manufacturer's stock numbers. (Georgia-Pacific Corp.)

157

dressed size. Nominal ("not real or actual") refers to the *rough* size of a board as compared to the finished, actual size. A board may be cut to a *nominal size* of 2" x 4" but after finishing and planing and, if green, after drying, the *actual* size would be much less; for example, 1½" x 3½", depending upon the end use and the lumber standard used. This does not mean, however, that a nominal size 2" x 4" board is originally cut by the mill at exactly 2" x 4" dimensions, the cut is slightly less. It is cut so that *after* finishing and drying the board will have specific, predetermined dimensions. The actual size for the various kinds of lumber is established by commercial standards, which the lumber manufacturers agree to follow. Consult the applicable standards (softwood or hardwood) for the sizes of a particular type of wood. *Appendix C* gives tables for softwood lumber sizes.

Shingles

Western red cedar, white cedar, redwood, and cypress are woods commonly used for making shingles. The grading varies with the kind of wood used. The western cedar is graded as: No. 1, No. 2, and No. 3. In cypress the grades include: No. 1, *bests*, *prime*, *economies*, and *clippers*. In white cedar the grades

are: *extra star A star*, *standard star A star*, and *sound butts*. Redwood comes in two grades: No. 1 and No. 2. Shingles of the highest quality are all clear, all heartwood, and all edge grain.

Shingles come in three lengths— 16, 18, and 24 inches—and in *random* widths; or *dimension* widths all cut to the same width. The thickness of shingles is indicated as ⁴⁄₂, ⁵⁄₂ and ⁵⁄₂½; that is, 4 shingles to 2 inches of butt thickness; 5 shingles to 2 inches of butt thickness; and 5 shingles to 2½ inches of butt thickness.

Shingles are usually ordered in *squares*. A square of shingles consists of four bundles of shingles: this is called a "square" because it will normally cover 100 square feet (10' x 10') of roof area. The amount covered will vary, however, depending on the shingle overlap. The shingle overlap is determined by the pitch of the roof and the length of the shingle.

Shakes

Shakes are very similar to shingles, except that shakes are split rather than sawed. Shakes, therefore, have a rough, natural grain surface. Shingles, on the other hand, have a smooth surface. Shakes come in 15, 18, 24 and 32 inch lengths. They are commonly tapered from one end to the other.

Ordering Lumber

Lumber Measurements. Lumber is sold by the *board foot, surface* or *square foot,* and *lineal foot* measurement.

Board Foot. Strip lumber, boards, dimension lumber, structural timbers, and shop lumber are sold by the *board foot,* see Fig. 14. A board foot is 1 inch thick, 12 inches wide, and 1 foot (12 inches) long (1″ x 12″ x 1′).

$$\frac{\text{Thickness in inches} \times \text{width in inches} \times \text{length in feet}}{12} = \text{board feet}$$

Allowing T to mean "thickness in inches" and W to mean "width in inches" and L to mean "length in feet," the formula may be written

$$\frac{T \times W \times L}{12} = \text{board feet}$$

Lumber sizes used in figuring board feet are the nominal sizes. Lumber less than 1″ thick is figured as 1 inch. For example, a piece $\frac{1}{2}″ \times 12″ \times 12″$ is considered as one board foot. Lengths are usually in even feet, usually under 24 feet. Lumber over 24 feet can be obtained on specification.

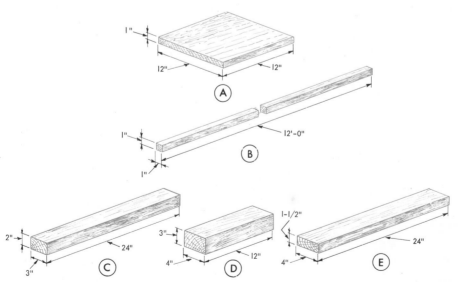

Fig. 14. The unit of measure for lumber is the board foot. Each of the above pieces is one board foot.

To find the board feet in a piece $1'' \times 6'' \times 12'0''$

$$\frac{1 \times 6 \times \cancel{12}}{\cancel{12}} = 6, \text{ or 6 board feet}$$

To find the board feet in a piece of dimension $2'' \times 10'' \times 16'0''$

$$\frac{2 \times 10 \times \overset{4}{\cancel{16}}}{\underset{3}{\cancel{12}}} = \frac{80}{3},$$

or $26\frac{2}{3}$ board feet

When the size is entirely in inches —$1'' \times 6'' \times 8''$

$$\frac{1 \times 6 \times 8}{144} = \frac{6}{18}, \text{ or } \frac{1}{3} \text{ board feet}$$

Surface or Square Feet. Thin lumber material ½- or ¼-inch thick, such as veneer, siding, and plywood is sold by the *square foot* —12 inches wide by 1 foot long— and is priced accordingly. A piece of ½-inch plywood $4' \times 8'$ would contain 32 square feet $(4 \times 8 = 32)$

Lineal Foot. Materials sold by the *lineal* or *running foot*, regardless of width or thickness, include moldings, interior trim, furring strips, and grounds.

Lumber Abbreviations. Several abbreviations and terms are commonly used in ordering, sizing, and surfacing lumber. These terms should be understood by the carpenter. They will be encountered both in ordering and working with wood. In ordering, the following information is required: number of pieces, thickness, width, length, kind of wood, grade of lumber, and the surfacing required. Also the name of the item, such as siding, flooring, etc., should sometimes be specified. For example: 8 pieces $2'' \times 4'' \times 14'$, D. F. Construction S1S1E. (D. F. stands for Douglas Fir; "construction" refers to the

TABLE III. LUMBER ABBREVIATIONS

S1S	Surfaced one side	D & H	Dressed and headed
S2S	Surfaced two sides	S/Lap	Shiplap
S4S	Surfaced four sides	D/S	Drop siding
S1E	Surfaced one edge	EXT	Exterior
S2E	Surfaced two edges	INT	Interior
S1S1E	Surfaced one side and one edge	STRUC–INT	Structural — Interior
S1S2E	Surfaced one side and two edges	STR	Structural
S2S1E	Surfaced two sides and one edge	M	Thousand
Ro	Rough, no milling	MBM	Thousand (feet) board measure
EM	End matched	Bd ft	Board feet
CM	Center matched	m c	Moisture content
D & M	Dressed and matched	AD	Air dried
T & G	Tongue and Grooved	KD	Kiln dried

grade.) If no surfacing (dressing) is desired, rough lumber or "saw sized" lumber should be specified. In all cases the lumber ordered should be of the appropriate size and surfacing for the intended use. If preservative treatments are re- quired, the type and amount of treatment and the final use of the lumber should be specified. Sometimes the moisture content (m.c.) must also be specified. Table III gives some of the common abbreviations used in the lumber industry.

Working Qualities and Uses of Wood

In selecting wood for a given purpose, the ease with which it may be worked is sometimes a factor, especially when hand tools are to be used.

Table IV gives the workability of common woods; this is based on the experience of the Forest Products Laboratory together with the general reputation of the wood.

TABLE IV.   WORKABILITY OF WOODS WITH HAND TOOLS

	SOFTWOODS	
Easy to Work	Medium to Work	Difficult to Work
Cedar, incense Cedar, northern white Cedar, Port Orford Cedar, southern white Cedar, western red Pine, northern white Pine, ponderosa Pine, sugar Pine, western white	Cedar, eastern red Cypress, southern Fir, balsam Fir, white Hemlock, eastern Hemlock, western Pine, lodgepole Redwood Spruce, eastern Spruce, Sitka	Douglas fir Larch, western Pine, southern yellow
	HARDWOODS	
Easy to Work	Medium to Work	Difficult to Work
Alder, red Basswood Butternut Chestnut Poplar, yellow	Birch, paper Cottonwood Gum, black Gum, red Gum, tupelo Magnolia Sycamore Walnut, black	Ash, commercial white Beech Birch Cherry Elm Hackberry Hickory, true and pecan Honey locust Locust, black Maple Oak, commercial red Oak, commercial white

Many of our woods have particular uses that are commonly associated with them. Of the great variety of lumber used in construction work the greatest bulk comes from the softwoods obtained from the conifers or needle-leaved trees. Therefore, in this discussion the softwoods are considered first.

Hardwoods or broad-leaved trees are seldom used for structural work. However, the hardwoods do play an important part in the building industry where they may be used for interior trim, floors, cabinets, and furniture, and occasionally hardwood is used for exterior trim.

Uses of Common Softwoods

Alaska Cedar. This cedar is used for cabinet work, doors, blinds, furniture, interior finish, ship and boat building, and novelties. It is easily worked and takes a good polish. It holds paint well, requiring little paint protection for weathering.

Port Orford Cedar. The better grades of Port Orford Cedar are used for shingles, shakes, siding, chests, lawn furniture, boats, and interior finish. The lower grades are useful for general construction purposes. This wood is of moderate strength and hardness.

Western Red Cedar. This wood is valuable for shingles, shakes, siding, porch columns, greenhouse construction, ship and boat building, and wooden novelties. The wood is easily worked, rather soft and weak. It has good nail-holding qualities and little shrinkage. It finishes well. Shingles made from western red cedar take and hold the stain of the finest tint without discoloration. They also hold paint well and require little protection for weathering.

Northern White Cedar. The northern white cedar is used extensively for shingles, shakes, tanks, silos, caskets, professional and scientific instruments, planing-mill products, and ship and boat building. This wood makes good fence posts, telegraph and telephone poles, and because of its decay-resistant qualities is in demand for use where contact with the ground is required. The wood is soft, brittle, and weak in structure. It has a low shrinkage and splits easily. It is highly resistant to decay.

Southern Cypress. Because of its decay resistance southern cypress is used extensively for outside work, gutters, shingles, siding, casings, water tanks, vats, tubes, and wooden buckets. Cypress is also desirable for interior trim as well as for wall covering. It is easy to work.

White Fir. The white fir wood is used chiefly as dimension lumber and common boards for construction work. It is used also for blinds, boxes and crates.

This fir is moderately low in strength and moderately soft. It is straight-grained with a medium and fairly uniform texture, and is easily worked. Its resistance to decay is extremely low.

Douglas Fir. Because of its great strength this wood is used chiefly for structural purposes. Wood from the outer portion of a Douglas fir log is suitable for the finest grades of interior finish woodwork, exterior siding, window sashes and frames, doors, long ladder rails, and many other similar uses. Large quantities of the wood are cut into veneer for plywood and other purposes.

The quality of wood and its color vary in the same tree. Some is pale reddish yellow in color, fine grained, fairly uniform in texture, moderately soft, and is easily worked. Other parts are deep red in color, coarse grained, uneven in texture, and splinters easily. In general, the wood of the Douglas fir has a tendency to check and split. It does not hold paint well unless it is given a special priming coat of paint, such as exterior aluminum. In proportion to its weight, Douglas fir is one of the strongest woods ever tested.

Eastern Hemlock. The bark of the eastern hemlock is valuable for tanning purposes. The soft, coarse-grained, splintery wood, although much inferior to pine or spruce, is used extensively for building purposes.

The wood is moderately low in strength and has a tendency to splinter; it is subject to ring shake, is not decay resistant, and does not hold paint well. However, the lumber holds nails well, and the knots are comparatively small.

Western Hemlock. The wood of this tree is used chiefly for framing, sheathing, and subfloors. Western hemlock is used also for sashes, doors, blinds, and general millwork. It has a uniform fine-textured wood, comparatively free from ring shakes. Its resistance to decay is low.

Southern Yellow Pine. The qualities of southern yellow pine make it especially valuable for construction work. The heartwood is resistant to decay; the sapwood, forming the greater portion of the timber, absorbs preservatives readily and is thus highly adaptable for treatment.

Longleaf Pine. Because of its great strength and rigidity, this wood is valued highly for structural purposes, such as for heavy timbers in factory construction, bridges, trestles, docks, and wharves. It is used also in lighter structural work for floor joists and sheathing. The wood, which is straight-grained, is highly resinous. It checks and does not hold paint well. Although the spring wood is soft, the summer growth is especially hard and flint-like, splitting easily when nailed.

Shortleaf Pine. This yellow wood is valuable for general utility purposes. It is used extensively for interior trim, flooring, sashes, doors and planing-mill products. It is softer and more easily worked than the longleaf pine. It is straight-grained and moderately resinous.

White Pine. White pine is an ideal pattern wood. It is also desirable for the making of products for which softwoods can be used but which must retain their shape and not be affected by moisture changes. White pine is used extensively for sashes, doors, blinds, and matches. The wood dries rapidly but with little shrinkage or swelling. When in contact with the soil, the heartwood is decay resistant.

This species is also commonly known under several different names; such as, northern pine, Minnesota pine, Wisconsin pine, cork pine, pumpkin pine, and soft white pine.

Sugar Pine. Much of the sugar pine is used in planing-mill products, sashes, doors, and or interior trim. It is also used for pattern wood. Because of the unusual size of the sugar pine, lumber can be obtained from the tree in large sizes free from defects. It is straight grained, easily worked, decay re-

sistant to some extent, and keeps its shape well.

Western White Pine. The western, or Idaho white pine, is used chiefly for sashes, doors, blinds, and matches. It is a little more difficult to work and swells and shrinks more with moisture changes than the northern white pine. The western white pine is known commercially as Idaho white pine.

Ponderosa Pine. The ponderosa pine is valuable for many purposes. It is used for millwork of all kinds, as well as for sashes and doors. It is also used extensively for both exterior and interior trim. The low-density cell structure makes it an excellent material for insulation purposes. It is easily worked. It has been given various names by the trade; the names depending upon the locality; such as, Arizona white pine and California white pine. That coming from Oregon is known as pondosa pine or Oregon pine.

Redwood. The redwood is especially desirable for use in places where wood is apt to decay easily; such as, crossties, fence posts, water tanks, pipes, gutters, flumes, greenhouses, and structural timbers for bridges. It is used extensively for exterior trim, shingles, shakes, and siding; as well as for sashes, doors, and other millwork products. The heartwood is decay resistant, not resinous, has a low shrinkage, and stays in place well. It also holds paint well, is easy to work, and has the advantage of being highly resistant to termites.

Eastern Spruce. The lower grades are used for framing or general construction of boxes and crates. The better grades are used as sounding boards for musical instruments. It is exceptionally strong for its weight, easy to work, but not decay resistant. (Included in the eastern spruce group are: white spruce, black spruce, and red spruce.)

Sitka Spruce. In aircraft construction the sitka spruce is used extensively because of its straight, uniform texture, strength, lightness, and shock-resisting qualities. It is used also for both exterior and interior finish, and for millwork products.

It undergoes only moderate shrinkage and is easily worked. It is sometimes called the *tidewater spruce.*

Uses of Common Hardwoods

Beech. It is used extensively for flooring, furniture, and laundry appliances. When treated it is used also for railroad ties. It is desirable for making butchers' blocks, woodenware, and similar products, as it does not impart a taste or odor to food and resists abrasion. The wood is hard, strong, and close-grained. It is also fine in texture. Its decay resistance is low.

Yellow Birch. Birchwood is used extensively for interior finishing and trim. It is also used for various millwork products, including cabinets, furniture, fixtures, dowels, and wood turning. Birch, when given a mahogany stain, makes one of the finest imitation mahoganies.

The wood is hard, stiff, strong, and shock resisting. The sapwood is easily affected by fungi.

Sweet Birch. Because of its hardness sweet birch is better for flooring than yellow birch. Otherwise the uses made of these two species are similar.

Butternut. Butternut makes a good wood for interior trim. It is used also for cabinet work and for furniture to replace black walnut which it closely resembles, although much lighter. It is one of the softer hardwoods and is not strong.

Red Gum. Red gum wood is used extensively for interior finish and trim. It is used also for millwork products, such as doors and furniture. Much of it is used for veneer stock. It takes a good finish and can be stained readily to imitate mahogany and walnut. The wood is strong and of a fine uniform texture.

Sugar Maple and Black Maple. These maples are two of the most important hardwoods and are used extensively for flooring and stair treads, fine furniture, pianos, ship keels, kitchen cabinets, shoe lasts, and bowling pins. The wood has a fine, crisp texture. It is generally straight-grained, extremely hard, tough, and strong. It does not swell or shrink to any appreciable degree, and takes a good finish.

White Oak. White oak is used in heavy timber construction where strength is demanded. It is also used in cooperage, flooring, interior trim, fine furniture, and cabinet work. White oak wood is extremely hard, stiff, and strong. It is porous and decay resistant.

Red Oak. Red oak is used extensively for flooring, but white oak is more desirable for fine furniture, panelling, and cabinet work. In appearance red oak is inferior to the white oak and is less decay resistant. In other properties, red oak is similar to white oak.

Black Walnut. The wood of black walnut is used for making fine furniture, panelling, and for cabinet work. It is highly prized for interior trim and for gun stocks. Great quantities of black walnut wood are cut into veneer stock. The wood has good shock-resisting qualities, and shrinks moderately in seasoning. Walnut is a hard, strong, stiff, and straight-grained wood. Some of the finest figured wood obtainable is cut from walnut stumps and crotches in the form of veneer. It takes an exceptionally good finish, and is comparable to the finest mahogany in this respect. It is

easily worked and holds its shape well. American black walnut is becoming increasingly scarce; it takes over a hundred years for a walnut tree to mature and there has been little re-forestation.

Mahogany. Mahogany is the standard cabinet wood of the world, and is the one by which all other cabinet woods are judged. It is highly prized for making the finest furniture, whether solid or veneered.

Although used chiefly for the making of fine furniture, mahogany plays an important part in building construction for interior finish work. It is used extensively in many of our best buildings for doors, panelling, and cabinets, as well as for window and door trim. Because of its inherent ability to hold its shape under variable moisture conditions, it is an excellent wood for boat construction and an ideal pattern wood.

Commercial Lumber

The commercial forest lands of the United States in 1962 included about 508 million acres from which approximately 33,178,000,000 board feet of timber was cut. Of the many different species of trees found in the United States only about 180 of them may be ranked as commercially important.

Local lumber dealers usually carry in their stock, for general building purposes, those species most easily obtainable and in greatest demand in that particular locality. Hence, as a rule, we will find in the local lumberyards of the Pacific Northwest: Douglas fir, spruce, ponderosa pine, western hemlock, and western cedar. In Illinois, lumber dealers usually carry in stock: western hemlock, western pine, ponderosa pine, southern yellow pine, western cedar, redwood, spruce, white fir, and Douglas fir. An eastern lumber dealer might carry in stock: eastern spruce and hemlock, northern white pine, cypress, ponderosa pine, southern yellow pine, and Douglas fir.

However, if given adequate time to secure the stock, most lumber dealers are able to obtain any kind of commercial lumber, either hard or soft, which an individual might desire.

Wood Joints

The whole idea of wood joints is to fit and interlock them in such a way that they have as much structural strength as possible when joined. Since there are, of course, many different kinds of structures, there are different types of joints, each more or less suited to a certain kind of construction.

With the development of strong mechanical fasteners, wood joints are less used in timber construction. In lighter construction, particularly in cabinetmaking, wood joints still play a very important part.

A joint is formed when one piece of wood is fitted against another piece; the two pieces may only be butted against each other or they may be interlocked or secured in place with glue, dowel pins, nails, or other similar fastenings. The joints illustrated here are by no means the only types in use; however, those shown are the ones most commonly used. For convenience, these are divided roughly into three groups, as follows:

1. Joining timbers in framing.

2. Joining boards at an angle for change in direction.

3. Joining boards at the edge to increase the surface area.

Since there is some overlapping in such a grouping of joints, the carpenter's choice is governed by the nature of his work and the kind of joint suitable for the particular situation at hand.

A joint must be well made, carefully fitted and secured to give complete satisfaction and service; to accomplish this feat requires skill and experience. A mechanic's ability can be judged quickly by the strength and appearance of the joint he is able to produce.

1. Joining Timbers in Framing. In increasing the length of timbers, consideration must be given to the strains and stresses which the joint or splice must bear, such as tension, compression, or cross strain, or a combination of these factors. These needs can be met with splices

similar to those shown in (A), (B), (C), and (D) of Fig. 15. For temporary structures timbers may be lengthened by use of the *lap joint* shown at (G), Fig. 15. Such a joint may be secured by use of bolts. Today, in timber framing, complicated joints seldom are made.

The most simple of all joints is the *butt joint* which is made by

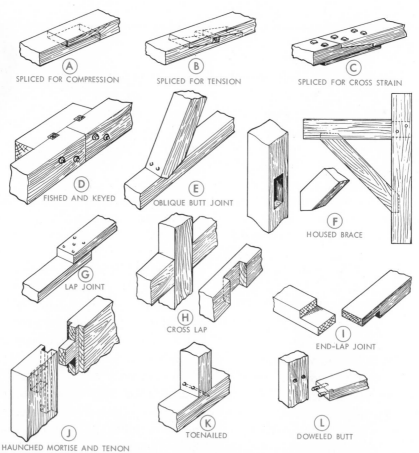

Fig. 15. Wood joints commonly used in timber framing and other woodworking.

merely placing two pieces of timber together with the end of one piece against the side or edge of the other and nailing the pieces firmly together after both have been trimmed square and true. In such a case the two pieces are perpendicular to each other. When the two pieces are arranged so as to form a *square butt joint* as shown at (*K*), Fig. 15, nails are driven diagonally through both pieces, an operation known as *toe-nailing*. An *oblique butt joint* is formed when two pieces of timber are not perpendicular to each other, but are trimmed to fit closely as illustrated at (*E*), Fig. 15. The *housed brace* shown at (*F*), Fig. 15, is a common type of brace construction. The illustration shows how such a joint is cut and fitted together. This type of construction gives additional strength to the joint, especially where there may be a tendency for one piece to slide along the other as in the case of a brace. Where timbers cross one another and are required to have one or both faces flush, both timbers are notched so as to fit over each other as shown in the *cross-lap joint* at (*H*), Fig. 15. Ends of heavy timbers or wall plates are usually cut so as to join as shown at (*I*), Fig. 15, and are known as *end-lap joints*. The cross-lap and end-lap joints are held together by spikes driven into the two pieces. A form of joint known

as a *tenon joint* is shown at (*J*), Fig. 15. In some cases the tenon has an additional haunch which adds considerably to its strength. The *haunched mortise and tenon joint* is used extensively in the making of doors. The piece of timber which is to be joined to the tenon and haunch has a mortise or slot cut through it to receive the tenon; the two pieces are then pinned or wedged together with wood pins. The *doweled-butt joint* shown at (*L*), Fig. 15, is used for making both temporary and permanent joints.

2. Joining Boards at an Angle for Change in Direction. Most of the joints used to connect boards at an angle for changing direction are used by the cabinetmaker and the millman. However, the carpenter uses joints constantly, especially when fitting and placing interior trim. Several different types of joints commonly used by the carpenter and other woodworkers are illustrated in Fig. 16. The *dado* shown at (*A*), Fig. 16, is often used for interior door jambs. These joints usually are secured with glue and nails. Joints used in the construction of drawers are shown at (*B*), (*C*), (*D*), and (*G*) of Fig. 16. When joining two pieces at an evenly divided angle the *spline miter* shown at (*F*), Fig. 16, is used. This type of joint is commonly used in the making of picture frames.

169

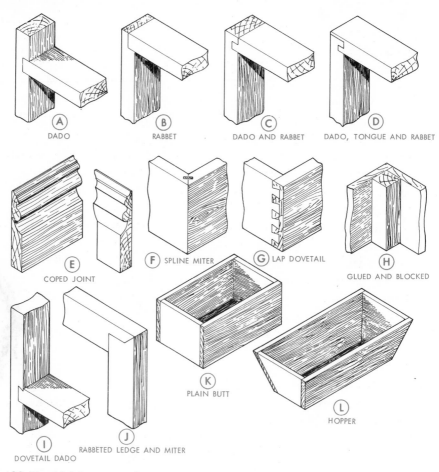

Fig. 16. Wood joints commonly used in cabinet construction and interior trim.

The construction used in a *glued and blocked joint* is shown at (*H*), Fig. 16. A *dovetail dado* and a *rabbeted ledge and miter* are shown at (*I*) and (*J*), respectively, Fig. 16. The type of joint used in making hoppers is known as a *hopper joint*. An illustration is shown at (*L*), Fig. 16. A joint commonly used by all carpenters and other woodworkers is the *plain-butt joint* shown at (*K*), Fig. 16.

3. Joining Boards at the Edge to Increase the Surface Area. There are two important factors in the making of the edge joints shown in Fig. 17. First, the boards must be selected according to grain; that is, the annual growth rings must run in opposite directions in adjacent boards. The curve of the annual rings must turn upward in one board and downward in the adjoining board as illus-

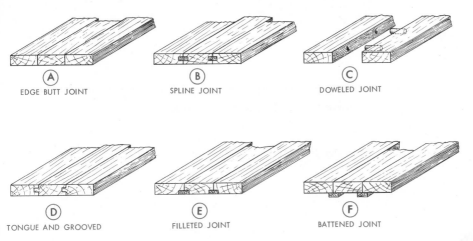

Fig. 17. Wood joints used in edge joining of boards.

trated in the ends of the boards joined at (A), Fig. 17. This method of joining boards will insure a true surface in glued boards which generally will remain true. Second, the edges of the boards must be joined straight, true, and square with the surface to insure good continuous contact throughout the entire length of the board. A shaped edge adds little if any strength to a glued joint. Examples of such joints are the *splined, doweled,* or *tongued and grooved* joints shown at (B), (C), and (D), respectively Fig. 17. The reason for the lack of added strength in such joints is due to the fact that, even though the surface area has been increased, the contact usually is imperfect. However, the use of such joints has a tendency to line up the board which is an advantage in construc-

tion work. In all six of the methods of edge jointing illustrated in Fig. 17 the boards usually are secured with glue. Wood strips intended to cover or close an open joint are illustrated at (E) and (F), Fig. 17. Such joints are known as *filleted*, shown at (E), and *battened*, shown at (F).

Dowels

Dowels are pins made of hardwood, usually birch. These pins are used to fasten wood members together. Before nails came into use, dowels were used extensively in timber framing, and in pinning of boards to walls and floors. Today their chief use is found in manufacturing doors and furniture. In many instances dowels are used to replace the mortise and tenon joint.

Checking On Your Knowledge

If you have read this chapter carefully you should be able to answer the following questions. If you have any difficulty, you should read the chapter again so that you will have the information well in mind before you go on with your reading.

DO YOU KNOW

1. Of what substance wood is composed?

2. How trees grow? How the fibers in wood are held together?

3. The size and shape of wood fibers or cells?

4. How the cells in hardwoods differ from the cells in softwoods?

5. The meaning of the terms *hardwoods* and *softwoods* as used in the lumber trade? Are hardwoods always *hard* and softwoods always *soft*?

6. A softwood that is *hard?* A hardwood that is *soft?*

7. The names of ten important commercial softwoods used in the United States and ten or more hardwoods?

8. The difference between *springwood* and *summerwood?* How they compare in strength?

9. How heartwood is formed? Where the sapwood is located in the tree?

10. The difference between *coarse-grained, straight-grained,* and *close-grained* woods?

11. In what two forms moisture is contained in standing trees?

12. How knots and pitch pockets are formed in wood?

13. The difference between *heart shake, wind shake,* and *starshake?*

14. What causes warping of lumber?

15. How lumber is graded and priced by lumber dealers?

16. How to find the number of board feet in a piece of structural timber?

17. How to determine the moisture content of any particular kind of wood?

18. The physical characteristics and common uses of the commercially important softwoods and hardwoods?

19. Which is more important for construction purposes, hardwood or softwood?

20. Why southern cypress is used extensively for water tanks, water buckets, and gutters?

21. The names of three woods that are used for making shakes?

Wood Products and Other Building Materials

<table>
<tr><td>Chapter</td></tr>
<tr><td>6</td></tr>
</table>

Wood is one of the most versatile and useful materials that nature has produced. In spite of this, and the many kinds of wood, there are still some places where wood, as it comes from the lumber mill, is not as useful as we would wish. With special uses in mind, industry has taken wood and transformed it into better and more useful forms. Wood has been modified for man.

Greater strength, larger pieces, dimensional stability, smoother surfaces, insulating properties, water resistance, durability, and maintenance-free finishes are some of the advantages that manufactured wood has over boards from trees.

In this chapter you will learn why plywood is preferred for certain uses, what properties make it superior to wood in some respects, and when the carpenter can use it to improve his work and produce better homes and woodwork.

Particleboard, hardboard, and wallboard are also covered. Treatments, coatings, and modifying materials are included, as well as some non-wood materials that supplement manufactured wood in some places.

Knowledge of these products will aid you, as a carpenter, to take advantage of the new technology in wood. The use of these wood products, however, should always conform to the local building codes.

Plywood Panels

Plywood panels are made up of 3 or more thin layers or plies of wood glued together, with the wood grain of adjacent layers running at right angles. See Fig. 1. Plywood panels usually contain an odd number of layers, 3, 5, 7, or more. The two outermost layers are called the *face veneer* and the *back veneer*. The face veneer, since it is often visible, is commonly of a quality wood selected for its beauty. The foundation of plywood panels is the center layer or core. It may be made of *veneer, lumber,* or *particleboard* (see Fig. 1). Some plywood panels may also be obtained with a fireproof mineral core. The most common and widely used plywood panels have a veneer core. The layers between the core and the face and back veneers in 5 and 7 ply panels are called *crossbands* or *inter plies.* Crossbands on each side of the core are paired and should be of the same species and thicknesses, and should have their grain running in the same direction.

In addition to the use of ordinary wood plies in plywood, some plywood panels use a modified wood impregnated with synthetic resin. Plywood may also be impregnated with fire retardant chemicals. Some of the plywood panels used for interior decoration come already finished with a varnish or lacquer. Plywood panel surfaces may also be overlaid with resin impregnated fiber or plastics. A variety of surface finishes, such as grooved or striated, may be obtained.

Special care must be exercised in installing prefinished panels so that the finish is not marred. Some finishes used on exterior paneling will not need painting for as long as ten years.

Plywood panels used in building construction come in a standard size of 4' x 8', though panels of 4' x 7' and 4' x 10' are also common. Plywood lap or bevel siding is also available. Thicknesses used in construction commonly run from $\frac{1}{4}$ to $\frac{3}{4}$th of an inch. Other sizes and thicknesses, however, may also be obtained. Table I gives the common plies and thicknesses of plywood.

Both interior and exterior plywood is manufactured. The interior types are either water resistant or moisture resistant and should be used where there is only a limited exposure to water and moisture. The exterior plywood is waterproof and is used where there is a continued exposure to the weather and wetting, or where unusual moisture conditions exist.

Grading. All plywood panels are graded as to quality, based on com-

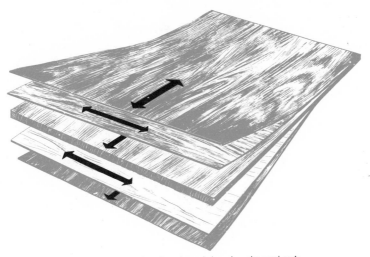

This opened view of a plywood panel shows how the wood grain of the plies runs in opposing directions to each other to counteract weakness with the grain.

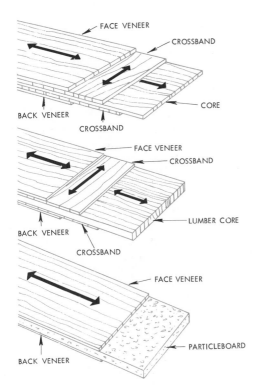

VENEER CORE: The most common plywood uses an all veneer core. The number of plies depends on the use. The more plies the greater strength.

LUMBER CORE: The core consists of lumber strips, one to four inches wide, edge glued together. Lumber cores with face wood on all four edges may be ordered.

PARTICLEBOARD CORE: The core is made of wood flakes and chips bonded together with resin to form a mat.

Fig. 1. Types of plywoods.

TABLE I PLYWOOD TYPES AND SIZES	
Veneer Core Plywood	
3 ply	1/8, 3/16, and 1/4 inch
5 ply	5/16, 3/8, and 1/2 inch
5 and 7 ply	5/8 inch
7 and 9 ply	3/4 inch
Lumber Core Plywood	
5 ply	3/4 inch
Particleboard Core Plywood	
3 and 5 ply	1/2, 5/8, and 3/4 inch

mercial standards. In total, three commercial standards are in effect: hardwood, softwood, and pine. Grading stamps are put on the plywood panels to indicate the kind and type of plywood. Usually these grading stamps indicate whether the plywood is to be used internally or externally. The grade of the face and back plies are also indicated. Fig. 2 shows a typical stamp used by the American Plywood Association for Douglas Fir plywood.

The designation "Group 1" (Fig. 2) refers to the type of wood. Under the softwood commercial standard there are four groups of wood types. The designation A-C refers to the quality of wood on the front veneer and back veneer. The softwood commercial standard lists four common grades: A, B, C and D.

Typical Back-stamp   **Typical Edge-mark**

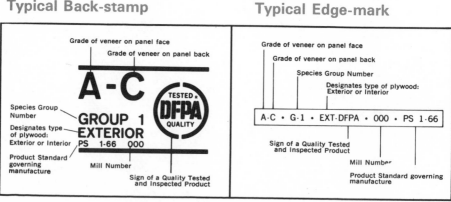

Fig. 2. Plywood marking. (American Plywood Assoc.)

A grade is smooth and paintable; neatly made repairs are permissible. This is the best grade commonly found in residential construction. (The highest grade, *N* grade, is used for cabinet work where natural finishes are desired.) *B* grade is a solid veneer in which some repair plugs are permitted. *C* grade and *D* grade permit more defects and faults with knotholes, splits, and repairs of varying degrees. In addition to these common grades, other special grades are also used.

Plywood Uses. Plywood panels are used throughout house construction. Some of the common uses are exterior siding, wall and roof sheathing, interior wall paneling, sub-flooring, flush doors, concrete forms, etc. The size, thickness, and grade employed would depend upon the specific use for which the plywood is intended. Table II gives the types of plywood, whether exterior, structural-interior, or interior, suitable to various locations in the house. (Structural-interior plywood is an improved interior type plywood that uses exterior glues.)

Advantages of Plywood. The balanced construction of plywood offers the utmost in strength, lightness, and practicability. The following factors influence its usefulness.

1. Plywood is comparatively light in weight.

2. Screws or nails can be driven close to the edge without danger of splitting the wood.

3. Plywood panels can be built to any size, while wood is limited to the width of the tree.

4. Plywood can be bent more readily than solid wood.

5. Plywood minimizes the tend-

TABLE II. PLYWOOD

LOCATION	EXPOSED TO WEATHER[1]	NOT EXPOSED TO WEATHER[2]
Ext wall finish	EXT	. . . .
Int wall finish	• •	INT, STRUC -INT or EXT
Int ceiling finish	• •	INT, STRUC -INT or EXT
Wall sheathing	EXT	STRUC -INT or EXT
Roof sheathing	EXT	STRUC -INT or EXT
Subflooring	EXT	STRUC -INT or EXT
Underlayment over subfloor	• •	STRUC -INT or EXT
Truss gussets	EXT	EXT [3]
Built-up structural members	EXT	EXT [3]
Soffits	EXT	. . . .
Porch or carport ceilings	EXT	. . . .

[1] Any edge or surface exposed to the weather, including underside of roof overhangs, soffits and ceilings of open porches and carports shall be exterior type. This does not apply to surfaces in ventilated attics or ventilated basementless spaces.

[2] Plywood wall finish in bathrooms shall have exterior glues.

[3] Structural-interior type having exterior glues may be used.

Credit: Minimum Property Standards, FHA 300

ency of wood to buckle or twist due to changes in moisture content.

6. Under normal use plywood will not shrink or swell appreciably.

7. Plywood has a greater strength across the grain than wood, and checking and splitting is negligible. This allows greater widths to be used. Table III compares the strength of plywood to that of ordinary wood. The reduction of the lengthwise strength in plywood is counterbalanced for some uses by the increase in crosswise strength.

TABLE III. WOOD AND PLYWOOD STRENGTHS

	ORDINARY WOOD		3-PLY PLYWOOD	
	Grain lengthwise (Percent)	Grain crosswise (Percent)	Grain of outer plies lengthwise (Percent)	Grain of outer plies crosswise (Percent)
Bending strength	100	8	82	17
Stiffness	100	4	96	9

Plywood Measurements. Plywood is measured by the square foot and is sold by the sheet, usually in sheets of 4′ x 7′, 4′ x 8′, 4′ x 10′ and 4′ x 12′. In calculating the number of sheets needed, determine the total number of square feet to be covered and divide by the number of square feet in the sheet. For example, if a wall 8 feet high and 14 feet long (with no openings) were to be covered:

$$8' \times 14' = 112 \text{ sq. ft.}$$

Divide 112 square feet by the square feet in a plywood sheet, using a 4′ x 8′ sheet:

$$4' \times 8' = 32 \text{ sq. ft.}$$
$$\frac{112 \text{ sq. ft.}}{32 \text{ sq. ft.}} = 3\frac{1}{2} \text{ panels}$$

Since *over* three panels are needed, order four.

In calculating the area to be covered, be sure to calculate the total square feet for *all openings*, such as for doors, windows, stair openings, etc., in the total area to be covered. To allow for waste, it is common practice to use only 50 percent of the total opening area. In calculating a room the total square feet of the four walls may be added together; then 50 percent of the total square feet for openings may be *subtracted*.

Plan to use scrap cuttings from one wall in another location on another wall. The layout and cutting of the panels would depend on the actual room layout and the exact location of openings. In cutting plywood a 10 point crosscut saw is used. A fine-toothed coping saw is used for cutting curves. In using a handsaw, keep the front veneer side up. In cutting with a power saw, however, keep the back veneer side up.

Plywood may be installed by nails or staples, by adhesive, by nails and adhesives, or by special fasteners or chips.

Structural Plywood Components

The use of structural plywood components which are fabricated in the shop and delivered as a unit, because of the economy and speed of erection, continues to grow. Panel units, such as stressed-skin and sandwich panels, are being extensively used in residential and large commercial construction. A trend toward panelized construction seems to be accelerating.

Stressed-Skin Panels. These consist of facings, normally plywood, glued on the two sides of an inner structural framework made of lumber. This type of construction acts as a unit and the load or stress on the panel is distributed by the internal framework. Insula-

tion is sometimes added to the stressed-skin panel within the framework. See Fig. 3. They are usually delivered to the job as a ready-made unit. Stressed-skin panels are used in floor, wall, and roof construction. They are commonly made in 4′ x 8′ units, though larger lengths for roofing are used.

Sandwich Panel Construction. These are similar to stressed-skin panels, except that the internal framework or core is composed of expanded or corrugated paper cores (honeycomb), or of insulation. They are also made in 4′ x 8′ units and used as wall panels and for floor and roof construction. Plywood, hardboard, particleboard, and

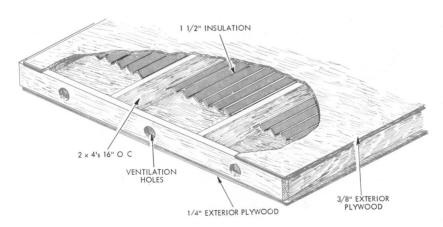

1 1/2" INSULATION

2 x 4's 16" O C

VENTILATION HOLES

1/4" EXTERIOR PLYWOOD

3/8" EXTERIOR PLYWOOD

Fig. 3. Stressed skin panels for roof decking.

fiberboard have been used for the facing.

Both stressed-skin panels and sandwich panels are made in curved panels for roof construction and canopies.

Plywood Box Beams. These are gaining acceptance for use in construction. They are built-up units, consisting of a plywood covering on lumber flanges. See Fig. 4. Plywood box beams are light in weight and have little shrinkage. They are especially useful for bridging wide spans (up to 120 feet), and have been used in residential construction as girders, lintels, and garage door headers.

Building Components. Many experiments have been made to develop building component parts so that they may be built on the job or away from the job in a shop. The panels consist of straight wall

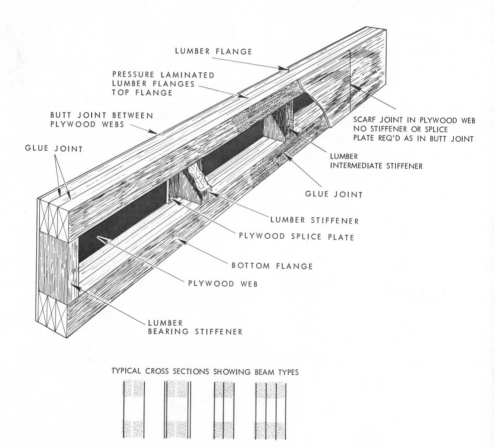

LUMBER FLANGE

PRESSURE LAMINATED
LUMBER FLANGES
TOP FLANGE

BUTT JOINT BETWEEN
PLYWOOD WEBS

GLUE JOINT

SCARF JOINT IN PLYWOOD WEB
NO STIFFENER OR SPLICE
PLATE REQ'D AS IN BUTT JOINT

LUMBER
INTERMEDIATE STIFFENER

GLUE JOINT

LUMBER STIFFENER

PLYWOOD SPLICE PLATE

BOTTOM FLANGE

PLYWOOD WEB

LUMBER
BEARING STIFFENER

TYPICAL CROSS SECTIONS SHOWING BEAM TYPES

Fig. 4. Plywood box beams.

units, units with doors or windows, gable end units, etc. See Fig. 5. Panels are designed using 2″ x 4″ members and plywood. Panels may vary in width but should be made in multiples of 16 or 24 inches if possible. They are made on the job site by some builders, although they can be made in a shop more economically. Jigs may be used to hold the framing members in place until they are nailed fast. Much labor is saved by precutting similar members such as studs and plates before assembly begins.

Prefabricated Houses. Buildings made in factories have been developed successfully in many parts of the country. Some buildings are made in halves or quarters so that they can be transported by truck and assembled at the site. They are limited to areas where deliveries can be made successfully and cheaply, and they are also limited in the number of different house plans available. Some of the work must be done at the building location, such as the foundation, plumbing connections, etc.

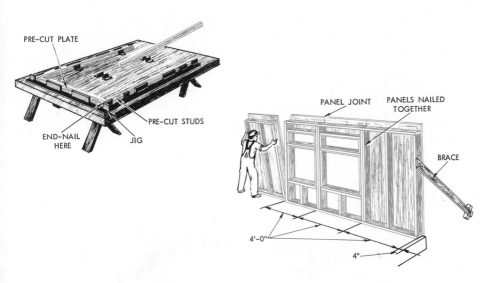

Fig. 5. A jig bench is used to hold the pieces of a panel in position until they are nailed. Panels are made so that they may be handled and fastened in place with ease.

Glued and Laminated Lumber

Glued Lumber. Ordinary lumber is also sometimes made larger (wider or thicker) or longer by gluing. Lumber pieces may be glued side by side (edge gluing), face to face, or end to end. (When three or more pieces are glued face to face they form a laminated beam or arch.) In gluing lumber end to end a plain scarf joint or finger joint is commonly used, see Fig. 6. (Lumber which is glued and is over 2″ in thickness is called laminated.)

End gluing is popular because it allows the use of individual short pieces of lumber to make up a single long piece. Edge gluing allows standard sized panels to be constructed. The production of large and longer pieces of lumber by gluing is made possible by the increase in glue holding power.

Glued-Laminated Structural Arches and Beams. These are being used for bridging wide spans. These structural members are built up of lumber solidly laminated together by pressure to form a unit. See Fig. 7. Unsupported spans of 30 to 100 feet are common, and unsupported spans of over 200 feet have been erected. Fig. 8 illustrates a laminated arch being lifted into place.

The increased cost of laminated construction is partially offset by the advantage of being able to use short lengths and narrow lumber. Lower grades of lumber may also be used without appreciable loss of structural strength. Fig. 9 shows some common arches and beams that may be constructed using laminated lumber.

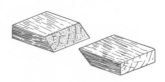

PLAIN SCARF JOINT

FINGER JOINT

Fig. 6. Glued joint types.

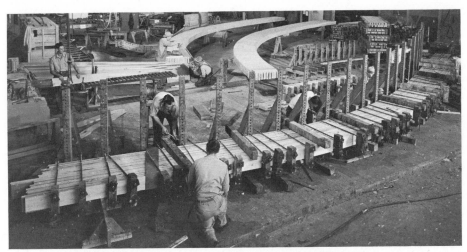

Fig. 7. Arch sections being clamped after gluing. (Timber Structures, Inc.)

Fig. 8. Hoisting arches for a fieldhouse dome with a crane. (Rilco Laminated Products Inc.)

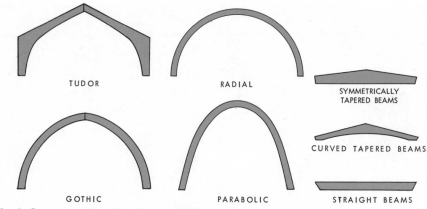

Fig. 9. Common types of laminated arches and beams.

Trusses

Trusses have been used in industrial and commercial buildings for many years and have permitted the covering of large areas without posts or bearing walls. A number of different designs are used to solve specific problems. Many builders have used trusses successfully in residential construction. There are several advantages. When trusses are used, the bearing partitions may be eliminated because the roof is supported by the two outside walls. Thus the building can be built as though it were one large room. Floors can be laid continuously from wall to wall, finished wall material can be applied, and ceilings can be hung across the whole building before partitions are installed. The trusses are usually made away from the job site on a jig or large platform. When delivered to the job they are installed quickly, and the building can be placed under a roof in a short time. The main disadvantage in the use of trusses is that they lend themselves mainly to buildings with rectangular shapes and with gable-end roofs. Intersecting ell-shaped buildings may use trusses with the transition from one roof to the other made with small trusses or with conventional jack rafters. Hip roofs can also be framed with the use of special trusses.

The design of a truss is a job for an engineer; the size and location of the members and the manner of making the joints varies with each span, slope and load problem.

Trusses may be spaced on intervals up to 8 feet apart along the plate. For small homes, however, they are usually spaced on 24 inch centers. Two types of trusses are generally used, the king post truss and the "W" truss. The king post is a simple truss of four members usually used for building with small spans. See Fig. 10. The "W" truss is made so that the load is distributed through more members. See Fig. 11. The method of making the joints where the members come together is by the use of gusset plates made of plywood which are glued and nailed in place, or by using steel connector plates made for this purpose. The size of the gusset plates, and the number and size of the

Fig. 10. The king post truss is a small truss with plywood gusset plates nailed and glued in place.

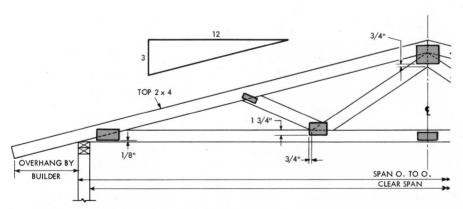

Fig. 11. The "W" truss provides a wide clear span. Steel connectors are used at the joints.

185

nails to be used to hold members together, is determined by the designer of the trusses.

When trusses are designed so that members overlap, bolts and split-ring connectors can be used.

(See Chapter VIII.) Circular grooves are cut in each member wherever two members meet. The ring is inserted and a bolt through the members draws the assembly up tight.

Processed Woods

Hardboard. Hardboard is a board material manufactured from wood fibers. Wood chips are broken down into their individual fibers, then the fibers are formed into mats and compressed by hot presses into a dry board. Lignin, a natural wood substance, bonds the fibers together. It is more dense, more durable, and more resistant to water absorption than other wood composition boards. No splitting or slivering occurs. Since it has no grain it has equal strength in all directions. Its working qualities are similar to that of wood and it may be bent into various shapes.

There are three basic types of hardboard: standard, tempered, and service. Standard hardboard is essentially the unchanged hardboard product as it comes from the manufacturer. Tempered hardboard is a standard hardboard to which small quantities of chemicals have been added to increase the stiffness, strength, hardness, working qualities, and resistance to water. Service hardboard is a hardboard with less strength and weight than the standard hardboard.

Hardboards are manufactured with one surface finished, S1S (smooth one side), or with two surfaces finished, S2S (smooth two sides). They commonly are made in panels 4' x 8' or 4' x 16', though 5' widths and 6' and 12' lengths are also standard. Thicknesses vary, but $\frac{1}{4}$", $\frac{5}{16}$", and $\frac{3}{8}$" are most used in residential construction. Some hardboards are manufactured for use as lap siding in 8 inch or more widths and in lengths up to 16 feet. Hardboard panels are commonly used in the interior of a house over gypsum board for decorative effect.

Various special hardboard products are available to meet particular requirements. Hardboards are produced with several different surface patterns, such as tile, embossed, striated, and grooved patterns. Pegboard is another form. Fig. 12 illustrates some of the common surface patterns. Factory applied finishes, including plastic

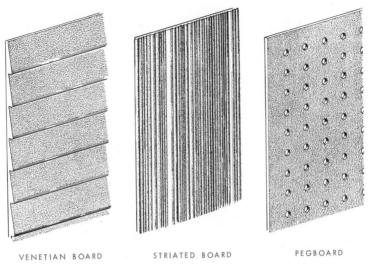

VENETIAN BOARD   STRIATED BOARD   PEGBOARD

Fig. 12. Typical hardboard designs.

coated surfaces, are also available, along with a wide color selection. Hardboards are sometimes laminated in multiple plies to obtain greater thicknesses.

Hardboard is calculated by the square foot and ordered in standard panel sizes. Thicknesses must be specified, and whether finished on one or two surfaces must be stated. Special thicknesses and sizes may also be obtained. Each panel has a grade stamp giving the manufacturer's name or trade mark, the symbol of the commercial standard, and the specific hardboard type.

Hardboard is used extensively in residential construction. See Table IV. External and internal (both wall and ceiling) panels are frequently used in many different textures and finishes. House sidings,

both horizontal and vertical, are common. Both hollow core and solid laminated doors are made from hardboard. In addition, hardboard, is used structurally for floor under-layment, decking, soffits, gable-ends, etc. Residential construction uses of hardboard are continually increasing.

Particleboard. Particleboard, sometimes called chipboard or flakeboard, is made from dry wood particles which are bonded together by pressure and heat with a resin bond. The size and type of the particles used determines the textures and properties of the board. The manufacture of particleboard is very similar to that of hardboard, except that for particleboard, particles rather than fibers are used and the binder is some type of resin

187

Fundamentals of Carpentry

TABLE IV. HARDBOARDS: TYPES AND APPLICATION*

APPLICATION	TYPE OF HARDBOARD	MAXIMUM OPEN FRAMING	Thickness	NAIL SPACING Intermediate Supports	Around Edges	FASTENING METHODS: Use any of the following for these hardboard applications
INTERIOR WALLS AND CEILINGS	Standard Hardboard and Tempered Hardboard	Solid Backing 16" 16" 24"	1/8" 3/16" 1/4" 5/16"	Adhesive only 8" thru body 8" thru body 8" thru body	4" 4" 4"	NAILS: Casing nail Finishing nail Special hardboard nail
	Low-Density Hardboard	16" 16"	3/16" 1/4"	8" thru body 8" thru body	4" 4"	Nails to be of sufficient length to penetrate ¾" into framing.
	Leather Textured or Tile Patterned Hardboard	Solid Backing	1/8"	Adhesive only		
	Wood Grain Embossed Hardboard	16"	1/4"	8" thru body	4"	
	Wood Grain Printed Hardboard	16"	1/4"	8" thru body	4"	
	Grooved Hardboard 4", 8" or Random	16"	5/16" 3/8"	8" thru body	4"	
	Scored Hardboard Striated Hardboard	16" 16"	1/4" 1/4"	8" thru body 8" thru body	4" 4"	
	Tempered S 2 S	Solid Backing 16" 16"	1/8" 3/16" 1/4"	Adhesive only 8" thru body 8" thru body	4" 4"	ADHESIVES: The following waterproof adhesives may be used when applied according to manufacturers recommendations: Tileboard cement Contact bond
	Perforated Hardboard (Leave 3/8" or more open space between hardboard and wall)	16" 16" 16"	1/8" 3/16" 1/4"	8" thru body 8" thru body 8" thru body	4" 4" 4"	
UNDERLAYMENT	Underlayment Hardboard		.215"	6" thru body	6"	NAILS: 7/8" Staples 1¼" ring grooved
FINISH FLOORING	Tempered Hardboard		1/4" 5/16"	12" thru body 12" thru body	6" 6"	NAILS: 1¼" coated casing
EXTERIOR CEILINGS	Low Density, Standard or Tempered Hardboard	16" 16"	1/4" 5/16"	6" thru body 6" thru body	4" 4"	NAILS: 1¾" box, siding or sinker
PANEL SIDING	Plain for use with Battens	16" 24"	5/16" Nom. 3/8"	8" thru body 12" thru body	4" 6"	NAILS: Galvanized special siding Galvanized box nail Stud penetration to be 1½" without sheathing, 1" with sheathing
	Grooved Hardboard Grooved Hardboard	16" 14"	5/16" Nom. 7/16"	8" thru body 12" thru body	4" 6"	
	Striated Hardboard Ribbed Hardboard	16" 24"	1/4" 5/16"	8" thru body 8" thru body	4" 4"	
LAP SIDING	(With or without Sheathing) 12" width 12' or 16' length	16"	Nom. 7/16"	16" along bottom edge thru 2 courses into studs		NAILS: Galvanized special siding Galvanized box nail Stud penetration to be 1½" without sheathing, 1" with sheathing
CONCRETE FORMS	Concrete Form Hardboard (Over Space Sheathing or Solid Backing)	See Mfgr's. Details				NAILS: 1¼" coated casing 1¼" coated casing

*Source: Practical Builder

188

rather than lignin. Particleboard is made not only by hot pressing but also by a hot extrusion process.

Particleboard comes in several standard sizes; 4' x 8' is most commonly used. Thicknesses range from $\frac{1}{10}$ of an inch up to 2 inches, however, $\frac{1}{4}$ to $1\frac{1}{2}$ inch is most commonly used in residential construction; $\frac{3}{8}$ inch is commonly used for exterior paneling.

Particleboard is commonly used for exterior siding, wall paneling (drywall), floor underlayment, and in the manufacture of doors. Its use in residential construction is mainly confined to the exterior of the building. Panels with various patterns, such as lap or board and batten, are available for exterior siding. Particleboards with a wide variety of pre-finishes are available; it also comes with wood finishes.

Fiberboard. Fiberboard, or fiber insulation board, is produced from wood or vegetable fibers in a manner very similar to that of hardboard, but a thermoplastic binding agent is used. Fiberboard also has a much lower density than either hardboard or particleboard, and has less stiffness and strength. It comes in 4 foot widths and in several different lengths; it may be obtained in varying thicknesses. The $\frac{1}{2}$ inch and $\frac{25}{32}$ inch thicknesses are most commonly used in residential construction. For sheathing, 2' x 8' boards are made. Acoustical tile, a type of fiberboard, is also available in various sizes. Fiberboard may be asphalt impregnated or asphalt coated to render it water resistant. Fire retardant chemicals may be added. Fiberboard is used in residential construction mainly for insulation, acoustical tile, sheathing, and interior finish (drywall).

Modified Woods

Woods, especially veneers such as used in plywoods, may be impregnated with resin compounds to increase their stability. Two basic types are manufactured: uncompressed resin-treated wood (impreg) and compressed resin-treated wood (compreg). In both treatments the resin compound is distributed uniformly throughout the wood. Because of a difficulty in impregnating wood, these treatments are only practical for thin pieces of wood, such as veneers.

Uncompressed resin treated wood (impreg) shows a decrease in moisture absorption and thus a decrease in swelling and shrinking. Checking and splitting, of course, is reduced. In addition, it shows a considerable

189

resistance to decay and a resistance to termite and marine borer attack. Hardness and acid resistance are also increased. At the same time, however, the wood becomes more brittle.

Compressed resin treated wood (compreg), like impreg, shows a similar decrease in swelling and shrinking, and also has a considerable resistance to decay and a resistance to termite and marine borer action. Hardness is greatly increased (10 to 20 times as much)

with the result that a high degree of polish may be obtained. However, at the same time, the wood becomes very brittle and is more difficult to work than ordinary wood.

Both impreg and compreg, because of their increased stability and durability, are used for making plywoods for use under special conditions. Only moderate application has been found for these modified woods in ordinary residential construction.

Wood Treatments

Many different chemicals may be used to treat wood or wood products. Chemicals may be applied to the surface or they may be permeated into the wood. Some treatments involve the actual chemical modification of the wood cell substances. In the case of composition woods, chemicals may be introduced with the bonding agent.

Chemical treatments are employed for several reasons: to produce desirable physical qualities, such as stiffness, water resistance, strength, weight changes, etc.; to increase the fire-retardant properties; to better the durability and preservative qualities of the material against the action of organisms, such as decay-causing fungus, termites, marine borers, etc.; and to

increase the insulative and acoustical properties. In each case, before using any of these treated woods the properties of the material should be known and should be related to the particular use. Manufacturer's specifications should be consulted as to the nature of the treated material and its recommended uses. In some cases particular care and storage may be required.

Not only must the material have the properties suitable for a particular use, but the side effect of the chemical treatments must often also be considered. For example, lumber treated with some wood preservatives, such as creosote, would not be suitable for house siding as the preservative might bleed from the wood penetrating any paint covering and causing objectionable stains. In addition, many treatments, especially those for wood preservation, use toxic chemicals. Special care, therefore, should be used in handling materials that have been treated with substances that might be poisonous. Gloves should be worn and shirt sleeves should be rolled down. Skin contact with toxic chemicals should be avoided. If contact should occur, wash the toxic material off and treat the area involved as if it were a burn. Caution should also be exercised around woods treated with volatile compounds as fire or explosive hazards may exist.

Non-Wood Building Materials

Many different kinds of non-wood materials are commonly used in residential construction. The most common are the masonry materials, such as concrete, concrete blocks, and the various kinds of bricks. These are of more concern to the mason than to the carpenter. But there are many other non-wood materials, however, that the carpenter will work with and be expected to be familiar with.

Non-wood materials are frequently used for exterior covering and for interior finish. Mineral fiber shingles are often used for exterior siding. Asphalt shingles are often used for the roof covering. Gypsum panels are used for wallboard, lath, and sheathing. Metals, such as aluminum and steel siding, steel I-beams, metal lath, metal studs, etc., are also commonly used. Both aluminum and steel siding are available and come with various baked-on enamel finishes. Ceramic and vinyl tiles have long been used as an interior finish, especially in bathrooms, and for flooring. Metal and vinyl-coated (vinyl on wood) windows and doors are also used.

Metal Studs. Metal studs have long been used in light commercial and industrial construction and they are also increasingly being used in residential construction. Metal studs are usually either webbed or hollow. See Fig. 13. Ordinary channel iron may also be used. Various sized studs are available but $2\frac{1}{2}$ inch and $3\frac{5}{8}$ inch (placed 16 inch O.C.) are most commonly used in residential construction; studs are available in 6 inch widths. The length varies depending on the width of the stud. Metal studs are used for non-load bearing walls. Plumbing and electrical equipment run directly through the stud. The studs fit into a track that is attached at the floor and

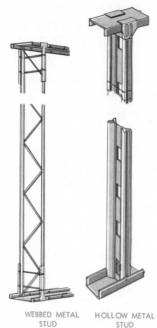

WEBBED METAL
STUD   HOLLOW METAL
              STUD

Fig. 13. Common types of metal studs.

ceiling. Fig. 14 illustrates a non-load bearing wall constructed of metal studs. Note that the drywall is nailed or screwed directly into the stud. The V-groove in the stud holds the fastener.

Gypsum Wallboard. One of the most common construction materials used in residential construction is gypsum wallboard. It comes in standard sizes of 4' x 8', 4' x 10', and 4' x 12'; other lengths up to 16 feet are also available, and widths of 2 feet may be ordered. The standard thickness is ½ inch although ⅜ inch and ⅝ inch are common. See Table V. Gypsum wallboard is commonly used in the interior of a house

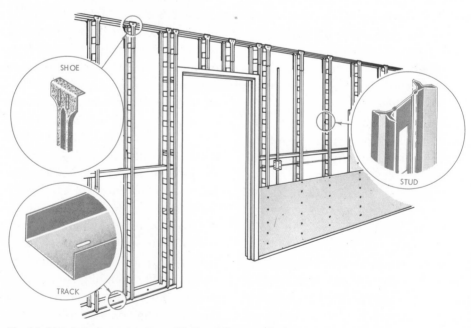

SHOE

STUD

TRACK

Fig. 14. Metal stud construction. (National Gypsum Co.)

TABLE V GYPSUMBOARD TYPES AND SIZES

Thick-ness	Edge	Width	Length	Approx. Weight Lbs. Per M Sq. Ft.	Recommended Support Spacing	Joint Treatment
5/8"	Tapered	4'	6,7,8,9,10,12,14	2,800	16" or 24" o c	Tape & Joint Compound
*5/8"	Square	2'	8,9,10,12	2,800	16" or 24" o c	No Treatment Required
1/2"	Tapered	4'	6,7,8,9,10,12,14	2,100	16" or 24" o c	Tape & Joint Compound
*1/2	Square	2'	8,9,10,12	2,100	16" or 24" o c	No Treatment Required
3/8"	Tapered or Sq.	4'	6,7,8,9,10,12,14	1,550	16" o c	Tape & Joint Compound
3/8"	Beveled	4'	6,7,8,9,10,12	1,550	16" o c	No Treatment Required
*3/8"	Square	2'	8,9,10,12	1,550	16" o c	No Treatment Required
**1/4"	Square	4'	8 & 10	1,100	16" o c	Tape & Joint Compound Batten Strips

The above materials are available with insulating foil back in sizes given, at slight additional costs.
Also available in 3/8" is predecorated Wallboards (Woodgrain, Vinyl Coated & Vinyl Surfaced).

*Gypsum Backing Board may be used as base layer
in two-ply wallboard construction

** 1/4 inch gypsum wallboard is recommended for use as a finishing
material over existing surfaces. It is not recommended for new construction.

Credit: Practical Builder

in *drywall construction.* (Drywall is a wall applied without the use of mortar or plaster.) Panels are composed of a gypsum rock base sandwiched between two layers of special paper. Insulating panels with an aluminum backing are available and standard fire resistant panels (with a base of gypsum rock mixed with glass fibers) are common. Panels may be either unfinished or finished. Vinyl finishes with various permanent colors and textures are available. (When installing gypsum wallboard with a color finish be sure to use nails of a matching color.) Gypsum board may be installed with nails, staples, drywall screws (Phillips), or clips. Adhesives may be used in combination with either nails, staples, or screws. A special drywall hammer should be used in installing the panels. The panels may be either sawed, or scored and snapped. Care should be exercised in handling the panels so that they do not chip or crack at the edges and corners.

Gypsum Lath. Gypsum lath usually comes in 16"x48", 24"x48", and 24" x 96" sizes. Other sizes are also available. The most common thickness is ⅜ inch, although a ½ inch thickness is manufactured. A special 1 inch board (called "coreboard") is also available. Gypsum lath is used as a base upon which plaster is applied. Some panels are perforated to allow the plaster to push through the holes for a better bond. (Wire lath is sometimes used for the same purpose.) Standard laths may be made more fire resistant by a core of gypsum rock and glass fiber. Insulating laths with aluminum backing are available in standard sizes.

Solid Vinyl. One of the most interesting recent developments is the use of solid vinyl materials in residential construction. Their major use is in exterior siding. Both vinyl panels and vinyl shingles are being used in a variety of sizes and finishes. Lap siding of vinyl is also used. In addition to being used as siding, solid vinyl is also used for roofing, gutters, window shutters, roof edging, and, in some areas, as flashing. (Consult local codes for the use of vinyl flashing.) Several advantages have been discovered in using solid vinyl building materials. (1) Because of the method of manufacture, uniformity of properties is attained. (2) Solid vinyl has good insulative qualities. (3) It requires little maintenance as the whole material is impregnated with coloring. Painting, therefore, is not necessary. When used as siding this means that no blistering, peeling, or flaking will occur. (4) Also, it will not rot and is impervious to termite attack.

In installing vinyl siding special care often must be observed. Since the siding is already pigmented and no painting is required, color coated nails must be used. The color coating of the nail, of course, must match the siding color. In nailing, a plastic cap is commonly fitted over the face of the hammer. This prevents damage both to the vinyl surface and to the color coating on the nail head. It is sawed like ordinary wood.

Another recent development in vinyl siding is the slide-on boards. Special grooved sheathing is used and the vinyl siding is installed by sliding the boards into the grooves. No nailing is required. Corner edging secures the siding in place. Siding boards may be easily replaced by removing the corner, sliding the old board out, and sliding a new board in.

Laminated Plastics. The plastics industry manufactures great quantities of laminated sheets under such trade names as Formica, Micarta, Textolite, etc. The laminations may be of various materials such as paper, asbestos, cloth, etc., bound together by a synthetic resin.

Attractive laminated counter and table tops are produced from resin treated wood surfaces. These are very popular due to the fact they are resistant to damage by burning cigarettes or alcoholic beverages.

Checking On Your Knowledge

These questions cover some of the newest and most interesting developments in building. Be sure you understand them and know the answers.

DO YOU KNOW

1. Five reasons why wood is manufactured into building products?

2. How plywood is made?

3. In what ways particleboard differs from plywood? Wallboard?

4. What is meant by "drywall" construction?

5. Two reasons for wood treatment?

6. The proper precautions to be used in handling treated wood?

7. What lamination means in connection with trusses? With wallboards?

8. How solid vinyl is being used in modern construction?

Building Insulation

Buildings are needed to protect people and products. Once the basic protection from rain, cold, and wind is provided, then the demand becomes one for greater comfort, convenience and appearance.

In the early days the inefficient heating systems impelled a search for better heating methods and also for better ways of saving the heat provided. The basic idea of using insulating materials in a house was a simple, practical one of keeping heat in so that less fuel would be needed. Insulation, however, also serves to keep heat *out* in summer.

The fact that insulating materials had a direct bearing on noise was also observed and new products for insulating against noise were developed. Fire retardant values must sometimes be considered.

New demands have caused the development of the many kinds and types of insulating materials on the market. The carpenter needs to know which one will provide the best combination of properties for each use. He needs to know how to apply them, what precautions have to be observed, and when and how to use multi-purpose materials. Today the carpenter must reckon with insulating from heat, cold, moisture, sound and fire. Tomorrow radiation, sonic boom, electronic beams and other problems yet to come may be added.

Thermal Building Insulation

Constructing buildings so they will have a higher degree of heat resistance is a problem to which various authorities have given much attention in recent years. The house should be built so that it will be comfortably warm in winter and relatively cool in summer; that is, a building should be constructed so as to retain the heat which is generated by the heating plant in the winter and keep out the heat developed by the hot rays of the sun during the summer. If the walls and roof can be constructed in such a way that the passage of heat through them becomes relatively difficult, fuel will be saved during the cold months and increased comfort will be provided during the hot weather. The use of thermal building insulation gives these desirable results. By *thermal insulation* we mean the use of materials which possess concentrated heat resistance; that is, materials which have a high degree of heat resistance per unit of thickness.

Our forefathers filled the wall spaces of buildings with sea grasses or sawdust and shavings, or back plastered them. (*Back plaster* consisted of lath and plaster in the stud space midway between the outside sheathing and the inside lath and plaster.) However, today we have available many different types of insulation in forms which are easy to handle. If properly installed these insulation materials are effective.

Thermal Insulation. Manufacturers have utilized many different kinds of materials in the process of developing thermal insulation. Now on the market in various forms these materials may be classified as: blanket and batt insulation (flexible), loose fill insulation, structural insulation board (rigid), reflective insulation, slab or block insulation, and miscellaneous insulation.

The intent of insulating is to surround all the *living area* in the house with some kind of thermal insulation. A protective shell should surround the house. See Figs. 1 and 2. Note that in Fig. 1 areas that are not living areas are not insulated; however, insulation is placed between the living area and the area which is not lived in, such as an unheated attic. Slab floors are commonly laid over a crushed rock fill covered with polyethylene film.

Thermal insulation serves other purposes than merely keeping heat in or out of a structure. It also serves to control condensation, as sound

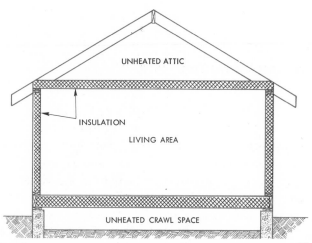

Fig. 1. Insulation for a one-story house over unheated crawl space. (National Forest Products Assoc.)

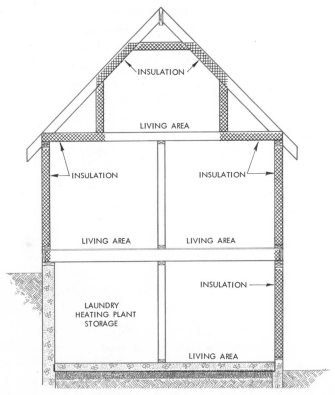

Fig. 2. Insulation for a one-and-a-half-story house with basement. (National Forest Products Assoc.)

proofing, and as a fire retardant material.

Condensation. Moisture comes from ordinary living conditions. Common sources of moisture in the home come from cooking, dish-washing, bathing, scrubbing, plants, and the perspiration of the occupants. Too much moisture, however, is as undesirable as too little.

Proper insulation is a necessity to prevent condensation from forming on the walls and ceiling and damaging the walls and ceiling. A vapor barrier (usually polyethylene sheets) should be applied on the warm side of the structure to keep the moisture from penetrating to the cold surface. Ventilators should be used in the attic area.

Crawl spaces with bare earth should be covered with a vapor barrier to prevent the moisture from entering and condensing.

Fire Retardant Ratings. Insulation materials are rated as to their fire retardant properties. This rating gives the time (in hours) a particular type of construction using specified materials can resist intense heat and flame and still support its design loads.

Only insulation and construction that conform to the minimum standards set by the local and state codes may be used. The particular application and the type of construction must also be considered. Some material or combination of materials that are suitable for residential construction have too low a fire rating for multi-family dwellings or for commercial or industrial construction.

Ratings are given by nationally recognized, independent standards associations and may be obtained from the manufacturer. These ratings are only guaranteed if the instructions for assembling the particular construction are followed exactly.

Acoustical Materials. Sound control is becoming increasingly important in all types of building construction. This is especially true in business and industry. Home buyers are also more-and-more insisting on the privacy given by well designed acoustical construction. Insulation, especially rigid insulation, is used in sound control in residential construction. To determine the efficiency of sound control, construction assemblies (such as a wall) are rated as to *sound transmission class* (STC). The higher the STC number the more efficient the construction in eliminating sound. Table I illustrates the meaning of STC numbers. An STC rating of 50 is highly desirable in the home and it is becoming almost essential in party walls in apartment houses, motels, hotels, etc. In some areas local codes may require a specific STC number for a particular type of construction.

Three techniques are used in the home for sound control: (1) trans-

TABLE I.   SOUND TRANSMISSION CLASS*

25	30	35	42	45	48	50
Normal speech can be understood quite easily	Loud speech can be understood fairly well	Loud speech audible but not intelligible	Loud speech audible as a murmur	Must strain to hear loud speech	Some loud speech barely audible	Loud speech not audible

STC numbers have been adopted by acoustical engineers as a measure of the resistance of a building element such as a wall to the passage of sound. The higher the number, the better the sound barrier.

*Source: Insulation Board Institute

mission paths for noise are blocked; (2) noise is absorbed within the area; and (3) the source of the noise is quieted. The first technique, the blocking of possible noise paths, falls partly within the area of design and house layout. Sound can be transmitted directly if heat registers or electrical outlets are back to back between two rooms. Loosely fitted doors, windows, etc., will also allow direct sound transmission. Sound deadening insulation board is used to block the transmission paths for noise. The second technique uses noise absorbing, acoustical insulation board or ceiling tile. The third technique is concerned with methods of quieting appliances, plumbing, heating systems, etc., within the home. Tables II and III illustrate some of the methods and materials used in the home for sound control. Table III also gives STC numbers for particular materials and construction techniques. The higher the rating the greater the sound barrier.

Flexible Insulation: Blanket and Batt

Flexible Insulation Material. Known as *blankets* or *quilts* and as *batts*, flexible insulations are made from processed wood fiber, mineral wool, fiberglass, and other fibers which in many cases are highly resistant to fire, moisture, and vermin, or have been treated to render them resistant to these hazards. The matted or felted fibers are encased generally with sheets of kraft paper and stitched or cemented together, then the paper is asphalt-saturated or coated.

Some blankets and batts have no paper covering or a paper covering on only one side. Those that have a paper covering on both sides will have one side treated so as to form a vapor barrier. Some flexible

TABLE II METHODS OF INSTALLING ACOUSTICAL UNITS

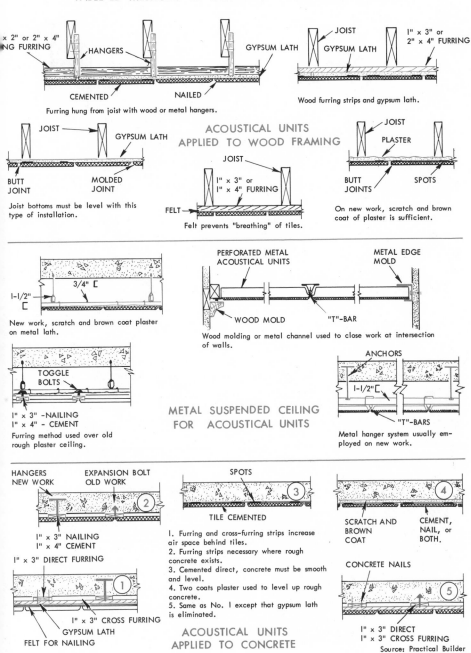

x 2" or 2" x 4"
NG FURRING

HANGERS

JOIST

GYPSUM LATH   GYPSUM LATH

1" x 3" or
2" x 4" FURRING

CEMENTED   NAILED

Furring hung from joist with wood or metal hangers.

Wood furring strips and gypsum lath.

JOIST

GYPSUM LATH

BUTT
JOINT

MOLDED
JOINT

Joist bottoms must be level with this
type of installation.

ACOUSTICAL UNITS
APPLIED TO WOOD FRAMING

JOIST

1" x 3" or
1" x 4" FURRING

FELT

Felt prevents "breathing" of tiles.

JOIST

PLASTER

BUTT
JOINTS

SPOTS

On new work, scratch and brown
coat of plaster is sufficient.

3/4" [

1-1/2"
[

New work, scratch and brown coat plaster
on metal lath.

PERFORATED METAL
ACOUSTICAL UNITS

METAL EDGE
MOLD

WOOD MOLD   "T"-BAR

Wood molding or metal channel used to close work at intersection
of walls.

TOGGLE
BOLTS

1" x 3" -NAILING
1" x 4" - CEMENT

Furring method used over old
rough plaster ceiling.

METAL SUSPENDED CEILING
FOR ACOUSTICAL UNITS

ANCHORS

1-1/2" [

"T"-BARS

Metal hanger system usually employed on new work.

HANGERS
NEW WORK

EXPANSION BOLT
OLD WORK

2

1" x 3" NAILING
1" x 4" CEMENT

1" x 3" DIRECT FURRING

1

1" x 3" CROSS FURRING
GYPSUM LATH
FELT FOR NAILING

SPOTS

3

TILE CEMENTED

1. Furring and cross-furring strips increase
air space behind tiles.
2. Furring strips necessary where rough
concrete exists.
3. Cemented direct, concrete must be smooth
and level.
4. Two coats plaster used to level up rough
concrete.
5. Same as No. 1 except that gypsum lath
is eliminated.

ACOUSTICAL UNITS
APPLIED TO CONCRETE

4

SCRATCH AND
BROWN
COAT

CEMENT,
NAIL, or
BOTH.

CONCRETE NAILS

5

1" x 3" DIRECT
1" x 3" CROSS FURRING

Source: Practical Builder

201

TABLE III SOUND INSULATION VALUE OF WALL PANELS

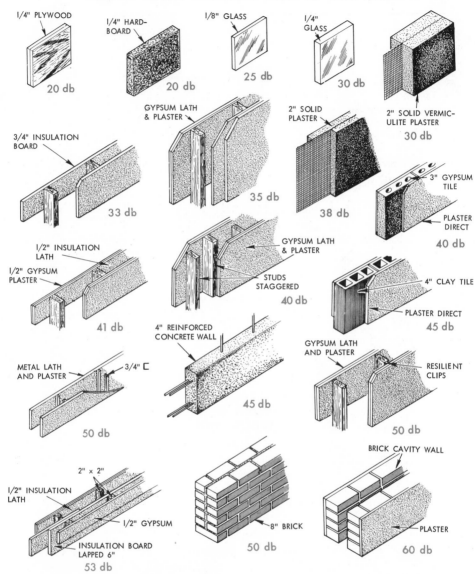

1/4" PLYWOOD — 20 db

1/4" HARDBOARD — 20 db

1/8" GLASS — 25 db

1/4" GLASS — 30 db

2" SOLID VERMICULITE PLASTER — 30 db

3/4" INSULATION BOARD — 33 db

GYPSUM LATH & PLASTER — 35 db

2" SOLID PLASTER — 38 db

3" GYPSUM TILE / PLASTER DIRECT — 40 db

1/2" INSULATION LATH / 1/2" GYPSUM PLASTER — 41 db

GYPSUM LATH & PLASTER / STUDS STAGGERED — 40 db

4" CLAY TILE / PLASTER DIRECT — 45 db

METAL LATH AND PLASTER / 3/4" Ϲ — 50 db

4" REINFORCED CONCRETE WALL — 45 db

GYPSUM LATH AND PLASTER / RESILIENT CLIPS — 50 db

2" x 2" / 1/2" INSULATION LATH / 1/2" GYPSUM / INSULATION BOARD LAPPED 6" — 53 db

8" BRICK — 50 db

BRICK CAVITY WALL / PLASTER — 60 db

The noise reduction factors given for these panels are average and conditions such as workmanship, quality of materials and other factors may raise or lower the efficiency of the panel.

They are shown primarily for comparison purposes and to illustrate how sound reduction depends on weight, thickness and air space. Those panels which have air space as an element, may have their efficiency increased by further separation of the solid surfaces.

Source: Practical Builder

insulation has a vapor barrier on one side and a sheet of reflective material on the other. Double foil insulation with foil on both faces is also available.

Fig. 3 illustrates the installation of blanket insulation. The thickness of blanket insulation varies from ½ inches to 6 inches. Batt insulation is usually 3 to 6 inches in thickness, although 1 and 1½ inch thickness are also available. Flexible insulation usually comes in 15 and 23 inch widths; 19 inch widths are also available. Both blanket and batt usually have a flange for stapling.

The difference between blanket insulation and batt insulation is one of length. *Batt insulation* is usually sold in units of 24 or 48 inches in length. This allows more ease in handling. *Blanket insulation* is defined as being *over* 48 inches in length. Blanket insulation comes in rolls of 40 to 100 feet and is cut to the length desired; 8 foot strips are also available. The 8 foot blanket strips are sometimes referred to as "batts" by the manufacturer.

Fig. 3. Applying fiberglas insulation blanket. (Owens-Corning Fiberglas Corp.)

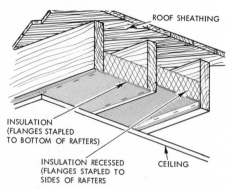

Fig. 4. Methods of installing flexible insulation between rafters. (National Forest Products Assoc.)

Installation of Blanket Insulation. The fibers in this type of insulation (both blankets and batts) are usually held in place between two layers of paper. Blanket insulation is made wide enough to fit in the usual stud and rafter spacings of 16, 20, or 24 inches. In case of thinner blankets, that is, ½ inch or ¾ inch in thickness, the material is bent and nailed against the framing members. However, in the case of 2-inch blankets, or thicker, and batts, the edges of the paper are cemented and turned up by the manufacturer to make a ¾-inch

flange on each side. These flanges are rather stiff and are strong enough for staples or nails to be driven through them to hold the insulation in place. Some manufacturers create a double ¾-inch fold along the edges, one to nail to the edge of the framing member, the other to act as a spacer. Fig. 4 illustrates flush and recessed flanges used in a roof ceiling. The use of recessed flanges is recommended when drywall is to be applied.

Fig. 5 illustrates how the air spaces are proportioned for both types. The insulation will be held securely in place and the joints sealed by the ceiling.

Fig. 6 illustrates how blanket insulation is used between studding. In applying blanket insulation, the vapor barrier faces in toward the living area; the backing, or foil if used, faces outward.

When flexible insulation is applied to masonry walls it is necessary to use furring strips. In order to create an air space between the insulation and the wall, it is advisable to use 2x1-inch furring

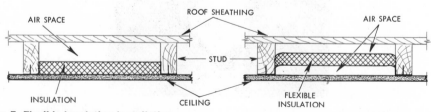

Fig. 5. Flexible insulation installation.

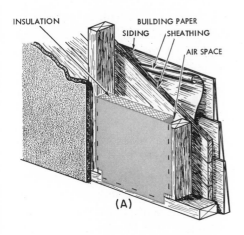

(A)

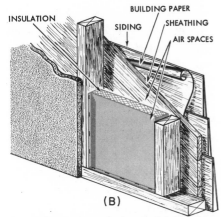

(B)

Fig. 6. Methods of installing wall insulation. (National Forest Products Assoc.)

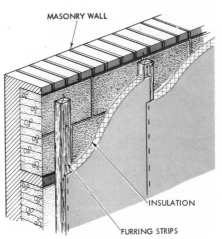

Fig. 7. Method of insulating masonry walls. (National Forest Products Assoc.)

Consequently, the insulating value of extra air space on the outside of the insulation material is lost. The insulation material must be tightly fitted in each stud space, not only on the sides but also across the top and at the bottom where the insulation material meets the floor. Cut the insulation over-long to be sure that there are no voids at the top or bottom.

Installation of Batts. Batts with flanges are installed in the same manner as blankets. However, plain batts without paper backing are installed simply by inserting them between framing members. The batts are held in place in walls by fitting them tightly against the sheathing and between the studs. To avoid leaving heat-leaking crevices, adjoining

strips. The furring strips also keep the paper away from the damp masonry. The insulation can be applied vertically between the furring strips, as in Fig. 7.

Much of the value of flexible insulation is lost by poor installation. Frequently careless workmen will push the material tightly against the sheathing in the stud spaces.

205

batts should be butted snugly together. Odd-shaped spaces are filled by cutting the batts to the proper size to fit into such spaces.

When the batts are installed between ceiling joists from above, the finished ceiling, if previously installed, supports the batts. If ceiling joists are inaccessible from above, the batts may be installed from the under side and a vapor barrier nailed immediately to the under side of the joists to hold the batts in place until the interior finish is installed. If necessary, wire, such as in Fig. 8, may also be used to hold the batts in the joists until the finish is installed. Friction, however, should oridinarily hold the batt in place.

A vapor barrier is recommended where plain batts are used. The barrier should be installed on the warm side of the wall or other construction as soon as the batts are in place. A vapor barrier should be used similarly when batts are installed between roof rafters. Polyethylene is commonly used as the vapor barrier.

Most manufacturers, as mentioned before, now furnish batts with a vapor-proof paper backing which serves not only as a vapor barrier but is used also for installing the batts. This backing usually is wider than the batt and serves as a flange by which the insulation may be nailed to the framing members. Batts with flanges are installed like blanket insulation except, of course, the batts are in smaller units. See Figs. 9 and 10.

Fig. 11 illustrates the techniques for installing both blanket and batt insulation.

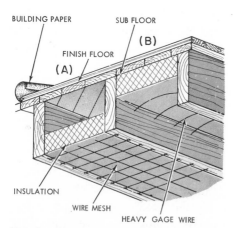

Fig. 8. Methods of installing insulation between floor joists. (National Forest Products Assoc.)

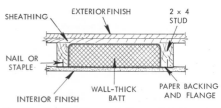

Fig. 9. Application of flanged batts between studding.

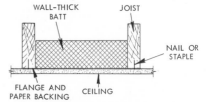

Fig. 10. Application of flanged batts between ceiling joists.

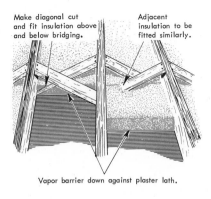

Make diagonal cut and fit insulation above and below bridging.

Adjacent insulation to be fitted similarly.

Vapor barrier down against plaster lath.

CEILING JOISTS (over heated areas)

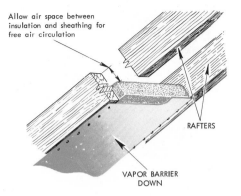

Allow air space between insulation and sheathing for free air circulation

RAFTERS

VAPOR BARRIER DOWN

RAFTERS (pitched roof)

Provide louvers or other permanent vents above insulated area

VENT

LIVING SPACE

VAPOR BARRIERS

VENTILATION

VAPOR BARRIER UP

Either vapor permeable asphalt felt, wood strips or lacing wire, to hold insulation against flooring.

CEILING JOISTS (over unheated areas)

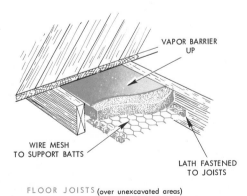

VAPOR BARRIER UP

WIRE MESH TO SUPPORT BATTS

LATH FASTENED TO JOISTS

FLOOR JOISTS (over unexcavated areas)

CONTINUOUS INSECT SCREEN

FURRING

If free air circulation parallel to rafters cannot be provided, install furring and insert screen as shown.

RAFTERS (flat roof or ceiling)

Fig. 11. Techniques for insulating various areas using batts and blankets. (Insulation Board Institute)

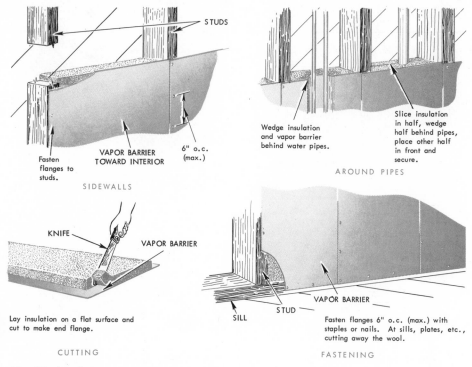

STUDS

Fasten
flanges to
studs.

VAPOR BARRIER
TOWARD INTERIOR

6" o.c.
(max.)

SIDEWALLS

Wedge insulation
and vapor barrier
behind water pipes.

Slice insulation
in half, wedge
half behind pipes,
place other half
in front and
secure.

AROUND PIPES

KNIFE

VAPOR BARRIER

Lay insulation on a flat surface and
cut to make end flange.

CUTTING

SILL

STUD

VAPOR BARRIER

Fasten flanges 6" o.c. (max.) with
staples or nails. At sills, plates, etc.,
cutting away the wool.

FASTENING

Fig. 11. Insulating Techniques Continued.

Fill Insulation

Fill Materials. Loose fill insulations are made generally from mineral substances and are supplied in granulated, cellular, and fibrous wool forms. As the name implies, fill-type insulation is installed to either completely or partially fill the spaces between the framing members.

Usually the fill material is pneumatically blown into the spaces to be insulated. However, it may also be poured from the bags directly into the spaces between the framing members. Fig. 12 illustrates the basic difference between loose fill insulation and flexible insulation. Loose fill is installed *after* the ceiling finish is in place. Blanket insulation is stapled to the bottom edges of the joists *before* the ceiling finish is applied.

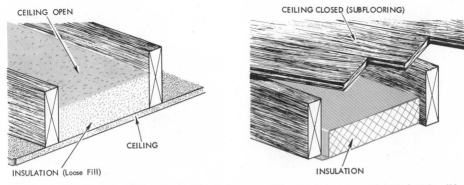

Fig. 12. Methods of installing insulation between ceiling joists under unheated attic. (National Forest Products Assoc.)

A granulated fill, mica pellets, is made from a mineral ore known as expanded vermiculite (aluminum magnesium silicate). This type of fill is found on the market under several different trade names. Perlite is another common granular fill and is made from volcanic siliceous rock which is greatly expanded under heat. Mineral wool is also used as fill, in granulated and nodulated form. Depending on what it is composed of, it is called rock wool, slag wool or glass wool. Granulated cork is used chiefly in refrigeration.

Powdered-fill and cellular-fill insulations are made chiefly of finely ground gypsum; they are sold under various trade names.

Particular care should be taken in handling loose fill insulation made from such materials as animal hair, minerals, and glass fibers. For instance, rock wool, which is made from fibers of molten rock, should be handled with gloves if used in the form of loose fill insulation. Also, care should be taken not to breathe in excessive amounts of dust and loose particles from fill insulation. This can be avoided by not excessively agitating the material while handling it, or by wearing a protective mask.

Figs. 13 and 14 illustrate how fill materials may be poured into the open spaces between ceiling joists.

Vapor Barrier. A vapor barrier, consisting of a polyethylene sheet, should be used with fill insulation. This vapor barrier is stapled directly to the studs; all walls that face the outside should have a vapor barrier. The purpose of a vapor barrier is to prevent the va-

209

Fig. 13. Mica pellets are poured between ceiling joists.

Fig. 14. Template is used to gage the depth of the insulation.

por within the building getting into the wall space and insulation where it might condense and form ice. Most flexible insulations now come with such barriers on one side, but for the fill type of insulation the barrier must be provided. This can be done by horizontally tacking a piece of vapor-proof polyethylene to the inside of the stud frame before applying the lath or plaster base.

The vapor barrier should be installed as work progresses on nailing the plaster base in place. Beginning at the bottom of the wall, the vapor barrier is applied, then the lath, plaster base, or interior finish is placed over it and nailed. The fill should then be poured from the bags into the stud spaces up to the height of the top edge of the vapor barrier. Another sheet of poly-

ethylene is then applied and the plaster base or interior finish is nailed in position. Insulation fill is again poured into the stud space until it is filled to the height of the top of the second piece of vapor barrier. This procedure should be repeated until the top of the wall is reached.

In the case of ceilings, joists, and rafters the entire area can be covered first with the vapor barrier and then with the plaster base. Then the fill is applied from above until the joist spaces are filled to whatever depth is desired. See Figs. 13 and 14.

In applying the vapor barrier, take care not to tear the sheet. If any tears do occur, however, be sure to repair them.

Pneumatic Filling. Fill insulation can be applied also by the

Fig. 15. Granulated wool being applied pneumatically. (Owens-Corning Fiberglas Corp.)

pneumatic method, blowing the material into place. See Fig. 15. This method is commonly used when insulating old buildings.

The siding is removed near the top of the wall and holes bored through the sheathing between the studs in order to get the fill into the wall spaces of old buildings.

Rigid Insulation Board

Rigid insulation board, also known as structural insulation board, is made out of wood and vegetable fibers. Many uses have been found for this material. It may be used as wall and roof sheathing to replace wood sheathing; as a plaster base to replace wood, metal, and gypsum lath; and as interior-finish wall covering in place of plaster or wood covering. In addition to these uses, structural insulation

211

Fig. 16. Applying insulating board. (Celotex Corp.)

board also serves as a thermal insulation whenever applied to outside walls or roof of a building. See Fig. 16.

Table IV shows the many sizes, thicknesses, and uses of this building material. Note that sound deadening board, an acoustical board, is also included in this category. The manufacturer of each of these products makes the boards in different sizes and thicknesses with a variety

TABLE IV. STANDARD INSULATION BOARD MATERIALS*

PRODUCT	THICKNESS	SIZES	EDGES	MAJOR USES
Building Board	½″	4′ x 8′ 4′ x 9′ 4′ x 10′ 4′ x 12′	Square	General purpose insulation board.
Insulating Roof Deck	Nominal 1½″ 2″ 3″	2′ x 8′	Fabricated long edges, short edges interlocking or square.	Flat, pitched or shed type roofs.
Roof Insulation	Nominal ½″ 1″ 1½″ 2″ 2½″ 3″	23″ x 47″ 24″ x 48″	Varies	Built-Up roofs and under certain types of roofing on pitched roofs.
Wall Board	⁵⁄₁₆″ or ³⁄₈″	4′ x 8′ 4′ x 10′	Square	General purpose utility board.
Ceiling Tile: Plain or Perforated	½″	12″ x 12″ 12″ x 24″ 16″ x 16″ 16″ x 32″	Fabricated or butt edges.	Decorative wall and ceiling finish.
Plank	½″	12″ x 8′ 12″ x 10′	Fabricated long edges	Decorative wall and ceiling finish.
Sheathing, Regular Density	½″, ²⁵⁄₃₂″	4′ x 8′ 4′ x 9′ 4′ x 10′ 4′ x 12′	Square	Wall Sheathing for all types of wood framed construction.
	½″, ²⁵⁄₃₂″	2′ x 8′	Long edges fabricated short edges square.	
Sheathing, Intermediate	½″	4′ x 8′ 4′ x 9′	Square	High Density product designed for use without supplementary corner bracing.
Sheathing, Nail-Base	½″	4′ x 8′ 4′ x 9′	Square	High Density product designed for use in frame construction to permit the direct attachment of wood and asbestos-cement shingles
Shingle Backer	⁵⁄₁₆″ or ³⁄₈″	11¾″ x 48″ 13½″ x 48″ 15″ x 48″	Square	Undercoursing for wood or asbestos-cement shingles applied over insulation board sheathing.
Insulating Formboard	1″, 1½″	24″, 32″ & 48″ widths; 4′ to 12′ in length	Square	Used as a permanent form for reinforced gypsum or light-weight aggregate concrete poured-in-place roof construction.
Sound Deadening Board	½″	4′ x 8′ 4′ x 9′	Square	In wall and floor assemblies to control Sound Transmission between units.

For additional thicknesses and sizes, consult manufacturer.

*Source: Insulation Board Institute

of colors and textures to suit the individual's need.

Application of Rigid Insulation Board. As mentioned, rigid insulation board is used as thermal insulation in a variety of ways; it should be applied according to manufacturer's instructions. The different kinds and lengths of nails recommended for use with the more common kinds of insulating board are given in Tables V and VI. A small clearance should be allowed between adjacent sheets to allow for expanding and contracting under different conditions.

Wall Sheathing Installation. Today, for insulation on buildings, the boards commonly used are 4 x 8-foot sheathing ½ or $^{25}/_{32}$ inch thick coated with asphalt. These boards are square on all edges. They should first be nailed to the intermediate studs, spacing the nails six inches on center, and then

spacing the nails along the edges three inches on center and ⅜ inches in from the edges. Stapling guns are also used in the application of insulation board. Staples follow the same nailing pattern as nails. The head of the staple should be parallel to the edge of the board.

Boards should be fitted tightly around all openings and all cracks should be sealed and flashed.

The builder will find it more economical to use 4x9-foot sheathing or even larger sheets if the building is low enough so that sheets can be used vertically with each sheet covering the full height. Nail these sheets to the intermediate studs first, spacing the nails six inches on center, then spacing the nails along the edges three inches on center, and ⅜ inch in from the outer edge.

Insulation boards should never be forced into place. Between ad-

TABLE V.   NAILS RECOMMENDED FOR VARIOUS STRUCTURAL BOARD PRODUCTS*

Product	Thickness	Nails Recommended See Table VI
Sheathing...............................	25/32"	I.O.P
Sheathing...............................	1/2"	H.N.O
Roof Insulation Board	1/2", 1"	O
Tileboard (Panels)............................	1/2"	A . B . C . D
Plank	1/2"	A . B . C . D
Interior Boards (Nails Exposed).................	1/2"	A . B . C
Interior Boards (Nails Covered)	1/2"	E. G. M. N
Wallboards (Nails Exposed).....................	3/8" or 5/16"	A . B . C
Wallboards (Nails Covered)....................	3/8" or 5/16"	E, G. M. N
Shingle Backer	3/8" or 5/16"	F.Q
Roof Deck Insulation	1 1/2"	I
	2"	K
	3"	L

*Source: Practical Builder

TABLE VI. DESCRIPTION OF NAILS USED FOR STRUCTURAL INSULATING BOARD PRODUCTS*

No.	Name	Size	Length	Gauge	Head	No. per lb.
A	Brad............................	3d	1 1/4"	14	11 ga.	568
B	Finishing........................	3d	1 1/4"	15 1/2	12 1/2 ga.	807
C	Insulation Board— Cadmium Plated.................. Diamond Point		1 1/4"	17	5/32"	1139
D	Box	3d	1 1/4"	14 1/2	7/32"	635
E	Box	4d	1 1/2"	14	7/32"	473
F	Galvanized Box	8d	2 1/2"	11 1/2	19/64"	121
G	Common	4d	1 1/2"	12 1/2	1/4"	316
H	Common	6d	2"	11 1/2	17/64"	181
I	Common	8d	2 1/2"	10 1/4	9/32"	106
J	Common	10d	3"	9	5/16"	69
K	Common	16d	3 1/2"	8	11/32"	49
L	Common	30d	4 1/2"	5	7/16"	24
M	Galvanized Shingle	4d	1 1/2"	12	9/32"	274
N	Galvanized Roofing..............		1 1/2"	12	3/8"	249
O	Galvanized Roofing..............		1 3/4"	12	3/8"	210
P	Galvanized Roofing..............		2"	11	7/16"	138
Q	Galv. Annular Grooved	6d	2"	13 3/4	5/32"	336

*Source: Practical Builder

joining boards and at the ends of the boards ⅛ inch spaces should be left. Most insulating boards are cut scant in width and length to allow for this spacing.

Pitched Roof Installation. Where rigid insulating board is to be applied directly to roof rafters of pitched roofs, either the four foot wide wall sheathing or building board may be used. The boards should be applied lengthwise and directly to all framing members with ample bearing for nailing along all edges. Nail to intermediate studs first, spacing the nails six inches on center; then along all edges spacing nails three inches on center, ⅜ inch from outer edges of wall sheathing. When wood shin-

gles or slate are to cover the roof, 1x3 inch nailing strips are applied over the insulation board, Fig. 17. Asphalt shingles, roll or metal roof-

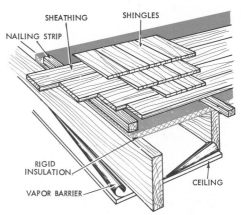

Fig. 17. Method of applying rigid insulation on sloping rafters. (National Forest Products Assoc.)

215

ing, or tiles require the installation of solid wood sheathing over which these types of roofing material are laid.

Flat Roof or Deck Installation. Rigid insulating board is designed especially as an insulation under built-up roofing. The most common sizes are 23x47 and 24x48 inches and the thicknesses are ½, 1, 1½, 2, 2½, and 3 inches. This board is used as insulation over wood, monolithic concrete, precast concrete, gypsum structural board, and steel decks.

It is advisable to use a vapor barrier over the deck and under the insulation. Where the insulation is to be applied in one layer, the entire roof area should be covered with two plies (lapped half) of heavy vapor-proof asphalt paper. The roof deck should be mopped with either hot asphalt or coal tar.

However, coal-tar pitch and asphalt should not be used together on the same job. Each piece of insulation board should be embedded firmly in the hot bituminous mopping. See Figs. 18 and 19. Over the top of this mopping the built-up roofing is laid according to whatever specification are desired.

When used as lath for a plaster base for walls, rigid insulating board should be applied with long edges at right angles to the framing or furring strips. Manufacturers' instructions should be followed where lath with special joints are used.

Rigid insulating board products used as interior finish include: building board, plank, and tileboard, the latter being known as panels. The proper application of insulating board for interior finish purposes is important. To obtain the best results, the specific instruc-

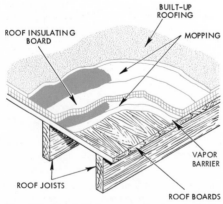

Fig. 18. Insulating a wooden roof deck.

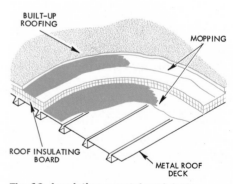

Fig. 19. Insulating a metal roof deck.

tions of the manufacturer, of each particular product used, should be followed.

R-Value. Most rigid insulation board is rated by the *Insulation Board Institute* as to its effectiveness in retarding heat transfer. Each type and thickness of board is tested and assigned a heat *resistance value* or *R-value.* This IBI rating is stamped on each panel. See Fig. 16. The higher the R-value, the more efficient the panel is in retarding the passage of heat. The most efficient standard panel is the $^{25}/_{32}$ inch fiberboard sheathing which has an R-value of "R 2.06." (Flexible insulation, depending on the type and thickness, has much higher

R-value. Flexible insulation with a R-value of 7 to 13 are common.) Table VII gives a listing of commonly used rigid sheathing materials arranged in order of effectiveness. All the materials used, of course, must be considered before the effectiveness of an insulated wall or ceiling can be determined.

TABLE VII. R-VALUES OF COMMON MATERIALS*

MATERIAL	R-VALUE
IBI Rated Insulation board sheathing (25/32")	R 2.06
IBI Rated Insulation board sheathing (1/2")	R 1.32
Lumber (nominal 1")	R 0.98
Gypsum (1/2")	R 0.45
Plywood (3/8")	R 0.47

*Source: Insulation Board Institute

Reflective Insulation

Reflective Insulation Materials. The reflective materials are distinguished from other types by the fact that, to be effective, they must always be installed in conjunction with air spaces so that the reflective surface is exposed to an air space of comparatively large size. The principle of this insulation is that of reflecting the radiated heat. An absolutely black body or surface absorbs all the radiation which strikes it and reflects or transmits none. Bright metallic reflective surfaces, on the other hand, such as

aluminum foil, have low absorption and reflect the radiation. Metallic surfaces are more efficient than the nonmetallic reflective surfaces such as wood. Reflective insulations now on the market are of four general types, namely:

1. *Aluminum foil,* a crimped blanket of one or two layers of reflective insulation which comes in various forms. The following types are used: heavy flat foil mounted on one or both sides of heavy kraft paper with asphalt; a plaster base consisting of steel reinforcing wire, backed

with metalated (aluminum foil) kraft paper; and an aluminum-colored paper similar to reflective insulation.

2. *Aluminum foil-backed gypsum board,* a gypsum wallboard with aluminum foil surface. It is available in large-sized sheets up to 48 inches wide and 12 feet long, also in small plaster-base or lath sizes 16x32 or 16x48 inches. In addition to the gypsum board, rigid insulation sheathing board comes with an aluminum foil on one side.

3. *Blanket or reflective insulation* is the same as blanket and flexible insulation, except that the surface of the paper is covered with an aluminum reflective foil or coating.

4. *Reflective coatings:* special papers coated with a polished reflective material. This comes either in single sheets or with two sheets laminated together. Reflective coated papers may be either used by themselves or may be part of another insulating product, such as blanket insulation.

Installation of Reflective Insulation. Reflective insulations are usually installed in much the same manner as flexible insulations; that is, either between and fastened to the sides of framing members or fastened to the edges of framing members. It should be remembered that proper installation is particularly important with this type of insulation because, to be of value,

the reflective surfaces must always be exposed to an air space of appreciable size. To be of maximum value, the air space should be ¾ inch or more in depth because the value of reflective insulation diminishes as the depth of the air space decreases below ¾ inch. As the depth of the air space to which the reflective surface is exposed diminishes toward zero, the insulating value of the reflective material also diminishes toward zero; that is, no value.

Reflective insulation should be installed in such a manner as to divide the total air space into two air spaces. When thus installed, the value will be greater if both sides of the material are reflective instead of only one.

If foil backed panels are used, they are installed in the same manner as any interior panel. The vapor barrier should face inward and the reflective surface should face outward towards the air space.

The method of installing a single flexible reflective insulation, using lath strips and nailing through the strips to the sides of the studs, is shown in Fig. 20. Another method of application suitable for flexible insulation is shown in Fig. 21. In this case the reflective insulation has flanges for nailing or stapling the material to the sides of the studs. The foregoing methods usually are suitable also for appli-

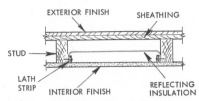

Fig. 20. Reflective insulation between framing members using laths.

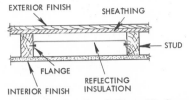

Fig. 21. Reflective insulation with flanges.

cation of these materials to furring strips of masonry walls, to ceiling joists, or to roof rafters.

Insulating lath of the reflective type are installed in the same manner as insulating board lath, with the reflective surface exposed to the air space and with plaster applied to the other surface.

Slab or Block Insulations

Slab or Block Insulation Materials. These slabs are small rigid units usually one to four inches or even more in thickness and ranging from 12x32 inches to 20x96 inches in size. These slabs are fire and moisture resistant, termite proof, and sealed against attack by fungus growth. This type of insulation is used principally for refrigeration and cold storage construction work. There are several types of this product available. (1) *Corkboard*, made from the bark of the cork oak by grinding the bark and compressing it while at the same time subjecting it to high heat. The heat liquefies the gum or rosin which binds the granules together and also seals them, producing a solid slab or pure corkboard, Fig. 22. (2) *Wood fiber and cement*, made by combining shredded wood or wood fibers with fire-resisting Portland cement. (3) *Mineral wool* with

Fig. 22. Commercial sizes of corkboard. (Armstrong Cork Co.)

219

binder, made from rock wool, wood pulp, and asphaltic binder. (4) *Rigid insulation slab* is made of the same materials as the rigid insulation board, but differs in the thickness and size of the sheets, and is of low density. Other slab and block insulations that are sometimes used are: (5) vermiculite and asphalt, (6) cellular hard rubber, (7) cellular glass, and (8) perlite and vermiculite concrete.

Installation of Slab Insulation. Slabs are designed for special purposes and are not in general use in building. As a special type of insulation, each manufacturer always recommends his own particular method for its application. These detailed instructions, of course, should be followed carefully. In many cases these instructions for installing the slabs require the use of special clips or other fastening provided by the manufacturer. Often, nailing is impractical because of the rigid form and thickness of most slab insulation materials. Slabs usually are held firmly in place by the use of cement.

Miscellaneous Insulations

Spray Type Insulations. A specially constructed air gun is used to apply spray type insulations to any surface, such as wood, masonry, or metal. Fibrous flakes are forcibly projected with an air gun simultaneously with an atomized adhesive. When the confetti-like flakes leave the nozzle of the air gun, they are coated with the atomized adhesive and when blown against the surface to be insulated a cellular blanket can be built up to any thickness desired.

Precast Masonry Units. There are a number of lightweight mason units which have insulation value due to their cellular construction or the lightweight properties of the aggregates of which they are made, Fig. 23. The lightweight aggregates available include: *Haydite*, a lightweight burned clay aggregate; *Celocrete* is an aggregate made by converting molten blast-furnace slag into hard, cellular clinkers which are crushed and screened to commercial sizes; *Waylite*, a light-weight aggregate pro-

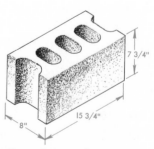

Fig. 23. Precast concrete masonry unit.

duced by passing molten blast furnace slag through a processing machine in which it is centrifuged and beaten in an atmosphere of steam. When mixed with Portland cement and cast in building units, these light weight aggregates have the required strength for wall construction as well as thermal heat insulation qualities.

Another form of masonry unit is the glass block. These glass units, molded into two half blocks and hermetically sealed into a single unit at the time of manufacture, are finished on the mortar-bearing surface with gritty mortar bond. The glass block is used in wall construction to produce attractive, light-transmitting panels. Because of the partial vacuum in the blocks, they have thermal insulation value in addition to being resistant to sound transmission. Glass blocks generally are translucent, but transparent blocks are obtainable.

Checking On Your Knowledge

The following questions give you the opportunity to check up on yourself. If you have read the chapter carefully, you should be able to answer the questions. If you have any difficulty, read the chapter over once more so that you have the information well in mind before you go on with your reading.

DO YOU KNOW

1. What areas are insulated in a house?
2. What causes condensation?
3. What fire retardant ratings are?
4. What STC ratings are and what STC rating is desirable?
5. Three means of sound control?
6. The difference between blanket insulation and batts?
7. How batts are installed?
8. Of what materials loose fill insulations are usually made?
9. What vapor barriers are used for and where they are installed?
10. The names and classification of six popular types of insulating materials?
11. The most common use of rigid insulation?
12. Some of the requirements for installing reflective insulation in order to insure satisfactory results?
13. What type of insulation is used principally for refrigeration and cold storage construction work?

Hardware: Rough

Since carpentry is such an old trade, some people may think its practices are all established and firmly set, and that important improvements are no longer being made. Such a belief is far from the truth. Because the work of the carpenter is practical, it is necessary for him to make every effort possible to improve the efficiency of his methods of construction. Competition in · his field requires him to keep up to date with the new products and building methods.

When you consider that the nail industry still employs the ancient *penny system* to indicate the length of the most commonly used nails, in contrast you must be impressed particularly with the progressive attitude of those engaged in the carpentry industry. On every hand there is evidence of the fact that

carpentry is one of the oldest of all trades, and yet it continues to develop new and better tools and methods of construction.

In carpentry, rough hardware consists of the many metal fastening devices used in constructing a building. Nails are the most commonly used items that come under the classification of rough hardware. There are, however, several other types of rough hardware that the carpenter will encounter and use on the job. Rough hardware used in carpentry work may be classified as follows:

1. Nails
2. Staples
3. Screws
4. Bolts
5. Anchors
6. Metal wood connectors
7. Miscellaneous

Nails

The most common method of fastening one wooden member to another is with nails; it is also usually the simplest method, and therefore the quickest, although it may not result in the strongest of joints. It is therefore expedient for the carpenter to be fully familiar with all the characteristic details of nails of various types, for without this knowledge, he will never achieve the status of a master craftsman.

Nails are divided into two general types: wire and cut nails. Hereafter when we refer to a *type* of nail we will be referring to this general category. There are many *kinds* of nails, whose uses will be explained, but nevertheless, all kinds of nails still fall into the two type classifications. *They are either wire nails, or cut nails.*

The three main characteristics of nails that you should know are:

1. The proper name of the nail.
2. The appearance of the nail.
3. The proper uses of the nail.

This knowledge will make your work easier and your construction better. The master carpenter constructs with the *minimum amount of time and material;* it is this which distinguishes him from the poorly trained carpenter.

Nails are made in many different sizes and various shapes of heads, points, and shanks, each type designed for a particular purpose de-

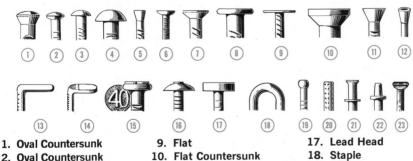

1. Oval Countersunk
2. Oval Countersunk
3. Oval
4. Round
5. Flooring Brad
6. Curved
7. Flat Countersunk
8. Flat
9. Flat
10. Flat Countersunk
11. Flat Countersunk
12. Cupped
13. Metal Lath
14. Hoop Fastener
15. Tree and Pole Dating
16. Umbrella
17. Lead Head
18. Staple
19. Brad
20. Headless
21. Scaffold Anchor
22. Shade Roller Pin
23. T-Nail

Fig. 1. Different types of nail heads available.

pending upon the nature of work, the kind of wood driven into, and the holding power required.

Nail Heads. Examples of a number of different shaped nail heads are shown in Fig. 1. The *flat-headed nail* is the one most commonly used. The *large flat* heads are used for soft materials such as roofing paper, fiber boards, and similar materials. The *brad* and the *deep countersunk head* are used for finish work when nails must be set below the surface. The *double* or *duplex headed* nail is used for temporary work which must be taken apart, including scaffolds and blocking; the extra head, which extends above the surface of the board, is easily hooked by a claw hammer or wrecking bar. The *T-nail* is used with portable air nailers as are the common flat headed nails.

Nail Points. Carpenters and other woodworkers use nails with various types of points as shown in Fig. 2. The *diamond point* is the one most commonly used. The *long diamond point* is found on nails used with parquet flooring, gypsum board, hinges, and some roofing materials. Such a point increases the holding power of the nail and also makes the nail easier to drive. This is because it does not remove any wood but compresses the wood which in turn presses against the nail. Small brads are made with the so-called *needle point*. Boat spikes and large spikes used for various types of woodwork have *chisel points*. Cut nails have *blunt points* as do also certain flooring and shingle nails. Clinch nails have the *duckbill point* which allows clinching of the nail without danger of breaking it.

Usually a nail with a long or needle point will hold better in softwood than a common or diamond point nail, providing the wood into which the nail is driven does not split easily. A blunt point will cut a path through the wood instead of pushing the fibers aside, thus preventing splitting; however, a blunt point reduces the holding power of a nail.

Nail Shanks. Since the holding power of a nail depends to a great extent upon the area of the surface

1. Chisel	5. Diamond	9. Blunt, Shooker
2. Chisel	6. Diamond	10. Screw
3. Diamond	7. Barbed, Beer-Case	11. Side
4. Diamond	8. Needle	12. Duck Bill

Fig. 2. Different types of nail points.

Fig. 3. Different types of nail shanks available.

of the nail in contact with the wood, various kinds of shanks have been designed to increase this surface, Fig. 3. Among these types of shanks the most common are the *square,* the *longitudinally grooved, annular* and the *spiral.* Holding power also is increased by *barbing* the shank, or by coating or etching the surface. Threaded nails, the annular, spiral and screw, are commonly used where increased holding power is required.

Splitting Prevented. Many types of wood split easily when nailed. These include practically all of the denser hardwoods and a few of the softwoods, such as white cedar, Douglas fir, and eastern hemlock. However, danger from splitting can be reduced or entirely eliminated by boring a pilot hole, by using lighter gage or blunt nails. When lighter gage nails are used instead of heavier gage nails, they should be coated, etched, ringed, spiral or barbed.

Experiments made with nails at the United States Forest Products Laboratory show that a good quality of cement coating will increase a nail's resistance to withdrawal immediately after driving it into softwoods from 85 to 100 percent, as compared to the plain nails. Little holding power is gained by using coated nails in hardwood. This increased resistance partially disappears with passing of time so that after a month or so only about one-half of the increased resistance remains. The chemically etched nail developed at the Forest Products Laboratory has from 180 to 200 percent higher holding power than a plain nail in softwoods; and from 90 to 175 percent more holding power in the denser hardwoods.

Metals, Coatings, and Finishes of Nails. Nails are made of various kinds of metals including steel, brass, copper, and stainless steel. The three last-named will resist different types of corrosion, such as that caused by exposure to salt brine, acids, alkaline solutions, or fumes.

Aluminum nails are also made and can be had in just about all the kinds that have been previously made of steel. There is a great advantage from the standpoint of non-rusting, but care should be taken not to use aluminum with certain other metals, such as copper, because of the risk of electrolysis; that is to say, that the metal would tend to decompose.

Different coatings and treatments are applied to steel nails to increase their holding power, reduce corrosion, add sanitary protection, and improve appearance. Coatings and finishes now in use are as follows:

Cement-coated
Resinous coatings
Nylon coated
Acid etching
Galvanized
Copper plated
Tin-coated
Brass-plated
Cadmium-plated
Nickel-plated
Chromium-plated
Blued
Painted
Parkerized
Japanned

Color coated nails are now commonly available for fastening prefinished panels. The nail color is matched to the color of the prefinished panel.

Besides the various finishes, some nails are also hardened so they can be driven into concrete or masonry while others are annealed to soften them so they can be riveted.

Stainless steel nails are also available for special purposes when their nonstaining characteristics offset the extra cost, such as in redwood exposed to salt air or chemical fumes that cause corrosion.

Sizes and Weights of Nails. The nail industry still adheres to the ancient *penny system* to indicate the length of the most commonly used nails, ranging in length from one inch to six inches. This penny system originated in England. Two explanations are offered as to how this curious designation came about. One is that the six penny, four penny, ten penny, and so forth, nails derived their names from the fact that one hundred nails cost sixpence, fourpence, and so on. The other explanation, which is more probable, is that one thousand tenpenny nails, for instance, weighed ten pounds. The ancient, as well as the modern, abbreviation for penny is *d*, which is the first letter of the Roman word *denarius* (a coin), in English monetary reckoning, *a penny*.

Nails shorter than 2d (two penny) or one inch, or those longer than 60d (sixty penny), or six inches, as well as many of the special nails, are listed by inches or fractions of an inch. The types of nails most commonly used by the trade are shown in Table I which show the length, gage, and the number of nails per pound.

Table II gives the kinds and quantities of wire nails commonly used in building construction.

TABLE I. COMMONLY USED NAILS: SIZE, GAGE AND NUMBER PER POUND*

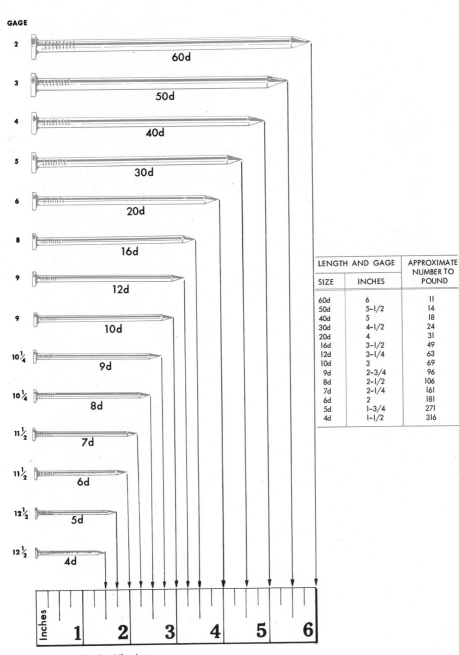

LENGTH AND GAGE		APPROXIMATE NUMBER TO POUND
SIZE	INCHES	
60d	6	11
50d	5-1/2	14
40d	5	18
30d	4-1/2	24
20d	4	31
16d	3-1/2	49
12d	3-1/4	63
10d	3	69
9d	2-3/4	96
8d	2-1/2	106
7d	2-1/4	161
6d	2	181
5d	1-3/4	271
4d	1-1/2	316

*Source: National Lumber Mfg. Assoc.

TABLE II. WIRE NAILS: KINDS AND QUANTITIES REQUIRED

Length, in inches	Am. Steel & Wire Co.'s Steel Wire Gage	Approx. No. to lbs.	Nailings	Sizes and Kinds of Material	Trade Names	12"	16"	20"	36"	48"
						Pounds				
2½	10¼	106	2	1x 4	8d common...	60	48	37	23	20
2½	10¼	106	2	1x 6	8d common...	40	32	25	16	13
2½	10¼	106	2	1x 8	8d common...	31	27	20	12	10
2½	10¼	106	2	1x10	8d common...	25	20	16	10	8
2½	10¼	106	3	1x12	8d common...	31	24	20	12	10
4	6	31	2	2x 4	20d common...	105	80	65	60	33
4	6	31	2	2x 6	20d common...	70	54	43	27	22
4	6	31	2	2x 8	20d common...	53	40	53	21	17
4	6	31	3	2x10	20d common...	60	50	40	25	20
4	6	31	3	2x12	20d common...	52	41	33	21	17
6	2	11	2	3x 4	60d common...	197	150	122	76	61
6	2	11	2	3x 6	60d common...	131	97	82	52	42
6	2	11	2	3x 8	60d common...	100	76	61	38	34
6	2	11	3	3x10	60d common...	178	137	110	70	55
6	2	11	3	3x12	60d common...	145	115	92	58	46
2½	12½	189	2	Base, per 100 ft lin...	8d finish......	....	1	....	....	....
2½	10¼	106	2	Byrket lath...	8d common...	....	48	....	....	....
2½	12½	189	1	Ceiling, ¾x4.........	8d finish......	18	14	....	....	....
2	13	309	1	Ceiling, ½ and ⅝....	6d finish......	11	8	....	....	....
2½	12½	189	2	Finish, ⅞............	8d finish......	25	12	....	....	....
3	11½	121	2	Finish, 1⅛..........	10d finish......	12	10	....	....	....
2½	10	99	1	Flooring, 1x3........	8d floor brads.	42	32	....	....	....
2½	10	99	1	Flooring, 1x4........	8d floor brads.	32	26	....	....	....
2½	10	99	1	Flooring, 1x6........	8d floor brads.	22	18	....	....	....
4	6	31		Framing, 2x4 to 2x16	20d common..	20	16	14		
3½	8	49		requires 3 or more sizes	16d common..	10	10	8		
3	9	69		and varies greatly.	10d common..	8	6	5		
6	2	11		Framing, 3x4 to 3x14	60d common..	30	25	20		
2½	11½	145	2	Siding, drop, 1x4.....	8d casing.	45	35	....		
2½	11½	145	2	Siding, drop, 1x6.....	8d casing.	30	25	....		
2½	11½	145	2	Siding, drop, 1x8.....	8d casing.	23	18	....		
2	13	309	1	Siding, bevel, ½x4....	6d finish..	23	18	....		
2	13	309	1	Siding, bevel, ½x6....	6d finish..	15	13	....		
2	13	309	1	Siding, bevel, ½x8....	6d finish..	12	10	....		
				Casing, per opening...	6d and 8d casing......	About ½ pound per side.				
1¼	14	568	12" o c	Flooring, ⅜x2........	3d brads......	About 10 pounds per 1000 square feet.				
1⅛	15	778	16" o c	Lath, 48"............	3d sterilized blued lath...	6 pounds per 1000 pieces.				
⅞	12	469	2" o c	Ready roofing........	Barbed roofing.	¾ of a pound to the sq.				
⅞	12	469	1" o c	Ready roofing........	Barbed roofing.	1½ pounds to the square.				
⅞	12	180	2" o c	Ready roofing........ (⅝ heads)	American felt roofing.....	1½ pounds to the square.				
⅞	12	180	1" o c	Ready roofing........ (⅝ heads)	American felt roofing.....	3 pounds to the square.				
1¼	13	429	....	Shingles*.........	3d shingle.....	4½ pounds; about 2 nails to each 4 inches.				
1½	12	274	....	Shingles............	4d shingle.....	7½ pounds; about 2 nails to each 4 inches.				
⅞	12	180	4	Shingles............	American felt roofing	12 lbs., 4 nails to shingle.				
⅞	12	469	4	Shingles............	Barbed roofing.	4½ lbs., 4 nails to shingle.				
1	16	1150	2" o.c.	Wall board, around entire edge...........	Plaster board nails flat head	5 pounds, per 1,000 square feet.				
1	15½	1010	3" o.c.	Wall board, intermediate nailings.......	2d...........	2½ lbs., per 1,000 square feet.				

Notes spanning the "Sizes and Kinds of Material" section:

I. Used square edge, as platforms, floors, sheathing, or shiplap.

II. When used D & M, blind nailed, only ½ quantity named required.

(Siding and Casing trade names marked: or 7d Siding Nails)

*Wood shingles vary in width; asphalt are usually 8 inches wide. Regardless of width 1000 shingles are the equivalent of 1000 pieces 4 inches wide.

Courtesy American Steel & Wire Co.

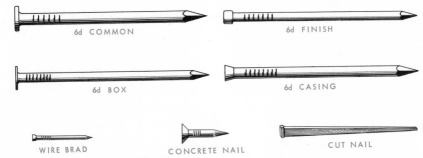

Fig. 4. Commonly used types of nails.

Kinds of Nails. *Common nails,* (Fig. 4) are available from 2d to 60d in length. As their name implies, they are the most commonly used kind of nail, and will usually be supplied if no other specification is made. They are used when the appearance of the work is not important; for example in the framing-in ‘of houses, and building of concrete forms.

Box nails, (Fig. 4) are similar in appearance to common nails, however they are not quite as thick and are only obtainable from 2d to 40d in size. Their applications are similar to common nails except that they are used on wood that splits easily.

Finish nails, (Fig. 4) are available in lengths from 2d to 20d. The head is barrel shaped and has a slight recess in the top. As the name implies, these nails are used for finished work where the final appearance is of importance, such as trimming in buildings, cupboards, and cabinets, as are any nails with small heads. The small head is intended to be sunk into the wood with a nail set.

Casing nails, (Fig. 4) are similar to finish nails with these exceptions; the head is conical, it is a thicker nail than the finish nail and it is available in lengths from 2d to 40d. It is used in finish work where the wood in which it is used is heavy enough to take a thicker nail than a finish nail. The use of this nail is governed by the knowledge and judgment of the carpenter.

Brad nail lengths (Fig. 4) are specified in inches, from $\frac{3}{16}$ inch to 3 inches. They can be obtained in a lighter gage than finish nails, from 20 to 10 gage. Brad nails are used for finish work.

Concrete nails (Fig. 4) are not specified by the penny system. They are available in lengths from $\frac{1}{2}$ inch to 3 inches, with a sinker head, and are usually hardened. Concrete nails are comparatively thick, from 10 gage to 5 gage and are used to fasten wood or metal to concrete, or masonry.

Cut nails (Fig. 4) are available from 2d to 20d in length; they are made by a shearing process from flat nail plate. For most applications, wire nails are now used instead of cut nails, but since cut nails cut the wood fibres and drive with the wood grain, they are less likely to split the wood, and are also used for fastening wood to harder materials like concrete. Cut nails are used for fastening wood to concrete and masonry. They can be obtained case-hardened.

Roofing nails (Fig. 5) are not specified by the penny system, they are available in lengths from ¾ inch to 2 inches, and have large cooler heads. Roofing nails are used to apply asphalt shingles, short ones on new roofs and long ones for re-roofing. They are also used to apply composition sheathing (Celotex, Firtex) to the studs. Most roofing nails are galvanized.

Shingle nails (Fig. 5) are sized from 3d to 6d. They are used for cedar shingles and have thin shanks with small heads. Two nails are used for each shingle.

Gypsum board nails (Fig. 5) are specified by their actual length; 1 inch to 1¾ inches. They are blue in color and are sterilized, for the carpenter usually holds them in his mouth while working. They are used for applying both rock lath and gypsum board. Rock lath is a base for plastering. Gypsum board or drywall is a finished product.

Masonry nails (Fig. 5) are hardened electrogalvanized and coated, their lengths range from 1¾ inches to 2½ inches. One of the uses is to apply galvanized area-way wall to the foundation wall of a building.

Double head nails (Fig. 5) are specified by the penny system, and are used in temporary construction such as form work and scaffolds. The advantage of using this nail is that it is easy to remove because the collar keeps the head away from the wood and the claws of a hammer can easily engage the head for removal. This eliminates the need to strike pieces of lumber to get them apart,

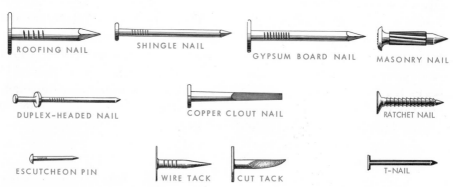

ROOFING NAIL SHINGLE NAIL GYPSUM BOARD NAIL MASONRY NAIL

DUPLEX-HEADED NAIL COPPER CLOUT NAIL RATCHET NAIL

ESCUTCHEON PIN WIRE TACK CUT TACK T-NAIL

Fig. 5. Some special types of nails.

which preserves the timber and extends its useful life.

Clout nails (Fig. 5) vary in length from ¾ of an inch to 1½ inches. Unlike most other nails the clout nail is intended to go through the second piece of material and then be clinched (bent over) for greater holding power. A *boat* nail is used in a similar manner.

Ratchet nails (Fig. 5) are a special type of annular nail used for nailing into metal studs to hold drywall and gypsum lath. The heightened annual rings hold on the V of the metal stud.

The *T-nail* (Fig. 5) is a specially designed nail used in pneumatic nailing machines. Common nails can be used in some nailing machines.

Escutcheon pins (Fig. 5) range from ³⁄₁₆ inch to 2 inches long. This nail is considered a finish nail, because it matches the hardware with which it is used. Escutcheon pins are used for fastening metal trim on store fixtures, and house numbers, where the nail heads will show.

Tacks (Fig. 5) are sold by weight, and are available as both wire tacks and cut tacks, as shown in Fig. 5. The larger the number of the tack, the longer it is. For example, a #8 tack is ⁹⁄₁₆ of an inch in length, a #6 is ½ of an inch. Some tacks are sterilized so that the carpenter can hold them in his mouth; they are also available with a galvanized or copper finish.

Staples are used to fasten metal, in the form of fence wire or metal screens to wood. They are also used for installing insulation or acoustical tile. Special tools in the form of tackers and staple hammers are often used to drive staples. Fig. 6 shows a selection of staples and on the left a new kind of staple which has great holding power due to its annular shank.

Dowel pins (Fig. 6) have no head. They are available from ¾ inch to 2½ inches in length, and have a barbed shank for greater holding power. They are used in mortise and tenon joints, and must be set.

Lead capped nails (Fig. 6) have a lead head which seals the nail hole. They are used for exterior work such as roof flashing and metal siding.

FENCE STAPLE   FENCE STAPLE   LEAD-CAPPED NAIL

DOWEL PIN   ROOFING NAIL (SCREW SHANK)   ROOFING NAIL (PLAIN SHANK)

Fig. 6. Nails and staples for special uses.

Lead capped nails are sold by weight.

Roofing nails with neoprene washers (Fig. 6) range in size from 1¾ inches to 2½ inches and are not specified by the penny system. They are obtainable with both plain and helical shanks, and are used for aluminum and fiberglass roof and siding installations. The helical shank provides greater holding power, while the neoprene washer makes a weather-proof seal.

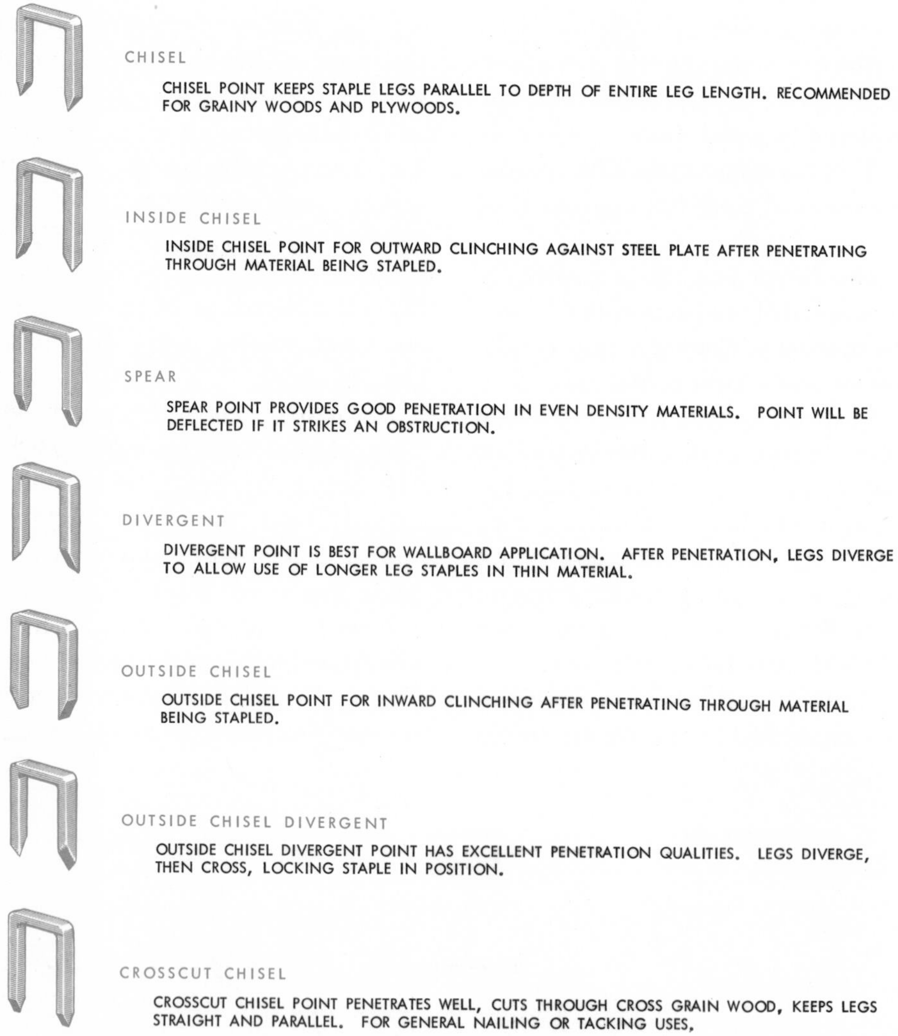

CHISEL

CHISEL POINT KEEPS STAPLE LEGS PARALLEL TO DEPTH OF ENTIRE LEG LENGTH. RECOMMENDED FOR GRAINY WOODS AND PLYWOODS.

INSIDE CHISEL

INSIDE CHISEL POINT FOR OUTWARD CLINCHING AGAINST STEEL PLATE AFTER PENETRATING THROUGH MATERIAL BEING STAPLED.

SPEAR

SPEAR POINT PROVIDES GOOD PENETRATION IN EVEN DENSITY MATERIALS. POINT WILL BE DEFLECTED IF IT STRIKES AN OBSTRUCTION.

DIVERGENT

DIVERGENT POINT IS BEST FOR WALLBOARD APPLICATION. AFTER PENETRATION, LEGS DIVERGE TO ALLOW USE OF LONGER LEG STAPLES IN THIN MATERIAL.

OUTSIDE CHISEL

OUTSIDE CHISEL POINT FOR INWARD CLINCHING AFTER PENETRATING THROUGH MATERIAL BEING STAPLED.

OUTSIDE CHISEL DIVERGENT

OUTSIDE CHISEL DIVERGENT POINT HAS EXCELLENT PENETRATION QUALITIES. LEGS DIVERGE, THEN CROSS, LOCKING STAPLE IN POSITION.

CROSSCUT CHISEL

CROSSCUT CHISEL POINT PENETRATES WELL, CUTS THROUGH CROSS GRAIN WOOD, KEEPS LEGS STRAIGHT AND PARALLEL. FOR GENERAL NAILING OR TACKING USES.

Fig. 7. Various types of staple points. (California State Department of Education)

Staples

Various kinds and sizes of staples are now commonly being used in both pneumatic and manually operated staplers. Many of these are used in building construction. The type of point often determines the use. Fig. 7 illustrates the types of points that staples may have. Steel, aluminum, bronze, and other metals are used to make staples. Steel, however, is most commonly used. A galvanized finish is available. Some staples are acid etched. Staples with various coatings are available, such as cement, nylon, paint, etc.

Hundreds of different types of staples are manufactured.

Manufacturer's catalogs should be consulted for the particular type to do a specific job. The crown width, the length, the type of point, and the wire gage varies. Crown width commonly varies from ⅜ of an inch to 1 inch. Length commonly varies from ½ of an inch to 2 inches. The wire gage is commonly 14 or 16 gage. Figs. 8 and 9 illustrate the various sizes for two typical types of staples. Staples come glued together for insertion into the stapler. The type and the size of the staple should be chosen to fit the specific job. The staple, of course, must fit the stapling device used.

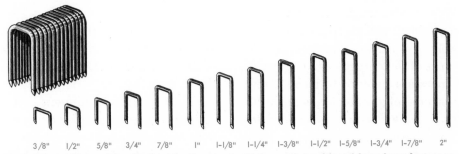

3/8" 1/2" 5/8" 3/4" 7/8" 1" 1-1/8" 1-1/4" 1-3/8" 1-1/2" 1-5/8" 1-3/4" 1-7/8" 2"

Fig. 8. These heavy duty staples are the most widely used machine driven long fasteners. They are available in 14, 15, or 16 gage, and in ⅜ to 2 inch lengths. (Spotnails, Inc.)

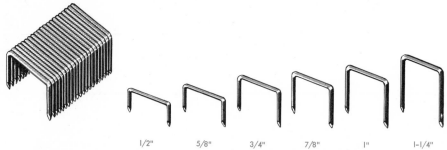

1/2"   5/8"   3/4"   7/8"   1"   1-1/4"

Fig. 9. The wide crown staples have a 1 inch crown and vary in length from ½ to 1¼ inch. They are used for crating, butt joining, asphalt shingles, and millwork. They provide extra width for extra bearing surface. (Spotnails, Inc.)

Screws

In addition to nails, screws are another means of fastening one member to another. Three types of screws will be considered in this chapter; wood, metal and machine screws.

Wood Screws

Wood screws are used extensively for all types of work in the building trades where various materials must be fastened to wood. The most important use of wood screws probably is for fastening building hardware. Wood screws are used also for fastening in place various trim members, as well as in cabinet construction. Because of their greater holding power, screws are superior to nails. Screws also present a neater appearance and have more decorative possibilities. They have the advantage of being more easily removed with less danger

of injury to materials. However, the use of screws often is discouraged because the screws cost more than nails and besides it requires less time to drive a nail into place than it does to drive a screw.

Sizes and Shapes. Wood screws are made in about 20 different stock lengths and thicknesses, ranging from ¼ inch to 5 inches. The diameter, or screw gage, is indicated by a number. The sizes range from 0 to 24. The higher the number the greater the diameter of the screw. This is the reverse of the wire gage used to indicate the nail diameter where the smaller the gage number the thicker the nail.

There are three different kinds of standard wood screws commonly used by the trade. These are named from the shape of the head and are

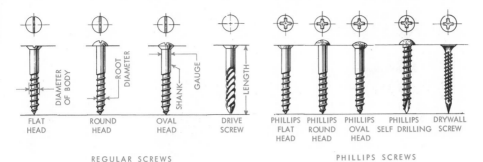

Fig. 10. Styles of standard wood screws.

known as *flat, round,* and *oval,* Fig. 10, left. Slots in the heads of screws were standardized many years ago. A more recently developed type of screw head is known as the *Phillips recessed head,* Fig. 10, right. Although this type of screw head requires a special type of screwdriver, the screw has the advantage of giving a neater appearance to the finished job. This screw also has a greater drawing power with less damage to the head when being driven into place. Another recently developed screw is the *self-drilling wood screw.* This screw has a cylindrical shank and a centered point and it cuts its own hole. It comes with a Phillips head (Fig. 10, right) or with a conventional slot head.

In addition to these screws, there are many specially designed screws ranging from the *headless* to the *ball head.*

A special flat head Phillips screw

that has come into common use is the *drywell screw,* See Fig. 10, right. A bugle head is used to prevent the drywall covering from tearing or the core from fracturing. In addition to the conventional thread (Fig. 11, top) for attaching drywall to wood framing, drywall screws also come with dual, high and low threads, see Fig. 11, bottom, for additional holding power. (The dual thread screw is recommended for attaching gypsum drywall to another gypsum panel.)

CONVENTIONAL THREADS

HIGH LOW THREADS

Fig. 11. Drywall screw thread types: conventional thread gives maximum resistance to stripping and withdrawal. High low thread gives excellent holding power. A double lead on the screw drives it quickly. (Source: U.S. Gypsum Co.)

235

DIAMOND POINT

SLOTTED DRILL POINT

Fig. 12. Drywall screw point types: *(top),* point drills into wood members without "drifting"; *(bottom),* point drills quickly through steel studs. (Source: U.S. Gypsum Co.)

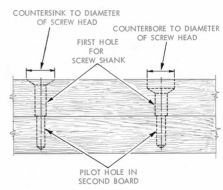

Fig. 13. Details for shank, pilot, and counterbore holes for flat head wood screws.

Two drywall points are commonly used. The diamond point, Fig. 12, top, is used for driving into wood. A slotted drill point, Fig. 12, bottom, is used for drilling into metal. In both cases the screw makes its own hole.

Drywall screws come in several different lengths. The type of drywall screw used and the length should be chosen to fit the specific job. A power screwdriver is commonly used for setting drywall screws.

When applying screws it is often necessary to bore pilot holes to receive them, especially in hardwoods, Fig. 13. This practice of boring pilot holes insures drawing of the materials together tightly. The pilot holes also make driving of the screws much easier and prevent damage to the screw as well as to the materials. The bit sizes which should be used when boring pilot holes and shank clearance holes for different sizes of screw gages are shown in Table III.

Finishes. Screws are made principally of steel although some screws are made of brass, copper, and bronze. The brass, copper, and bronze screws are used where corrosive action from moisture, chemical solution, or fumes require this type of screw. To meet the demand for decorative as well as utility values, screws are also made in the following finishes:

Nickel	Silver plate
Cadmium	Gold plate
Zinc phosphate	Japanned
Galvanized	Parkerized
Hot tinned	Lacquer
Spartan	Antique copper
Statuary bronze	Sand brass
Chromium	Steel blued

TABLE III. BIT SIZES FOR BORING PILOT HOLES AND SHANK CLEARANCE HOLES FOR WOOD SCREWS

NUMBER OF SCREW	BIT OR DRILL SIZES								NUMBER OF AUGER BIT (To counter-bore for sinking head by 16ths) Slotted or Phillips
	For Shank Clearance Holes		For Pilot Holes						
			Hardwoods				Softwoods		
	Twist Bit (Nearest size in fractions of an inch) Slotted or Phillips	Drill Gauge No. or Letter (To be used for maximum holding power) Slotted or Phillips	Twist Bit (Nearest size in fractions of an inch)		Drill Gauge No. (To be used for maximum holding power)		Twist Bit (Nearest size in fractions of an inch)		Drill Gauge No. (To be used for maximum holding power)	
			Slotted	Phillips	Slotted	Phillips	Slotted	Phillips	Slotted	Phillips	
0	1/16	52	1/32	—	70	—	1/64	—	75	—	—
1	5/64	47	1/32	—	66	—	1/32	—	71	—	—
2	3/32	42	3/64	1/32	56	70	1/32	1/64	65	75	3
3	7/64	37	1/16	1/32	54	66	3/64	1/32	58	71	4
4	7/64	32	1/16	3/64	52	56	3/64	1/32	55	65	4
5	1/8	30	5/64	1/16	49	54	1/16	3/64	53	58	4
6	9/64	27	5/64	1/16	47	52	1/16	3/64	52	55	5
7	5/32	22	3/32	5/64	44	49	1/16	3/64	51	53	5
8	11/64	18	3/32	5/64	40	47	5/64	1/16	48	52	6
9	3/16	14	7/64	3/32	37	44	5/64	1/16	45	51	6
10	3/16	10	7/64	3/32	33	40	3/32	5/64	43	48	6
11	13/64	4	1/8	7/64	31	37	3/32	5/64	40	45	7
12	7/32	2	1/8	7/64	30	33	7/64	3/32	38	43	7
14	1/4	D	9/64	1/8	25	31	7/64	3/32	32	40	8
16	17/64	I	5/32	1/8	18	30	9/64	7/64	29	38	9
18	19/64	N	3/16	9/64	13	25	9/64	7/64	26	32	10
20	21/64	P	13/64	5/32	4	18	11/64	9/64	19	29	11
24	3/8	V	7/32	3/16	1	13	3/16	9/64	15	26	12

Metal Screws

Metal trim is rapidly replacing wood trim in fireproof construction. Since carpenters also apply metal trim they should become familiar with some of the fastenings used with metal.

Sheet-Metal Screws. Self-tapping screws are used in sheet-metal work, shown in Fig. 14. The larger sizes are driven into clean-punched or drilled holes, but in lighter metal

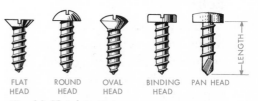

FLAT HEAD   ROUND HEAD   OVAL HEAD   BINDING HEAD   PAN HEAD   LENGTH

Fig. 14. Metal screws.

only pierced holes are necessary for starting the screws. These screws come in lengths ranging from 1/8 of an inch to 2 inches with diameters

237

ranging from a No. 2 to No. 14 screw gauge. This type of screw is used to fasten two pieces of metal together without riveting or soldering. The pan head metal screw has a self drilling point and is used for fastening metal studs to metal, such as metal stud runner.

Metal screws are used in light steel framing. Houses and all other buildings now being built by carpenters of steel plates and studs, along with joists and other parts of the structure, are being assembled by means of sheet metal screws. An example of such practice is the quonset hut.

Machine Screws. For the assembling of metal parts, *machine screws* are used. These screws are made regularly in steel and brass with the four types of heads—*flat, round, oval,* and *fillister*—shown in Fig. 15.

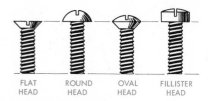

FLAT HEAD ROUND HEAD OVAL HEAD FILLISTER HEAD

Fig. 15. Machine screws.

The same style can be obtained also in the Phillips recessed heads. Sizes are designated as to length in inches, from $\frac{1}{8}$ of an inch to 3 inches, and as to diameter, from $\frac{1}{16}$ of an inch to $\frac{3}{8}$ inch or more. The number of threads per inch may vary, depending upon the standard used.

Machine screws are used to fasten butt hinges to metal jambs, lock cases, and door closers to their brackets. They are available with both coarse and fine threads.

Bolts

Bolts are another means of fastening one member to another. Let us consider the machine bolt, carriage bolt, lag bolt or screw, stove bolt and handrail bolt.

Machine Bolts. These have square heads and like most bolts, come with a nut (Fig. 16). Their lengths range from $\frac{3}{4}$ inch to 30 inches. They are used for heavy construction. The diameter of the bolt is the same as the thickness

of the nut. Hexagon heads and nuts can usually be obtained by special order. One use of these bolts is the fastening of the beam to the stanchion in house construction.

Carriage Bolts. This bolt has an oval head and a square shank just under the head to prevent the bolt from turning (Fig. 16). Lengths range from $\frac{3}{4}$ inch to 20 inches. They are sold with nuts and the threads are the same as those of

| CARRIAGE BOLT | MACHINE BOLT | LAG BOLT | FLAT HEAD STOVE BOLT | ROUND HEAD STOVE BOLT | HANDRAIL BOLT |

Fig. 16. Types of commonly used bolts.

machine bolts. When it is necessary to nail to a metal surface, a strip of wood known as a nailer is first fastened to the metal surface, and carriage bolts are often used for this purpose since the head is pulled into the wood, permitting other members to be nailed to the nailer without interference from the bolt head.

Lag Bolts or Screws. A bolt that does not have nuts, since the threads are self binding (Fig. 16). They are used to fasten wood to metal, except when used as the medium with lag expansion shields. Their length ranges from 1 inch to 16 inches. They are used in heavy construction.

Stove Bolts, with Round or Flat Heads. Stove bolts range in length from 3/8 inch to 6 inches (Fig. 16). They have either round or flat heads, and are used in light construction. Stove bolts up to 2 inches in length are threaded to the head and those longer than 2 inches are threaded to a maximum of 2 inches.

Handrail Bolts or Screws. These bolts are sold in one size only, 5/16 inch in diameter and 3 3/8 inches long (Fig. 16). Handrail bolts are used to fasten sections of stair handrail together, and have self-binding threads on one end and nut on the other. These devices are supplied with the stair crooks.

Anchors

The following descriptions are not intended to be a complete list, but rather a representative cross-section of available devices.

The fastening of wood and other materials to concrete and masonry has always been a problem for the carpenter. Anchors and fastenings

239

for such work can be divided into three general categories. The first group includes anchors installed *during* the initial construction. The second group includes anchors installed in solid concrete or masonry *after* the initial construction. The third group includes anchors installed in hollow masonry (or plaster which has a hollow space behind it) after the initial construction.

Anchors Installed During Construction

Several different types of connectors are used to fasten wood to masonry.

Anchor Bolts. These bolts are used to fasten sills to masonry foundations. Anchor bolts are also used to fasten the plate to brick walls. See Fig. 17.

Ties and Metal Straps. Ties (Fig. 18, left) are used to secure siding to masonry walls. Metal ties are used to hold the masonry wall and the frame superstructure together. Joists are sometimes fastened to walls by a metal strip at the center of the span, Fig. 18, right.

The ends of joists also anchored to masonry walls. See Fig. 19. The ends of the joists are cut so that in the event of fire the falling joist will not rupture the side of the building.

Sleeper Clips. Metal clips are used to embed and anchor wooden sleepers in concrete, Fig. 20. These wooden sleepers are used to provide a base for nailing. Sleeper clips are available 2, 3, and 4 inches wide.

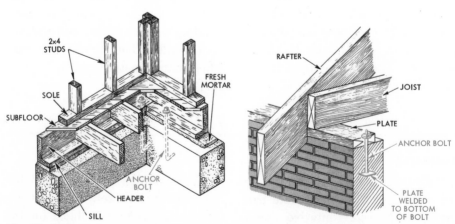

Fig. 17. Anchor bolts are used to secure the sill to the foundation and plate to brick wall.

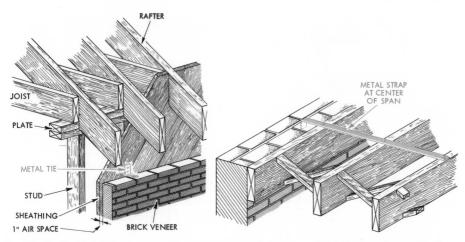

Fig. 18. *(Left)* Metal tie secures frame and masonry veneer. *(Right)* Strap connects floor and wall.

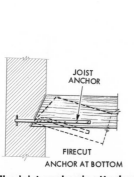

Fig. 19. The joist anchor is attached at the bottom. Dashed line shows how joist would fall without breaking the wall.

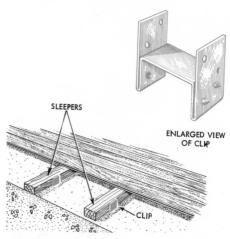

Fig. 20. Sleeper clips.

Anchors Installed After Initial Construction in Concrete or Solid Masonry

Star Dryvin Expansion Device. This is furnished complete with either single or double head nail, Fig. 21. Lengths range from ⅞ inch to 3½ inches. The shield holds the fixture, while the nail expands the lead wrapper on the bottom end.

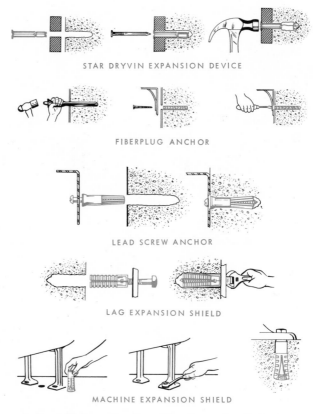

STAR DRYVIN EXPANSION DEVICE

FIBERPLUG ANCHOR

LEAD SCREW ANCHOR

LAG EXPANSION SHIELD

MACHINE EXPANSION SHIELD

Fig. 21. Anchors used after initial construction. (Star Expansion Co.)

Rawlplug Anchor. A fiber anchor that is fitted with a hollow metal core for use with wood screws. It can be used in almost any material, and is not affected by temperature, moisture, shock or vibration. Sizes run 6, 8, 10, 12, and 14. These size numbers refer to the size of screw for which they were designed although they will take one size smaller. Larger sizes are designed for use with lag screws.

Lead Screw Anchors. These are used in a similar way to rawl-plugs, and take three different sizes of screw, Fig. 21. Lengths range from ¾ inch to 1¾ inches.

Plastic Anchors. Plastic anchors are now being commonly used for light loads. These are similar in appearance to the lead screw anchors. Sheet metal screws are used to expand the anchor.

Expansion Screw Anchors.

These may take a machine screw or the larger sizes take a machine bolt. They consist of two parts, the conical member is tapped, and a lead sleeve slides over it. A pilot setting punch which comes with this anchor sets the lead sleeve tight in the hole. Sizes range from ⅛ inch machine screw to 1 inch machine bolt.

Lag Expansion Shields. These (Fig. 21) take a lag bolt. There is no nut in these anchors. The lag bolt screws itself further in as it is tightened. Used in heavy construction, sizes vary from ¼ inch to ¾ inch.

Machine Expansion Shields. These take a machine bolt, and are used in heavy construction, Fig. 21. There is a tapered nut in the bottom which locks when the bolt is tightened, and thereafter will be securely anchored even if the bolt is removed. The smaller sizes are for ¼ inch bolts and the larger ones for up to 1 inch bolts.

Pin Bolt Drives. They are available with flat or round heads. The diameter is ¼ inch and the length ranges from ¼ inch to 2 inches. They are used in concrete or solid masonry. The fixture is inserted in a prepared hole, and then the furnished pin is driven in.

Self Drilling Snap-Off Anchors. The fastener itself drills the hole and is then snapped off and left in place. The insertion of a screw

expands the fastener to give a secure hold.

They may be drilled into place by an impact hammer or by a specially designed manual tool. Fig. 22 illustrates the self drilling snap off anchor and the method by which it is installed. Goggles should be worn when installing this anchor.

Hammer Driven Fasteners. The studs (Fig. 23) are driven directly into steel and concrete using a tool guide and hammer. (See Chapter III.) No predrilling is necessary. The hammer driven fastener is used for the same purposes as the powder driven fastener. (See Fig. 24.) However, with the hammer driven fastener no explosives are necessary. The safety procedures are simple and possibility of accident is greatly reduced.

Powder Driven Fasteners. This tool may be used throughout the job for attaching fasteners into concrete, steel, and other difficult-to-penetrate materials. The manufacturer's specifications should be consulted on how to use this fastener and what materials it may be used with. Certification is required for the operation of this tool; safety goggles must always be worn. (See Chapter III for detailed safety information on the use of this fastening device.)

Several different types of fasteners may be used with powder fastening tools. Fig. 24 shows the pins

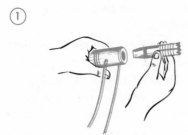

Insert tapered end of snap-off anchor into chuck head attached to any impact hammer.

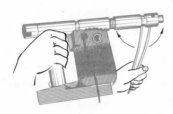

Operate impact hammer to drill into the concrete. Rotate chuck handle while drilling.

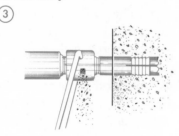

The drill is self-cleaning. Cuttings pass through the core and holes in the chuck head.

Withdraw the drill and remove grit and cuttings from the drill core and from the hole.

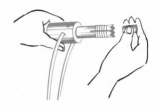

Insert hardened steel cone-shaped red expander plug in cutting end of drill.

Reinsert the plugged drill in the hole and operate the hammer to expand anchor.

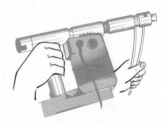

Snap off chucking end of anchor with a quick lateral strain on the hammer.

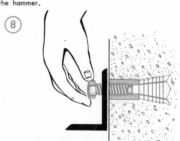

The anchor is now ready to serve as an internally threaded steel bolt hole to support any bolted object.

Fig. 22. Installation of snap-off type anchor. A wide selection of anchor sizes and lengths are available. (Phillips Drill Co.)

THREADED STUDS			SCREW FASTENERS		DRIVE PINS				WIRE LOOP FASTENERS		
Use 1/4 - 20 nut			No. 10 screw thread		For concrete or steel						
*SHANK LENGTH	THREAD LENGTH	STUD DIA.	HEAD DIA.	LENGTH	LENGTH	SHANK DIA.	LENGTH	SHANK DIA.	OVERALL LENGTH	SHANK LENGTH	SHANK DIA.
3/4	3/8	5/32	5/16	1/2	1/2	1/8	1-1/2	9/64	1-3/8	3/4	5/32
3/4	5/8	5/32			3/4	1/8	2	5/32	1-5/8	1	5/32
1-1/4	3/8	5/32	5/16	3/4	1	9/64	2-1/2	5/32	1-7/8	1-1/4	5/32
1-1/4	5/8	5/32	5/16	1	1-1/4	9/64	3	5/32	LOOPS - 1/2, 5/8, 7/8, 1-1/4		

DRILL HOLDER adaptor for guide tool, discs for greater head bearing surface and shock reducing hammers available.
*Threaded studs of 2-1/2 and 3-1/4 in. available; these require barrel extension adaptor.

Fig. 23. Hammer driven studs. *(Practical Builder)*

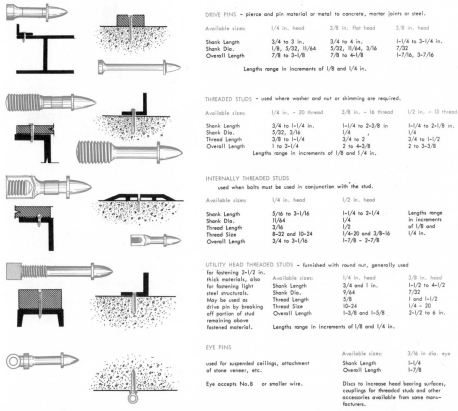

DRIVE PINS – pierce and pin material or metal to concrete, mortar joints or steel.

Available sizes:	1/4 in. head	3/8 in. flat head	3/8 in. head
Shank Length	3/4 to 3 in.	3/4 to 4 in.	1-1/4 to 3-1/4 in.
Shank Dia.	1/8, 5/32, 11/64	5/32, 11/64, 3/16	7/32
Overall Length	7/8 to 3-1/8	7/8 to 4-1/8	1-7/16, 3-7/16

Lengths range in increments of 1/8 and 1/4 in.

THREADED STUDS – used where washer and nut or shimming are required.

Available sizes:	1/4 in. - 20 thread	3/8 in. - 16 thread	1/2 in. - 13 thread
Shank Length	3/4 to 1-1/4 in.	1-1/4 to 2-3/8 in	1-1/4 to 2-1/8 in.
Shank Dia.	5/32, 3/16	1/4	1/4
Thread Length	3/8 to 1-1/4	3/4 to 2	3/4 to 1-1/2
Overall Length	1 to 3-1/4	2 to 4-3/8	2 to 3-3/8

Lengths range in increments of 1/8 and 1/4 in.

INTERNALLY THREADED STUDS
used when bolts must be used in conjunction with the stud.

Available sizes:	1/4 in. head	1/2 in. head	
Shank Length	5/16 to 3-1/16	1-1/4 to 2-1/4	Lengths range
Shank Dia.	11/64	1/4	in increments
Thread Length	3/16	1/2	of 1/8 and
Thread Size	8-32 and 10-24	1/4-20 and 3/8-16	1/4 in.
Overall Length	3/4 to 3-1/16	1-7/8 - 2-7/8	

UTILITY HEAD THREADED STUDS – furnished with round nut, generally used for fastening 2-1/2 in. thick materials, also for fastening light steel structurals. May be used as drive pin by breaking off portion of stud remaining above fastened material.

Available sizes:	1/4 in. head	3/8 in. head
Shank Length	3/4 and 1 in.	1-1/2 to 4-1/2
Shank Dia.	9/64	7/32
Thread Length	5/8	1 and 1-1/2
Thread Size	10-24	1/4 - 20
Overall Length	1-3/8 and 1-5/8	2-1/2 to 6 in.

Lengths range in increments of 1/8 and 1/4 in.

EYE PINS
used for suspended ceilings, attachment of stone veneer, etc.

Eye accepts No. 8 or smaller wire.

Available sizes:	3/16 in dia. eye
Shank Length	1-1/4
Overall Length	1-7/8

Discs to increase head bearing surfaces, couplings for threaded studs and other accessories available from some manufacturers.

Fig. 24. Common type of powder driven fasteners; a large variety of sizes and lengths are available. Plastic tip keeps stud in place and is dissipated when the fastener is fired. *(Practical Builder)*

and studs used, and illustrates their common application. Fasteners come in a wide variety of lengths and sizes. In selecting a fastener, make sure that it is the proper fastener for the job; it must be the correct length and size, it must be suitable for use with the material to be penetrated, and it must fit the particular powder fastener gun being used.

As may be seen in Fig. 24, pins and studs are commonly used to fasten steel to steel, wood to steel, steel to concrete and wood to concrete. Pins may be driven through the two materials to be fastened in one operation. Studs are driven into the base material and the material to be fastened is bored and bolted on the base material.

Anchors Installed in Hollow Masonry or Plaster Which Has a Clear Space Behind It

Toggle Bolts. These, Fig. 25, top, have a wing head which is fitted with interior springs which cause the head to open after it has passed through the hole. An advantage of the spring wing toggle is that the constant tension on the machine screw helps to absorb vibration. Toggle bolts (tumble) (Fig. 25, middle) are designed to be used horizontally and are not recommended for vertical use. The sizes for both types range from ⅛ inch to ½ inch machine screw.

Fig. 25. Anchors used in hollow masonry. (Star Expansion Co.)

Hollow Wall Screw Anchors. There is a nut set in the bottom which, when the machine screw is tightened, draws that end up tight to the back of the material in which it is used. See Fig. 25, bottom. The flange on the face remains on the outside surface of the wall, and once tightened, the screw may be removed without losing the anchor. Sizes range up to that designed for a wall 1¾ inches thick.

Metal Wood Connectors

Timber Connectors. Metal devices employed in the contact faces of lapped members to transfer loads from one member to another are know as *timber connectors*. The joints of these devices are held together by one or more bolts. They are valuable especially in heavy timber framing, such as trusses, towers, piers, and wharfs, where through their use the strength of the joints is increased manyfold,[1] thus increasing the possibilities for the use of lumber. They also sim-

[1]Strength values for timber connectors have been established by the United States Forest Products Laboratory, Madison, Wisconsin, and the Timber Engineering Company, Washington, D.C.

plify the process of connecting timbers, doing away with the former interlocking wood joint, which required much more time for construction.

Two types of timber connectors designated according to application are *rings* and *plates*, Fig. 26(A). Grooves are cut in the wood to receive the rings and plates; the clamping plate and spike grids placed between the timbers are forced into the wood by drawing up the bolts. Fig. 26(B) illustrates the uses of timber connectors.

Timber connectors are also commonly used with large timbers and especially with laminated arches

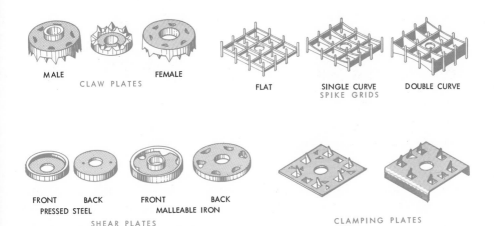

MALE   FEMALE

CLAW PLATES

FLAT   SINGLE CURVE   DOUBLE CURVE
SPIKE GRIDS

FRONT   BACK   FRONT   BACK
PRESSED STEEL   MALLEABLE IRON

SHEAR PLATES

CLAMPING PLATES

Fig. 26A. Timber connectors used with bolts.

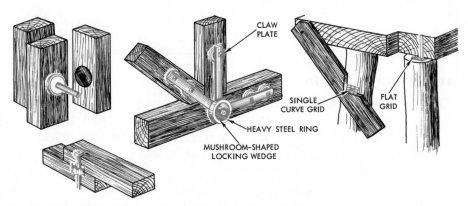

Fig. 26B. Timber connectors showing method of installation.

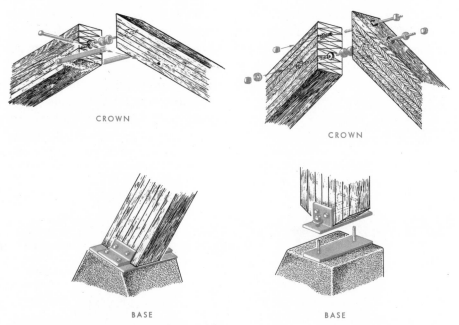

CROWN

CROWN

BASE

BASE

Fig. 27. Methods of anchoring large arches.

and beams. Figs. 27 and 28 illustrate some of the standard ways of anchoring large beams and arches.

Truss Clips. Fig. 29 illustrates a clip connector used in assembling trusses or in joining lumber end to end. Depending on the size of the connector, each clip has an effec-

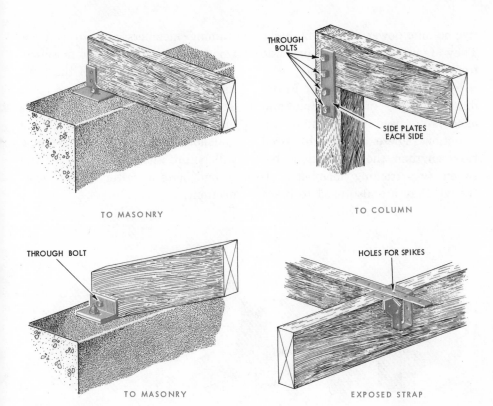

TO MASONRY

THROUGH BOLTS

SIDE PLATES EACH SIDE

TO COLUMN

THROUGH BOLT

TO MASONRY

HOLES FOR SPIKES

EXPOSED STRAP

Fig. 28. Methods of anchoring large beams.

Fig. 29. Truss clips have an effective holding power of 20 to 60 nails. (Panel Clip Co.)

249

tive holding power of 20 to 60 nails. They are either galvanized or made from a non-rusting material.

Framing Connectors. Many different types of connectors and anchors are used in residential construction. These are usually used to strengthen the connections between two framing members, although they are also used to brace framing members and to connect wood framing members to masonry. Fig. 30 illustrates some of the common types of framing anchors. Fig. 31 also shows a framing anchor that may be used in roof, wall, ceiling and floor framing. The long flange will permit the anchor to grip the second plate in rafter to plate connections.

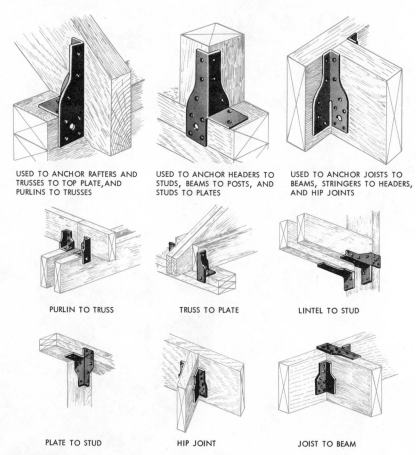

USED TO ANCHOR RAFTERS AND TRUSSES TO TOP PLATE, AND PURLINS TO TRUSSES

USED TO ANCHOR HEADERS TO STUDS, BEAMS TO POSTS, AND STUDS TO PLATES

USED TO ANCHOR JOISTS TO BEAMS, STRINGERS TO HEADERS, AND HIP JOINTS

PURLIN TO TRUSS

TRUSS TO PLATE

LINTEL TO STUD

PLATE TO STUD

HIP JOINT

JOIST TO BEAM

Fig. 30. Common types of framing anchors. (Cleveland Steel Specialty Co.)

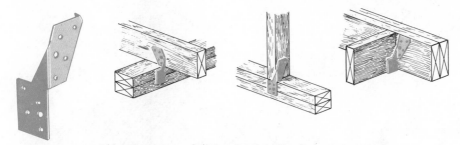

Fig. 31. Long flange framing anchor. (Timber Engineering Co.)

Joist Hangers. Hangers are used to secure a stronger connection. Fig. 32 shows two common types which may be used. They are also used to keep the joists on the same level as the header or beam they are fastened to, thereby saving headroom.

Nailing Clips. Nailing clips (Fig. 33) are often used to connect joists to steel beams and channels. This type of clip comes in various sizes to fit the steel beam used.

Wallboard Clips. Various kinds of clips are used to hold members together directly, or hold them together by tension in opposing clips. Clips may be used where there is

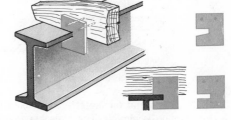

Fig. 33. Nailing clips.

no overlapping of members, and where it is desirable to have semi-independent members in construction to minimize stresses, as well as for other purposes, such as reduction of sound transmission. Various different types of clips, depending on the use, are available.

U-shaped clips and furring strips are sometimes used with drywall for both ceiling and wall construction to reduce the sound transmission. See Fig. 34. Nail "pops" are also reduced when this method of construction is used. Clips and furring strips are usually used where

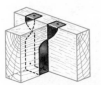

Fig. 32. Joist hangers.

251

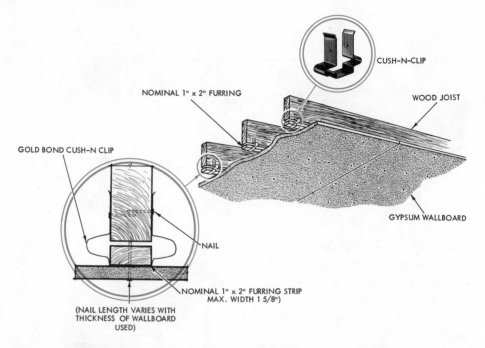

CUSH–N–CLIP

NOMINAL 1" x 2" FURRING

WOOD JOIST

GOLD BOND CUSH–N CLIP

NAIL

GYPSUM WALLBOARD

NOMINAL 1" x 2" FURRING STRIP
MAX. WIDTH 1 5/8")

(NAIL LENGTH VARIES WITH
THICKNESS OF WALLBOARD
USED)

Fig. 34. Clips and furring strips are used in "floating" ceiling construction. Floating wall construction is similar. The clips are made of spring steel which causes them to spring away from the joists after nailing. Drywall wood screws may also be used. (National Gypsum Co.)

sound transmission reduction is important, in such structures as motels, stores, offices, and apartments.

Two layers of wallboard may also be used to obtain high resistance to sound transmission. See Fig. 35. This wall system uses several different types of flexible clips to secure the ⅜" gypsum backer board; the finish wallboard is nailed or screwed to the backerboard base. Again, this type of construction is

used where sound control is desirable, in commercial buildings and between apartment party walls.

Metal Fasteners for Light Carpentry. The metal *mending plate, angle iron, tee iron, corner angle iron,* and *corrugated iron fasteners* need little explanation as they have been in general use for many years, Fig. 36. Also shown in this illustration is the *Skotch fastener,* which is a newer device. This has great holding power, is easily applied, and is

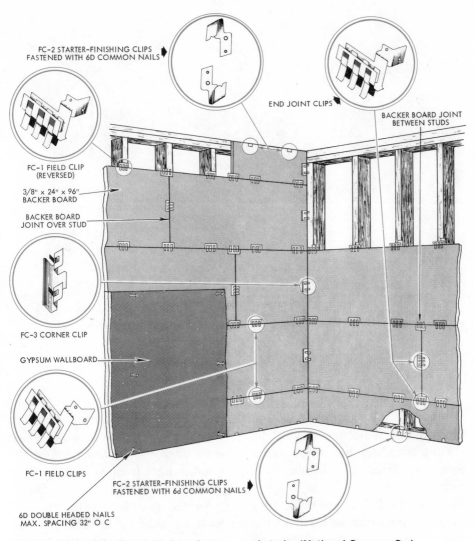

FC-2 STARTER-FINISHING CLIPS
FASTENED WITH 6D COMMON NAILS

END JOINT CLIPS

BACKER BOARD JOINT
BETWEEN STUDS

FC-1 FIELD CLIP
(REVERSED)

3/8" x 24" x 96"
BACKER BOARD

BACKER BOARD
JOINT OVER STUD

FC-3 CORNER CLIP

GYPSUM WALLBOARD

FC-1 FIELD CLIPS

FC-2 STARTER-FINISHING CLIPS
FASTENED WITH 6d COMMON NAILS

6D DOUBLE HEADED NAILS
MAX. SPACING 32" O C

Fig. 35. Clips used with backer boards over wood studs. (National Gypsum Co.)

available in two sizes. The *Miklin metal corner* is a great aid in making screens as it will insure a strong joint and eliminates the need of a mortise and tenon.

Mending plate (Fig. 36), sizes range from 2 to 12 inches; they are made of steel, or zinc plated steel. Screw holes are staggered for greater structural strength.

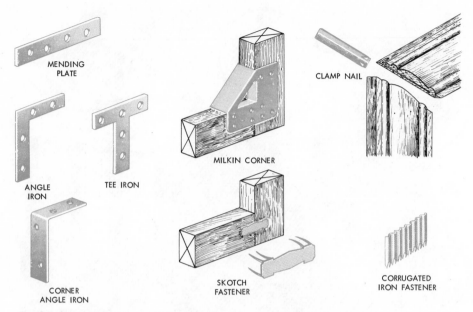

MENDING PLATE

CLAMP NAIL

ANGLE IRON

TEE IRON

MILKIN CORNER

CORNER ANGLE IRON

SKOTCH FASTENER

CORRUGATED IRON FASTENER

Fig. 36. Metal fasteners used in cabinetmaking and other light construction work.

The *angle iron* or *plate* (Fig. 36), is made of the same materials as the mending plate and is ideal for bracing or reinforcing corner joints. Sizes are from 1½ inches to 8 inches.

T *irons* (Fig. 36), are made from the same materials as other plates, and are used for center bracing. Sizes range from 1 inch to 8 inches.

Corner angles (Fig. 36), are used for either inside or outside corners, depending upon which side of the angle is countersunk for the screw heads. Sizes range from 1 inch to 8 inches.

Corrugated fasteners (Fig. 36), are used to fasten two pieces of wood together. Their lengths range from 3 inches to 8 inches, and their depth or height, the choice of which is dictated by the thickness of the wood, ranges from ¼ inch to ⅞ of an inch.

Skotch fasteners (Fig. 36), are used for making or strengthening any type of wood joint. The curved prongs draw both sides of a joint firmly together. Skotch fasteners are available in three sizes.

Miklin metal corners (Fig. 36), are used on inside corners, and come in sizes for 1 inch and 1¼ inch wood stock. They are made of sheet metal and are nailed to the coner. A rigid corner results, because the Miklin corner acts as a diagonal brace.

Clamp nails (Fig. 36), consist of a steel spline with a clamp action that draws a joint together as it is driven into two saw kerfs; the wide end is driven in first. Clamp nails are used on elaborate stair parts, cabinets, furniture, sash and door trims.

Miscellaneous Rough Hardware

There are many other things that go into a building that may be classified as rough hardware. The type of construction (whether light or heavy) determines to a great extent the type and extent of the rough hardware. Some of this rough hardware, however, is applied by trades other than the carpenter's. Flashing, for example, is considered a rough hardware item. The carpenter, however, does not normally install flashing. *Metal corners*, on the other hand, would be installed by the carpenter. See Fig. 37.

As a general and rough rule the carpenter installs all non-wood products (and the hardware associated with them) that have replaced wood products that the carpenter normally installed in the past. Thus, carpenters install the metal bracing (Fig. 38) that has replaced the wood bracing between studs and joists. Metal furring strips and the channel for metal studs (along with the studs) are also installed by the carpenter. Trade jurisdiction agreements will determine the extent of the job.

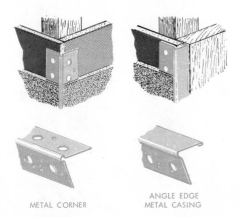

METAL CORNER

ANGLE EDGE
METAL CASING

Fig. 37. Metal corners. (Bestwall Gypsum Co.)

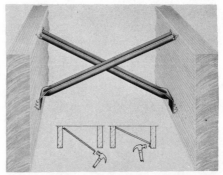

Fig. 38. Metal cross bridging may be used in place of bracing set into the face of the stud, and in place of wood bracing between joists. (Cleveland Steel Specialty Co.)

Checking on Your Knowledge

These questions will test your understanding of this chapter. If you can answer these easily, go on to the next chapter. If some of them puzzle you, go back and read over the chapter. A second reading will always bring out points you missed the first time.

DO YOU KNOW

1. How the length of a nail is specified and its abbreviation?

2. The purpose of the double-headed nail?

3. The reason of galvanizing some types of nails?

4. Why some nails are made of steel and others of aluminum, copper, or stainless steel?

5. Some advantages in using staples as fastenings?

6. The two major kinds of screws?

7. The principal use of screws?

8. When anchors are used?

9. The three kinds of installation of anchors?

10. The advantages of using metal connectors?

Hardware: Finish

Finish hardware is made up of a somewhat special group of wood fastenings in that, although widely used in carpentry, they are not considered *structural fastenings*. In other words, they are not typically used to give support to structural members, but are used mostly to permit the movement of parts, or to secure or close moving parts. Thus, most finish hardware consists of hinges, locks, catches, and pulls. Other finish hardware consists of miscellaneous items such as door stops and coat hooks.

A whole book could be devoted to the discussion of the various uses of finish hardware, their selection, and their method of installation. We can here only mention the large variety of hinges, locks, etc.

Obviously, the choice of finish hardware, whether it be a hinge, lock, or pull, depends primarily on its intended use. You would not, for instance, use a light strap hinge for a heavy hardwood door. A butt hinge would be more appropriate for such a door.

In other words, finish hardware should not only be chosen for *function*, but also for the *amount and length of service* that should be expected from it. In addition to function and service, finish hardware can also be selected for its *decorative effect*. There are many types of hardware that are similar in function and service requirements, differing only in their design or decorative value.

Hinges

A hinge is a movable joint upon which a door, gate, etc., turns. It consists primarily of a pin and two plates which may be attached to a door and the door frame to permit the opening and closing of the door. Fig. 1 illustrates the parts and basic design of a common hinge.

There are four basic hinge classification of hinges (see Fig. 2):

Full mortise
Half mortise
Full surface
Half surface

Hinges are further classified on the basis of whether a *loose pin* or a *tight pin* is employed. A loose pin may be removed; a tight pin is secured to the hinge.

Many different types of hinge are manufactured to meet various design requirements; however, the type of hinge which requires the most careful selection is the door hinge. The width, length, and weight of the door determines the weight of the hinge, and whether plain or ball bearing hinges are to be used. The width and thickness of the door determine the size of

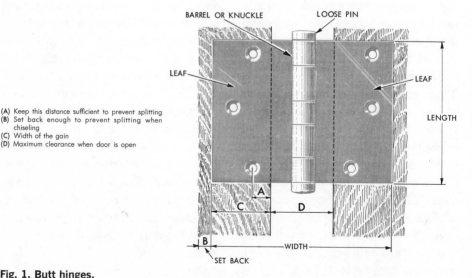

(A) Keep this distance sufficient to prevent splitting
(B) Set back enough to prevent splitting when chiseling
(C) Width of the gain
(D) Maximum clearance when door is open

Fig. 1. Butt hinges.

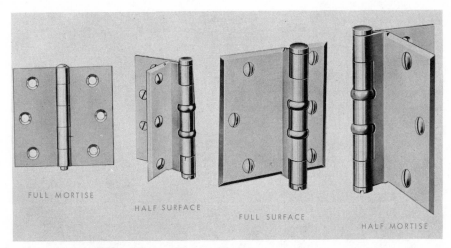

FULL MORTISE

HALF SURFACE

FULL SURFACE

HALF MORTISE

Fig. 2. A selection of door hinges. (Stanley Works)

the hinge. A rule which can be applied to the selection of door hinges is as follows:

The width of the hinge for doors up to 2¼ inches is equal to twice the thickness of the door, plus the trim projection, minus ½ inch. For doors from 2½ inches to 3 inches thick, the same rule applies, but ¾ of an inch should be subtracted instead of ½ inch. If the result of this calculation falls between regular sizes, the next larger size should be selected. Suggested rules for placement of door hinges are as follows:

Top hinge; 6-7 inches from head jamb rabbet to the top of the hinge barrel. (Or as specified.)

Bottom hinge; 10-11 inches from bottom edge of barrel to finish floor. (Or as specified.)

Third hinge; (although a third hinge is not always required, its use represents good construction practice) centered between top and bottom hinge. A selection of door hinges is shown in Fig. 2. The hinges should be set back at least ¼ inch from the edge of the door.

Ball bearing hinges (Fig. 3) are used for heavy doors, or on doors which are subjected to heavy use, such as doors in schools, office buildings and department stores.

Template hinges conform to government specifications. They will exactly fit the sinkage and screw hole locations in metal doors and jambs. They are also available with non rising pins.

Olive knuckle butt hinges (Fig. 3) have fixed pins with a loose leaf, and must be selected according to the way in which the door is to open. These hinges are longer than

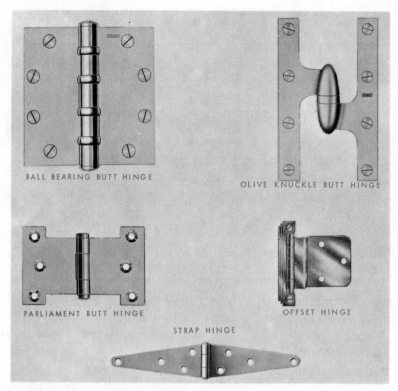

BALL BEARING BUTT HINGE

OLIVE KNUCKLE BUTT HINGE

PARLIAMENT BUTT HINGE

OFFSET HINGE

STRAP HINGE

Fig. 3. A selection of special hinges. (Stanley Works)

they are wide, and are used for cupboard and intercommunicating doors.

Parliament butt hinges (Fig. 3) have either a fixed or loose pin. They have a greater width than length and are used in churches on communion rails.

Offset hinges (Fig. 3) are used on lip cupboard doors.

Strap hinges and *T hinges* (Fig. 3) in most cases have a fixed pin. They are obtainable in light, heavy or extra heavy metal, according to their application. Strap hinges and T hinges are commonly used on carpenter-built doors and gates.

Double action spring floor hinge (Fig. 4), as its name implies, has a spring return action, which is effective in both directions. The spring action is generally concealed

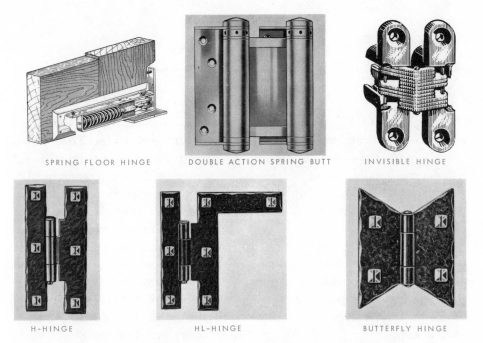

Fig. 4. Special hinges and door hardware. (Ornamental hinges: Stanley Works)

in the door in residential installations, and in the floor below the door in commercial installations. It is designed for doors which have a thickness between 1⅛ inches and 1¾ inches.

The *double action spring butt* (Fig. 4) is used in commercial installations. Its design requires a hinge strip on the jamb. It is designed for use on doors that can be pushed open from either side and will close under spring action.

Invisible hinges (Fig. 4) are made so that no portion of the hinge is visible when the door is closed. They fit snugly into a mortise cut into the door and jamb, and because of this, much of the weight of the door is taken off the screws. Invisible hinges are made to open 180 degrees and are reversible.

Many kinds of *ornamental hinges* are manufactured, and find their main use in the construction of cupboards. Illustrated in Fig. 4 are an "H" hinge, an "H-L" hinge, and a butterfly hinge.

Door Trim

Surface bolts (Fig. 5) are generally used vertically on doors, cupboards and casement windows. They are available in various weights and lengths, and it is important to select the proper strike plate.

Flush bolts (Fig. 5) are used vertically on top or bottom of doors, or both. They are made in various sizes and for many purposes. Some have a flush type lever, while others have a knob.

Extension flush bolts (Fig. 5) are used vertically, set in the edge of the inactive door of a pair of doors. They are available in various widths and their length ranges from about 5 inches to 48 inches. The lever for the top extension bolt should center about 72 inches from the floor, and the bottom, about 12 inches from the floor.

Cremone bolts (Fig. 5) are used vertically and are designed for use with large french windows and doors. They are operated by means of a knob or lever handle and open from the inside.

Barrel bolts (Fig. 5) are a surface type of bolt used horizontally. They are a less expensive variety of surface bolts and are considered rough hardware.

Chain door fasteners (Fig. 5) are made in many styles. They permit exterior doors to be opened sufficiently wide for communication and yet prevent forcible entrance.

Foot bolts (Fig. 5) are used vertically on the bottom inside surface of garage and swing doors. As their name implies, they are designed to be foot operated.

Chain bolts (Fig. 5) are used vertically on the top inside surface of doors and are considered to be the companion bolt to foot bolts. They hold the top of the door closed.

Exit fixtures (Fig. 5). Automatic exit fixtures are used on doors opening outward, and are often called "panic bars." Public buildings are required by law to use this fixture on certain exterior doors. Because human life may depend upon their proper operation, it is of the utmost importance that they be properly fitted. They are specified according to the hand of the door, for they cannot be reversed, and are obtainable in rim or mortise type.

Pneumatic door closers (Fig. 5) are used for the same purpose as hydraulic door closers, but on lightweight doors. Their checking medium is air, and a set screw adjusts

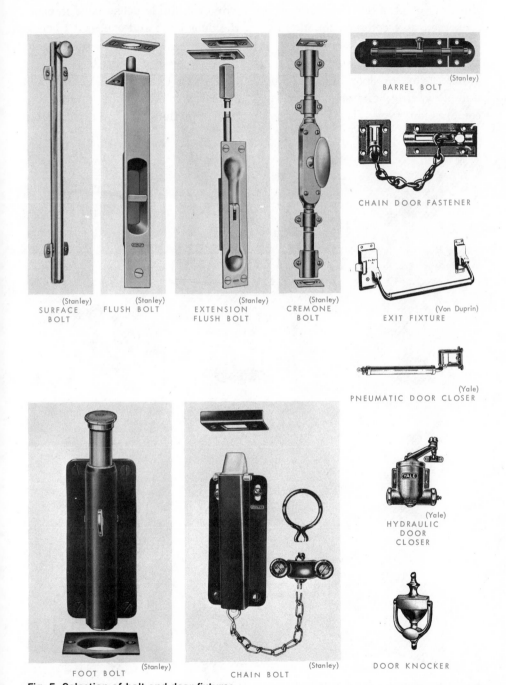

(Stanley)
BARREL BOLT

(Stanley)
SURFACE
BOLT

(Stanley)
FLUSH BOLT

(Stanley)
EXTENSION
FLUSH BOLT

(Stanley)
CREMONE
BOLT

CHAIN DOOR FASTENER

(Von Duprin)
EXIT FIXTURE

(Yale)
PNEUMATIC DOOR CLOSER

(Yale)
HYDRAULIC
DOOR
CLOSER

(Stanley)
FOOT BOLT

(Stanley)
CHAIN BOLT

DOOR KNOCKER

Fig. 5. Selection of bolt and door fixtures.

the time of closing. They are used on screen and combination doors.

Hydraulic door closers (Fig. 5) are mounted on the surface of the jamb, casing, or door bracket. The helical spring, either torsion or compression type, closes the door while the fluid checks it as it nears the door jamb and causes it to close slowly. The arm can be set to hold the door open if desired.

Door knockers (Fig. 5) add to the appearance of a door, apart from their function. They are available

DOOR STOP

BULLET CATCH

DOOR HOLDER

DOOR HOLDER

ELBOW CATCH

FRICTION CATCH

MAGNETIC CATCH

MORTISED

BAR

HOOK

Fig. 6. Miscellaneous small building hardware. (Door stop and holder: Stanley Works)

in a great number of designs and sizes, for exterior doors as well as in smaller sizes called guest room knockers, which are becoming increasingly popular.

Other Building Hardware Used on Doors and Windows

Door stops (Fig. 6) vary in style, some are used on the baseboard, while others are used on the floor. They protect the door locks and the wall from being marred or damaged.

Door holders (Fig. 6) vary in design, their purpose is to hold the door open at a given point.

Catches (Fig. 6) are used on cabinets and cupboards. The bullet catch is mortised in the edge of the door top, bottom side, or even the frame, whereas friction and elbow catches are applied to the inside surface.

Sash lifts (Fig. 6) are used on the bottom rail of double-hung windows. The flush sash lift is mortised into the rail while the bar and the hook are screwed to the rail.

Locks

Three different types of locks are commonly used in residential building construction: the tubular, the cylindrical, and the mortise lock. *Tubular lock* sets are used mainly for interior doors, for bedrooms, bathrooms, passages, and closets. They can be obtained with pin tumbler locks in the knob on the outside of the door and turn button or push button locks on the inside. There are several variations to this arrangement. Fig. 7 illustrates a tubular lock set.

Cylindrical lock sets are sturdy heavy duty locks, designed for maximum security for installation in exterior doors. See Fig. 8. Manufacturers' instructions supplied with the locks should be followed carefully.

An ordinary *mortise lock* is illustrated in Fig. 9. More elaborate mortise locks are made with cylinder locks, with a handle on one side and a knob on the other side, or with handles on both sides. This type of lock is used principally on front or outside doors. The present trend is away from using mortise locks.

When ordering lock sets for a door specify: the manufacturer's list number, the keying required, the type of strike required, the hand of the door, the door thickness, the door material, and the finish desired on the lock set. Con-

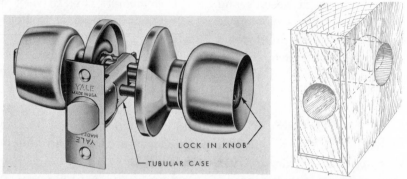

Fig. 7. Tubular lock set is installed by drilling 2 holes and mortising lock face. Locks of this type are supplied for several different applications. (Yale & Towne Mfg. Co.)

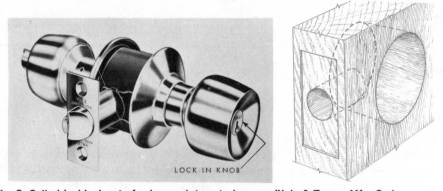

Fig. 8. Cylindrical lock sets for heavy duty exterior use. (Yale & Towne Mfg. Co.)

Fig. 9. Mortise lock. (Yale & Towne Mfg. Co.)

sult manufacturer's catalogs for specific information.

Hands of Doors. For the purpose of buying door hardware, it is necessary for the carpenter or builder to have some knowledge of the standard rules regarding locks intended for right-hand or left-hand doors or casements.

1. Whether a door is to be right-handed or left-handed is always determined from the *outside*.

2. The *outside* of a door is the street side of an entrance door and the corridor side of a room door.

The *outside* of a communicating door, that is from one room to another, is the side from which the butts or hinges are not visible when the door is closed. The *outside* of a closet, cupboard, or bookcase door is the room side, thus reversing the rule which applies to other doors.

3. When you stand *outside* a door, if the butts are on your right it is a right-handed door; if the butts are on your left it is a left-handed door. If, when standing outside, the door opens from you, or inward, it will require a lock with a

Fig. 10. When doors open away from you, they are right- or left-handed depending on which side has the butts.

Fig. 11. When doors open toward you, they are right- or left-handed depending on which side has the butts. A lock with a reverse bolt is required.

regular bevel bolt and the lock is described as either *right-handed* or *left-handed*, depending upon whether the butts are to your right or left. A lock with a regular bevel, for a right-handed door, is shown at Fig. 10, left. A lock with a regular bevel, for a left-handed door, is shown at Fig. 10, right. If, when standing outside the door, it opens toward you or outward, the door will require a lock with a reverse bolt and the lock is described as a *right-handed* or *left-handed* lock, depending upon whether the butts are to your right or left. A right-handed lock with a reverse bolt is shown at Fig. 11, left. A left-handed lock with a reverse bolt is shown at Fig. 11, right.

Fig. 12 shows how the door hand would look when viewed properly. In ordering, specify LH, RH, LHR, or RHR if the lock is not reversible.

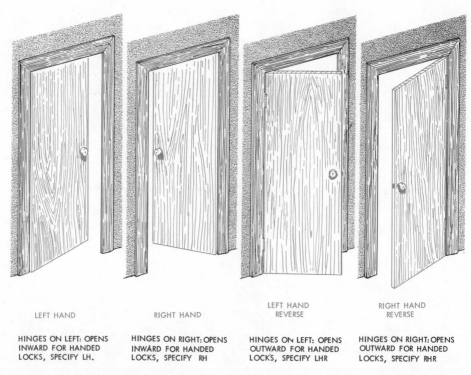

LEFT HAND	RIGHT HAND	LEFT HAND REVERSE	RIGHT HAND REVERSE
HINGES ON LEFT: OPENS INWARD FOR HANDED LOCKS, SPECIFY LH.	HINGES ON RIGHT: OPENS INWARD FOR HANDED LOCKS, SPECIFY RH	HINGES ON LEFT: OPENS OUTWARD FOR HANDED LOCKS, SPECIFY LHR	HINGES ON RIGHT: OPENS OUTWARD FOR HANDED LOCKS, SPECIFY RHR

Fig. 12. Hands of doors. Face the outside of the door to determine its hand. The outside is the street side of an entrance door and the corridor side of a room door. The outside of a communicating door is the side opposite the hinges.

Ventilation Equipment

Ventilators are also classed as finish hardware. Fig. 13 illustrates six different types of venting devices. Frequently two of these are used in combination, such as the ridge ventilator and the continuous under-the-eave (soffit) ventilator. Venting devices come in a wide variety of materials and finishes. Sizes vary, depending on the structure and the venting needs.

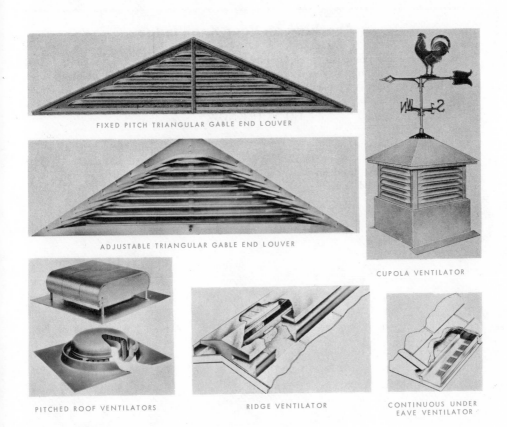

FIXED PITCH TRIANGULAR GABLE END LOUVER

ADJUSTABLE TRIANGULAR GABLE END LOUVER

CUPOLA VENTILATOR

PITCHED ROOF VENTILATORS

RIDGE VENTILATOR

CONTINUOUS UNDER EAVE VENTILATOR

Fig. 13. Ventilating devices. (H. C. Products Co.)

Miscellaneous Finish Hardware

Bathroom and kitchen accessories, shelf brackets, coat hooks, letter boxes, house numbers, curtain fixtures, etc., are also classed as finish hardware. The variety in design is unlimited. Only with extensive on-the-job experience will the carpenter become familiar with the many different types and applications of finish hardware.

Checking on Your Knowledge

The following questions will check your knowledge of the chapter. If you can answer all of them readily you will have a good understanding of the material. If not, then go over the chapter again.

DO YOU KNOW

1. The four basic types of hinges?
2. How to space butts on a door?
3. Three other items used on doors?
4. The three types of locks?
5. How to describe door hardware?
6. Two types of ventilators?
7. Three other kinds of finish hardware?

Adhesives

Chemistry has been creating many new products in all fields. The carpenter has benefited by the new kinds of manufactured wood products, new finishes, and new materials. One field that has benefited greatly has been that of adhesives. Today there are many products on the market that were unheard of only a few years ago.

While some of the adhesives being used seem like the old fashioned kinds, the chances are great that only the name is the same. New formulas, new chemicals, and new processes have greatly improved even the old-time materials so that they are stronger, better, and easier to handle than ever before.

Every carpenter should become acquainted with the new adhesives as they can aid greatly in producing better work and making the application of many kinds of materials much easier and faster. This is one of the fields that should be explored regularly in order to keep up with the latest developments.

Newer materials that have become prominent in the field of carpentry have brought changes in the methods used for fastening them in place. One of the great developments has been in the use of adhesives to replace nails and screws, especially when applying pre-finished walls, ceilings, and floors.

The two kinds of adhesives used are glues and mastics. *Glues* are obtainable in either liquid or dry form. The dry form is commonly used and mixed on the job into a liquid. In mixing glues, be sure to follow manufacturers' instructions. *Mastics* are much thicker than glues and usually have an asphalt, rubber, or resin base. They commonly come already mixed.

Glues

As a means of fastening joints, glue is not used as extensively by the carpenter as it is by the cabinet-maker or the millman. However, in small quantities, the use of glue is essential in the construction of stairs, some joints in interior trim, and cabinetwork built on the job. Glues are also used in building beams, arches, and curved members of glued laminated construction.

There are approximately eight general types of glue commonly used:

Liquid glue	Blood albumin glue
Casein glue	Vegetable glue
Animal glue	Synthetic resin glue
Epoxy resin	Cellulose cement & rubber compounds

The properties, uses and methods of application of the different types of glue vary, and the selection of a glue depends upon such factors as the rate of setting, water resistance, and tendency to stain wood; as well as the strength factor. Clamping is usually required for a strong bond.

Liquid Glue. Glue in liquid form is easily handled, which is one of its main assets. It is made from fish and animal products, and comes ready for use. There are many different kinds available on the market. Liquid glue is used chiefly for small jobs and repair work. Its hold-ing power is not as great as that of some other forms of glue, and it also has a rather low resistance to water and moisture.

Casein Glue. This glue is made principally of casein which is mixed with caustic lime. Casein is the dried curd of cow's milk. Other ingredients used in the manufacture of casein glue are trade secrets. Casein glue is marketed in powder form and is prepared for use by the addition of water, mixing well, and allowing the mixture to stand for a short period of time before applying. One great advantage of casein glue is the fact that it is easily prepared, and another advantage is its relatively high water resistance. The better grades are highly water-proof, a quality which makes this glue desirable in construction work.

Animal Glue. There are some 21 grades of animal glue, which have been extensively used for many years. The best grade is that made from animal hides. However, animal glues are not very practical for construction work, because they are not water resistant. Another factor which makes their use for construction work impractical is that the glue must be heated carefully before it is applied to the wood, which must also be warmed. The necessary heating of the wood and glue demand shop facilities which are not usually available on the construction site.

Blood Albumin Glue. Glues made from a base of blood albumin have been in use for many years, but their main extensive use is in the making of plywood and other veneer work. They are mixed from the various ingredients at the time of use, and are applied by hand or with mechanical spreaders. They are quick setting, but most of them require hot setting, which imposes certain limitations upon their extensive use.

Vegetable Glue. Vegetable glues, vegetable protein glues, or vegetable starch glues as they are variously known, are used mainly for making plywood, and other veneer products for interior use. The glue is prepared by the user, by heating the vegetable-starch powder with water and then cooling the mixture to room temperature before use. Vegetable glues set at room temperature and develop their strength by loss of water to the surrounding wood. Vegetable glues are not very resistant to moisture or water.

Synthetic-Resin Glue. The synthetic-resin glues, or as they are more simply called, the resin glues, were introduced about 1935, and their development and acceptance on a large scale is still increasing.

These resin glues originate from raw materials derived from coal, air, petroleum or natural gas, and water. Although the intermediate raw materials are available, the complex production methods required for the resins and the fact that some of them are covered by current patents makes the small scale production of resin glues by the individual user not ordinarily practical.

Synthetic resins are usually divided into two general groups, thermoplastic and thermosetting. The thermoplastic resins never harden permanently but soften or melt when the temperature is raised and harden again when it is lowered. This reversible hardening process involves no actual chemical change. The thermosetting resins however, undergo irreversible chemical change either at room temperature or at a higher temperature, to develop their strength and durability. After this reaction has taken place, the resin cannot be dissolved or melted again.

Some resins are sold in a single package, ready for use, or as a powder to be mixed only with water. Many others however, must be prepared for use by mixing resin, catalyst, filler, extender and water or other solvents at the time of use.

The principal advantages of some of the resins over other types of glue are the high degree of durability that they can impart to a wood joint when properly used, their adaptability to high volume production, and in some cases favorable cost.

Cellulose Cement and Rubber Compounds. Cellulose cement and rubber compounds are usually sold in liquid form ready to apply to wood. However, they have limited applications as woodworking glues. Cellulose cements are pressed cold, whereas most rubber compounds require heat. The relatively high cost of these compounds tends to impose further limits on their extensive use.

Epoxy Resin. This is a new material that does not depend on drying for strength. The strength is developed as a result of chemical reaction between the resin and catalyst. The two parts of the material are supplied in separate cans or tubes and are mixed before being used. As the mixed resin and catalyst react the strength of the bond increases. For this reason, only the amount that is needed should be mixed, otherwise the resin sets and has to be discarded. These resins have great strength when correctly mixed and may be used for joining dissimilar materials, such as wood to concrete or metal.

Mastics

Mastics, or pasty type cements, are being used more and more for installing wallboard, paneling, and certain kinds of flooring. Most manufacturers of these have mastics which they recommend for use with their products.

The mastics on the market are quite diverse. Some are thick pastes and can be used where there is no moisture problem, others are waterproof and can be used on concrete floors and in kitchens, laundries, and bathrooms. Some require a hot application; these are usually handled by specialists who have the equipment to heat the mastic and keep it in a fluid condition during use.

Many mastics come in cans ready for use and only need to be applied. Three general methods of application are used. For small tiles and panels the mastic is placed on the back of the floor or wall covering in blobs or patches. (Scrape the area of the tile where the mastic goes clean before applying the mastic). The covering is pressed into place and the mastic spreads out to form a bond with the underlying material. This method can only be used where there is a smooth sound

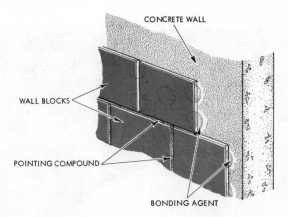

CONCRETE WALL

WALL BLOCKS

POINTING COMPOUND

BONDING AGENT

Fig. 1. Wall tile may be applied by using an adhesive. This method of applying adhesive is called "buttering."

surface to work against. It is a quick method of applying tiles and is readily adapted to the application of tiles to ceilings and walls. See Fig. 1.

A variation of this is to apply the mastic in a thin coat over the base with a special type of notched trowel. This trowel has notches that leave a series of ridges of mastic. When the finished covering is applied the mastic is forced out to form a solid bond. This is suitable for walls and floors where the troweling can be done without difficulty. See Fig. 2.

Some newer types of adhesive are applied with a brush. The object is to coat the entire backing so that the applied tiles or blocks are firmly held over their entire back surface. Fig. 3 illustrates the application of acoustic tile to a ceiling using this method. The carpenter in using mastics to apply floors and walls should keep in mind not only that good coverage is needed but also that care should be taken so that the mastic does not come up between the cracks and mar the finish. This can be largely avoided if the mastic is spread evenly and the floor or wall material is put in place without any sliding motion that would cause the mastic to pile up along the edge and squirt up between the joints.

Mastics are also applied with an adhesive gun. A canister containing the mastic is placed in the gun and is forced out to form a bead. (See Fig. 4, bottom.) Some adhesive guns have a permanent barrel into which the mastic must be forced.

275

Fig. 2. Block floors may be laid in a mastic fill either over concrete or wood flooring (E. L. Bruce Co.)

Fig. 3. Acoustical tile being applied to ceiling. (Celotex Corp.)

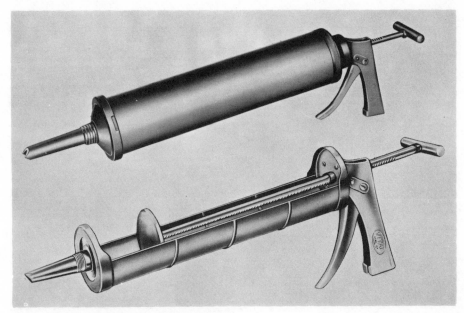

Fig. 4. Adhesive guns (U.S. Gypsum Co.)

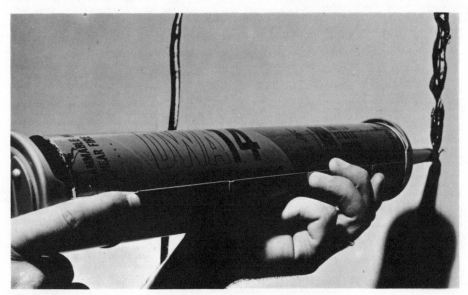

Fig. 5. Adhesive gun being used to apply a bead to wall. (U.S. Gypsum Co.)

TABLE I. ADHESIVES: TYPES AND PROPERTIES*

(1) ANIMAL GLUES. Solvents: Water. Nature: Melted and applied hot. Some are liquids applied cold. Bonds: Excellent for wood, leather, glass, paper. Poor for metals. Strength: Very high on wood. Up to 10,000-12,000 psi in shear. Temperature resistance: Medium for heat, good for cold. Creep resistance: Good. Water resistance: Very poor. Cure: Initial gel and then air-drying @ room temperature.

(2) ASPHALTIC MIXTURES. Solvents: Water, aromatics, carbon tetrachloride and disulphide. Nature: Thermo-plastic. Natural asphalts usually hard and brittle when cold. Bonds: Good for metals, rubber, or glass, floor coverings, roofing felts. Strength: Low to fair, depending upon grade and temperature. Temperature resistance: Poor for heat, good for cold. Melting point may be as high as 200°F., or as low as 50°F. Creep resistance: Very poor. Water resistance: Good to excellent. Cure: Elevated temperatures or cooling to room temperature.

(3) BLOOD ALBUMIN GLUES. Solvents: Water. Nature: Usually dry powder. Bonds: Fair for wood. Good for leather and paper. Poor for metals or glass. Strength: Good. Temperature resistance: Fair for both heat and cold. Creep resistance: Good. Water resistance: Poor. Cure: Dries at room temperature or low heat, 150-200°F.

(4) CASEIN GLUES. Solvents: Water. Nature: Usually dry powder. Sometimes called thermo-setting. Bonds: Good to medium for wood to wood, or paper. Strength: Up to 1650 psi in shear, on wood. Temperature resistance: Medium resistant to both heat and cold. Creep resistance: Good. Water resistance: Very good. Cure: Air drying or chemically reacted.

(5) CELLULOSE CEMENTS. Solvents: Water emulsion, ethyl acetate or acetone. Nature: Thermo-plastic. Fused by heating. Bonds: Good for glass, wood, paper, leather. Not for rubber. Strength: good. 1000-1400 psi on wood, in shear. Temperature resistance: Fair to good for both heat and cold. Creep resistance: Good. Water resistance: Water mixed, poor. Other solvents, fair to medium. Cure: Air drying and setting.

(6) CHLORINATED RUBBER. Solvents: Ketones or aromatics. Nature: Usually liquid. Bonds: Medium for wood, metals or glass. Good for paper. Strength: No data. Temperature resistance: Medium for both heat and cold. Creep resistance: Poor. Water resistance: Medium to good. Cure: Dries at room temperature.

(7) EPOXY RESIN. Solvents: No solvent needed. Nature: Thermo-setting. Bonds: Excellent for wood, metal, glass, masonry. Strength: High. 1000-7000 psi on wood. Temperature resistance: Excellent for both heat and cold. Creep resistance: Good to poor, depending upon compounding. Water resistance: Fair to excellent, depending upon compounding. Cure: Catalyst and hot-press (up to 390°F.) or strong catalyst @ room temp.

(8) MELAMINE RESINS. Solvents: Water, alcohol. Nature: Thermo-setting. Powder with separate catalyst. Applied cold. Colorless, non-staining. Bonds: Excellent for paper or wood. Poor for metals or glass. Strength: No data. Temperature resistance: Excellent for both heat and cold. Creep resistance: very good. Water resistance: Excellent. Cure: Hot-press @ 300°F.

(9) UREA RESINS. Solvents: Water; alcohol, or alcohol hydrocarbons blends. Nature: Thermo-setting. Bonds: Excellent for wood, leather, paper. Poor for metals or glass. Creep resistance: Good. Water resistance: Fair. Cure: some heat desirable, but some types will cure @ room temperature.

(10) NEOPRENE RUBBER ADHESIVES. Solvents: Water emulsions or volatile solvents. Nature: Thermoplastic, with some thermo-setting characteristics. Bonds: Excellent for wood, asbestos board, metals, glass. Strength: Up to 1200 psi in shear. Temperature resistance: Good for heat or cold. 100 to 400 psi @ 180°F. Creep resistance: Fair to good. Water resistance: Excellent. Cure: Some heat desirable.

(11) NITRILE RUBBER ADHESIVES. (Sometimes called Buna N rubber.) Solvents: Water emulsions or volatile solvents. Nature: Both thermo-plastic and thermo-setting types available. Bonds: Wood, paper, porcelain enamel, polyester skins. Strength: Thermo-setting, to 4000 psi shear, thermo-plastic, to 600 psi. Temperature resistance: Good for both heat and cold. Creep resistance: Good to fair. Water resistance: Excellent. Cure: heat cure preferable.

(12) PHENOLIC RESINS. Solvents: Water, alcohol, ketones. Nature: Dry or liquid. Bonds: Good to excellent for wood, paper. Medium to poor for glass and metals. Strength: Good. Temperature resistance: Excellent for both heat and cold. Creep resistance: Excellent. Water resistance: Excellent. Cure: Some set @ room temperature, some require hot-press.

(13) POLYVINYL RESINS: Solvents: Water, ketones. Nature: Liquid, usually an emulsion. Bonds: Good for wood or paper. Strength: Up to 950 psi in shear on wood. Temperature resistance: Fair for heat, good for cold. Fuses @ 220-350°F. Creep resistance: Fair to poor. Water resistance: Fair to medium. Cure: Air drying and setting @ room temperature.

(14) RESORCINOL RESINS. Solvents: Alcohol, water, ketones. Nature: Thermo-setting. Usually liquid with separate catalyst. Bonds: Wood, paper. Poor for glass or metals. Strength: On wood, up to 1950 psi in shear. Temperature resistance: Excellent for cold. More heat resisting than wood. Creep resistance: Very good. Cure: Room temperature or moderate (200°F.) heat.

(15) SODIUM SILICATE. Solvents: Water. Nature: Liquid. Bonds: Good for wood, metals. Excellent for paper, or glass. Strength: No data. Temperature resistance: Excellent for heat or cold. Creep resistance: Good. Water resistance: Poor. Cure: Dries at room temperature or moderate (150-200°F) heat.

(16) SOY-BEAN GLUE. Solvents: Water. Nature: Dry or water mixed. Bonds: Fair for wood or glass; poor for metals or rubber. Strength: No data. Temperature resistance: Fair for heat, poor for cold. Creep resistance: Good. Water resistance: Poor. Cure: Dries at room temperature.

(17) STARCH AND DEXTRIN GLUES. Solvents: Water. Nature: Dry and liquid available. Bonds: Wood, leather, paper. Strength: Fair to medium for wood or paper; poor for metals or glass. Temperature resistance: Fair for both heat and cold. Creep resistance: Fair. Water resistance: Poor. Cure: Dries @ room temperature.

(18) NATURAL RUBBER ADHESIVES. Solvents: Water emulsions, aromatics, various hydrocarbons. Nature: Latex emulsions or dissolved crepe rubber. Bonds: Good for rubber, glass or leather. Fair for wood or ceramics. Strength: Rather low, 340 psi in tension, on wood. Temperature resistance: Fair for both heat and cold. Creep resistance: Poor. Water resistance: Good. Cure: Dries @ room temperature.

†Source: Practical Builder

(See Fig. 4, top.) Adhesive gun application is usually used with pre-finished panels and drywall. Fig. 5 illustrates how the bead may be applied to the wall.

Mastics must have a smooth, clean surface as a base. Old paint, flaking plaster, and rough wood are not satisfactory as they affect bonding of the mastic and may cause it to fail. Materials are available to overcome these difficulties. Special paints and filling materials can be used to create a smooth surface for the mastic. Leveling cements may be needed to eliminate unevenness in concrete floors and walls. If the wall or floor being covered is in contact with damp ground some type of moisture-proofing may be needed or a waterproof mastic should be used.

The carpenter should be sure that the conditions of sound, smooth, moisture-proof surfaces are obtained before applying the mastic. Frequent checking with the manufacturer of the wallboard or flooring will bring the necessary information for securing sound installation under adverse conditions.

Table I gives the properties and uses of some of the common types of adhesives. Not all of these are commonly used for wood joints or for installing paneling or tiles. Adhesives come under many different brand names. Check the specifications and recommended uses before using. Many manufacturers state the recommended adhesives for use with their product.

SAFETY: RULES FOR ADHESIVES

Many of the new adhesives contain chemicals that may present some safety hazards. Consequently the following precautions should observed when using any adhesive.

1. Check label on container for specific cautions.

2. Use with good ventilation only.

3. Be sure that all flames are kept away, and that no switches or electric tools are operated nearby. Close off area so that no one can wander in accidentally with any flame of any kind (pipes, cigars, cigarettes, torches, etc.).

4. Avoid breathing of vapors for any length of time.

5. Remove any adhesive from hands right away. Avoid getting in mouth or eyes. Many people are sensitive to some of the solvents used.

6. Be sure to store all adhesives where they are inaccessible to other persons, and where they are not subjected to high heat.

Checking on Your Knowledge

The following questions will check on your knowledge of the chapter. If you have difficulty with them read over the portions of the chapter where the meaning was missed the first time.

DO YOU KNOW

1. What the two main divisions of adhesives are?

2. When epoxy resin types are preferred?

3. How to prevent mastic from squirting up between joints?

4. A good method for applying flooring with adhesives?

5. When a gun is the best means of application?

6. Why adhesives are preferred for prefinished materials?

Appendix

Contents

A. 282 Devices Made on the Job
Sawhorse
Saw vise
Workbench
Stepladder
Straightedge
Miter box
Door jack
Shoulder box
Tool case
Suitcase tool box

B. 304 Steel Square: Advanced Work
How to Use Unit-Length Rafter Tables
Brace Layout
Brace Measure
The 12th Scale on Framing Square

C. 317 Softwood Lumber Standards
Finish, Flooring, Ceiling, Partition and Stepping
Siding
Boards, Dimension and Timbers
Shiplap, Centermatch and D & M
Worked Lumber (factory flooring, heavy roofing, decking, etc.)

D. 323 First Aid Equipment

E. 325 Review of Working Drawings, Conventions and Symbols
Scale
Types of Lines
Working Drawings
Floor Plans
Elevations
Sections
Details
Transverse or Longitudinal Sections
Schedules
Symbols
Carpentry Specifications

Devices Made on the Job

The carpenter makes some of his equipment on the job. To simplify the making of this equipment, drawings and instructions suggest materials commonly found on the construction job or obtainable at any lumberyard. Detailed instructions have been worked out as an aid to the beginner or apprentice, on *how to make* the following devices.

Sawhorse
Saw vise
Workbench
Stepladder
Straightedge
Miter box
Door jack
Shoulder box
Tool case
Suitcase tool box

Lumber used in construction is designated or spoken of in *lumberyard sizes*, rather than the exact dimensions. For example, a piece of lumber 1⅝x3⅝ exact size is called a *2x4;* a board 25/32x9½ is called a *1x10*. However, it does not necessarily follow that a 1x10 will be exactly 25/32x9½ inches; nor a 2x4 exactly 1⅝x3⅝ inches; the exact size depends somewhat upon the moisture content. Lumber will swell in wet weather and shrink in dry weather, but when the 1x10 board was kiln dried and planed at the planing mill it was exactly 25/32x9½ inches. This information is given as a precaution and to encourage the beginner to measure his materials when exact sizes are demanded.

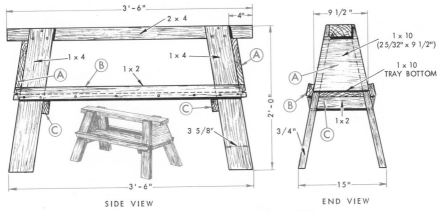

Fig. 1. A sawhorse, an essential part of a carpenter's equipment.

How to Make a Sawhorse

The sawhorse is an essential part of the carpenter's equipment, Fig. 1. It serves as a workbench and supports his tools. It also serves as a scaffold to stand on while working. A great many times a carpenter's mechanical ability is tested by the kind of sawhorse he can build when he starts out on a new job. The length and height of the sawhorse will depend somewhat upon the carpenter's individual needs and the type of work for which the sawhorse is intended to be used. The dimensions given in this instruction unit will serve the average person and job. It is advisable to make the sawhorse out of soft and lightweight material, such as No. 1 spruce or white pine.

MATERIALS

Top .... one piece 2x4 by 3'8″
Legs .... one piece 1x4 by 9'0″
Ends and tray .... one piece 1x10 by 5'6″
Reinforcements .... one piece 1x2 by 9'0″

PROCEDURE

1. Legs. Select a straight and smooth piece of soft 1x4 for the legs.

a) Lay the framing square on the 4-inch face of this board, as shown in Fig. 2, taking *4* inches on the tongue and *24* inches on the blade of the square. Draw the line *1*, along the tongue. This will be the line for the bottom cut of the leg. *Note:* The square is held so that the figures on both tongue and blade are along the same edge of the board.

b) Measure 24⅝ inches from this line along the same edge of the board and make a check mark. Reverse the square, as shown in Fig. 3, and hold it at the same figures as before (*4* and *24* inches). Draw the line *2*

283

Fig. 2. Leg layout—bottom cut.

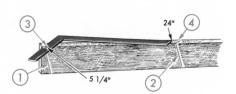
Fig. 3. Leg layout—top cut.

Fig. 4. Layout for side cuts of leg.

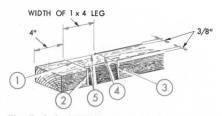
Fig. 5. Gain joint for receiving leg.

along the tongue through the check mark. This will be the line for the top cut of the leg. *Note:* The lines *1* and *2*, for the top and bottom cuts, should be parallel to each other.

c) Turn the board on edge and lay out the side cuts, *3* and *4*, Fig. 4, by holding the framing square to the figures 5¼ inches on the tongue and *24* inches on the blade; the tongue of the square should touch the line *1*, the bottom cut. Draw the line *3* along the tongue.

d) Reverse the square and draw the top side cut *4*, Fig. 4. *Note:* The lines *3* and *4* should be parallel to each other.

e) With a crosscut saw, cut to the lines, sawing on the waste side of the line.

f) With a block plane, smooth up the cuts to the lines.

g) Using this one leg as a pattern, lay out and cut the other three legs.

2. Top. Select a straight, smooth, and soft piece of 2x4 for the top member of the sawhorse. Cut it to the required length.

a) Lay out the gain joints, Fig. 5, which will receive the legs. *Note:* In studying the side view in Fig. 1, it will be observed that the legs of the sawhorse are set at an angle of 4 inches to the 24 inches of height. Although the legs are back 4 inches at the top, at the bottom they are in line with the end of the top piece.

b) Measure 4 inches in from the end of the top piece, as shown in

Fig. 5. Use the square as a guide and draw line *1* across the top.

c) Turn the top piece on one side and lay the framing square on the edge, holding the square to the 4-inch mark on the tongue and the 24-inch mark on the blade; the tongue of the square should touch line *1.* Draw line *2* along the tongue. *Caution:* Be sure to have the angle in the right direction; i.e., angling outward toward the end of the 2x4.

d) Draw line *3,* Fig. 5, using the leg pattern to get the exact width of the gain joint.

e) Square line *4* across the top edge.

f) Draw the gain joint on the opposite edge by setting a T bevel to the angle formed by line *2,* Fig. 5.

g) For the depth of the joint, set the marking gauge to ⅜ inch and gauge and draw lines *5. Note:* The depth of the gain joint is from ⅜ inch at the top to nothing at the bottom; this will give the desired angle to the legs, as shown in the end view, Fig. 1.

h) Lay out the two gain joints on the other end of the top piece.

i) Before cutting out the joint, check the layout for the following points:

(1) The lines of each joint on the edge of the top member must angle outward at the bottom.

(2) The lines of each joint must be parallel to each other.

(3) The width of the joint should not exceed the width of the leg.

j) Cut out the gain joint with saw and chisel. Be sure to cut on the waste side of line, leaving just the line, to insure a tight fit for the leg.

k) Nail each leg to the top member with three 8-penny coated box nails.

3. Ends. Lay out the two end pieces (*A*), Fig. 1, on a piece of 1x10. Be sure to have the grain run from one leg of the horse to the other leg. The end pieces are wedge-shaped. The angle can be obtained by taking 5¼ inches on the tongue of the framing square and 24 inches on the blade, marking along the tongue. The length of this piece, on the long edge, is equal to the width of the tray, 9½ inches. Lay off this distance and draw the other angle. Cut and nail the two end pieces in place with 8-penny coated nails, nailing them tightly up under the top member.

4. Tray. Select a 1x10 board for the tray bottom. Its width is determined by the width of the bottom or widest part of the end piece (*A*), Fig. 1, the length is equal to the length of the sawhorse measuring from the outside of the end pieces marked (*A*). Lay out the tray bottom and cut the notches for the legs. Fit the piece in place, nailing it tightly against the end pieces. Plane off any excess stock from the edges of the tray bottom. *Note:* The tray bottom must fit closely around the legs; therefore, when cutting out the notches for the legs do not cut to the layout lines, but leave sufficient stock to make a tight fit. To insure a good fit, remove excess stock carefully with a chisel, little by little.

5. Reinforcements. In order to make sure the sawhorse is properly built and strong enough to serve the purpose for which it is intended, some reinforcement is advisable.

a) The sides of the tray are formed by the two pieces marked (*B*), Fig. 1. The sides are made from a piece of 1x2, which should extend past the legs far enough to support the end pieces marked (*A*). Saw the side pieces to the proper length and nail them into place with 8-penny coated box nails. This will make the tray tight and firm enough to provide a place for a workman to stand.

b) The pieces indicated by (*C*), Fig. 1, are additional supports and reinforcements for both bottom and sides of the tray.

c) Finally, test the completed sawhorse by placing it on a true surface or level plane. If constructed according to the instructions given in this unit, the sawhorse should be firm and solid when standing on a true surface.

How to Make a Saw Vise

Several kinds of metal saw vises are available on the market. However, Fig. 6 shows a saw vise which can be made by the carpenter on the job. Such a vise has the advantage of having its jaws at a convenient height for filing. The correct height is about 4 inches below the arm pits of the workman who does the filing.

MATERIALS

Legs ....softwood, two pieces 2x4 by 4'4"

Jaws and braces ....softwood, one piece 1x4 by 9'6"

Tightener ....hardwood, one piece 1x2 by 1'6"

Hardware ....flat-head screws, eight No. 10x1½" carriage bolts, two ⅜"x4"

PROCEDURE

1. Legs. Select two straight pieces of softwood for the legs shown in Fig. 6.

a) Cut two pieces of 2x4 as shown at (*A*), to the desired length to suit the height requirements of the user.

b) Bevel the top as illustrated at (*B*).

c) Bore two ⅜" holes for the 4" bolts.

d) To make the arms, lay out lines (*X*) and (*Y*) and cut along these lines.

e) Lay out and cut the notches to hold the jaws shown at (*C*). *Note:* The jaws are tilted slightly to insure a tight grip of the saw on the top edge.

f) Lay out and cut two notches

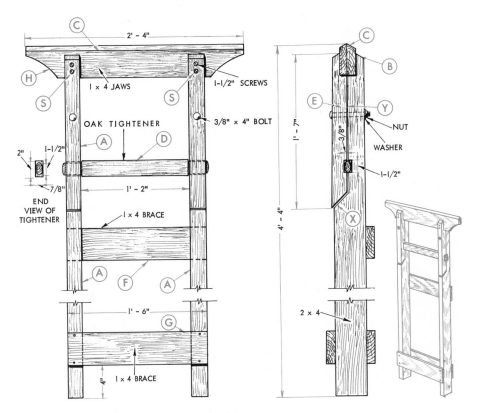

Fig. 6. A saw vise which can be made on the job.

⅜″x1½″ to receive the oak tightener (hardwood) shown at (D).

2. Jaws. Take two pieces of softwood board 1x4x28 inches, lay out the jaws and cut them off square; then bevel the top edges shown at (C), and cut and smooth the edges of the curved portion, as shown at (H) in the illustration, Fig. 6.

3. Braces. Take three pieces of softwood board 1x4x18 inches, lay out and cut off square for the braces shown at (F) and (G), Fig. 6.

4. Tightener. For the tightener use hardwood, such as oak.

a) Lay out and cut a piece ⅞x2x18 inches as shown at (D), Fig. 6.

b) Lay off 2 inches at each end and cut to an oval shape, smooth with sandpaper. See illustration Fig. 6.

5. Assembly. Before beginning to assemble the various parts for the saw vise, check each part carefully to make sure it has been prepared according to instructions.

a) Nail the two lower braces (*G*) into place with 8-penny coated nails.

b) Fasten one jaw to the legs marked (*A*) with four No. 10x1½″ screws, like those shown at (*S*), Fig. 6.

c) Lay the tightener in place. Then place the arms (*E*) in position, slip the two bolts into place and fasten with washers and nuts, shown in Fig. 6.

d) Fasten the other jaw to the two arms with screws, shown at (*S*).

e) Nail the third brace (*F*) into place. The position of this brace is governed by the height of the knee of the operator when he has one foot on brace (*G*).

f) Lastly, test the vise to make sure it will hold a saw in a tight grip. This may save delay in work at a later time.

How to Make a Workbench

A workbench makes it possible for the carpenter to carry the bench to his work instead of carrying his work to the bench. Such a workbench is a great convenience, especially in finishing work, such as fitting doors and windows. A portable vise fastened to one end of the workbench will hold the work while it is being planed and fitted. The movable ledge on the front of the bench can be adjusted to accommodate large doors, sash, or cabinet doors while fitting and applying hardware, such as hinges.

MATERIALS

Legs (four) ....one piece 2x4 by 12′0″
Top ....one piece 2x12 by 6′0″
Movable ledge ....one piece 2x4 by 6′0″
Braces and cleats ....one piece 1x6 by 12′0″
Shelf ....one piece 1x8 by 5′0″
Angle braces ....one piece 1x4 by 6′6″
Shelf back and supports ....one piece 1x2 by 8′0″
Hardware ....two bolts ⅜″x6″

1. Legs. For the legs, select a 2x4 of softwood. Cut the piece into four lengths for the legs of the workbench shown in the thumbnail sketch, Fig. 7.

a) Cut off two pieces from the 2x4 for the front legs 2′ 8¼″ in length. Both ends of these legs should be cut square.

b) Lay out and bore (at the angle shown, 15°) the ½-inch holes, 3 inches O.C. (on center). The bolts which hold the movable ledge are inserted in these holes.

c) The top and bottom of the rear legs are cut at an angle. See Fig. 7, end view at left. To obtain the correct angle for cutting these legs, hold the framing square to the figures 3½ inches on the tongue and 12 inches on the blade. Mark along the tongue; that is, the 3½-inch side of the square. The length of the rear legs is 2′ 9½″ with end cuts parallel to each other.

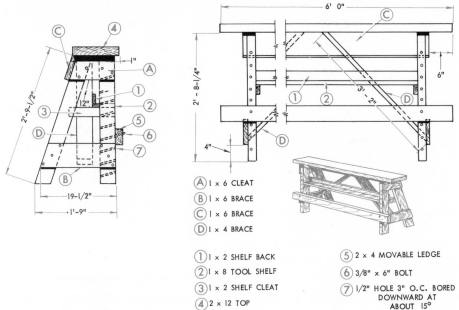

A) 1 x 6 CLEAT
B) 1 x 6 BRACE
C) 1 x 6 BRACE
D) 1 x 4 BRACE

1) 1 x 2 SHELF BACK
2) 1 x 8 TOOL SHELF
3) 1 x 2 SHELF CLEAT
4) 2 x 12 TOP

5) 2 x 4 MOVABLE LEDGE
6) 3/8" x 6" BOLT
7) 1/2" HOLE 3" O.C. BORED
    DOWNWARD AT
    ABOUT 15°

Fig. 7. Diagram shows construction of workbench.

See layout for legs of the sawhorse, Figs. 2 and 3.

2. Braces A and B. Lay out and cut braces (A) and (B) for both ends of the workbench.

a) Take a piece of board 1x6 and cut off two pieces 19½ inches in length for the two lower braces.

b) For the two top braces cut off two pieces from the 1x6 board, 12 inches in length. Each brace should be cut square on one end with the other end cut at an angle. The angles for both top and bottom braces should be cut in the same way the angles were cut for the top and bottom of the rear legs.

c) Nail the braces in place as shown in Fig. 7.

3. Top. Lay out and cut a piece of 2x12 plank to a length of 6 feet. Nail the plank to the top of the legs, keeping the legs back 6 inches from each end of the top piece, as shown in Fig. 7, illustration at right.

4. Brace C. For this brace use a 1x6 board cut to a length of 5 feet.

a) Square the board at each end and nail it to the rear legs of the bench under the top piece as shown in Fig. 7, illustration at top right.

b) Before nailing the brace in place, check the spread of the legs

289

at the bottom, making the spread the same as at the top.

c) Nail a piece of 1x2 across the bottom of the legs to hold them in place until all the braces have been securely fastened.

5. Braces D. These braces should be cut from a piece of 1x4. Each brace is 3'2" in length and is cut at an angle of 45 degrees.

a) The framing square can be used to lay out the angles at each end of the board. A 45-degree angle can be laid out by holding the square on the edge of the board to the same figure on both the tongue and blade. For example, 10 inches on the tongue and 10 inches on the blade; or 6 inches on the tongue and 6 inches on the blade.

b) After the angle cuts have been made, nail the braces into place as shown in the illustration, Fig. 7.

6. Shelf. First, cut two pieces of 1x2 to a length of 12 inches for *supports* for the shelf.

a) Nail these pieces to the inside of the legs 12 inches down from the top piece.

b) For the shelf take a piece of 1x8 measuring 5 feet in length. Cut, fit, and nail this into place on the two supports.

c) After the shelf is in place, cut a piece of 1x2 to the length of 5 feet and nail it into position as a back for the self.

7. Movable Ledge. Use a piece of 2x4 for the movable ledge.

a) Cut the 2x4 to a length of 6 feet.

b) Hold the piece in position against the front legs and mark the center of two bolt holes on the ledge, one hole at each end.

c) Bore two $\frac{5}{16}$-inch holes at the same angle as the holes in the front legs. Then drive two $\frac{3}{8}$-inch carriage bolts, 6 inches long, into place to hold the ledge in position. See thumbnail sketch, Fig. 7, which shows the ledge in place.

How to Build a Stepladder

The ordinary folding stepladder is not strong enough to withstand the rough usage of a construction job. Therefore, it is necessary for the carpenter to build his own stepladder which is more suitable for his particular type of work. A stepladder with housed steps, 1x4 rigid legs, and thorough bracing is a sturdy piece of equipment, Fig. 8. The most convenient height is about 4 feet and 6 inches. However, the height can be altered to meet the individual needs of the workman for whom the ladder is designed.

MATERIALS

Legs, steps, and rear brace ......three
pieces 1x4 by 10'0"

Top ....one piece 1x8 by 2'0"

Braces ....one piece 1x2 by 14'0"

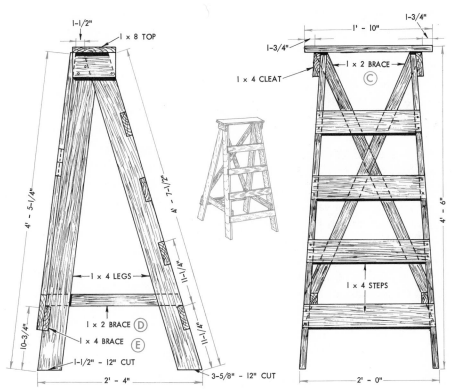

Fig. 8. Stepladder: diagram shows construction and thumbnail sketch.

PROCEDURE

1. Legs. For laying out the legs with a framing square, follow the method used when laying out the legs of the sawhorse, Figs. 2 and 3.

a) On a piece of 1x4 lay out the length of the front legs each *4* feet 7½ inches as shown at (*A*), Fig. 8. The cutting lines, for the top and bottom of the legs, must be parallel to each other. The correct line for the angle cut can be obtained by placing the framing square on the board in a position similar to

that for the legs of the sawhorse, as shown in Fig. 2. However, to find the guide line for the angle cut for the top and bottom of the front legs of the stepladder, hold the square to the figures *3⅝* inches on the tongue and *12* inches on the body, or blade. Draw a guide line along the tongue of the square and cut on this line.

b) Beginning at the bottom of each of the front legs, space lines for the steps along the front edges of these legs, 11¼ inches apart, and lay off the width of the steps, as shown in Fig. 8. Draw lines on the side of the legs and gauge the depth of the cutouts equal to the thickness of the steps. Cut on the waste side of the lines and chisel out each notch, little by little, to the gauge marks shown in Fig. 8.

c) On a piece of 1x4, lay out the rear legs shown at (B), Fig. 8, the length of each of the rear legs being 4 feet 5¼ inches. The angle cut for the top and bottom can be obtained by placing the framing square on the board in a position similar to that shown in Fig. 2, holding the square to the figures *1½* on the tongue and *12* on the blade. Draw a guide line on the 1½-inch side; that is, along the tongue of the square, as shown in Fig. 2.

d) The top of the rear legs has an additional angle cut for fitting against the front legs. Cut this angle according to the measurements given in Fig. 8.

e) Lay out and cut the notch for the 1x4 brace (E) near the bottom of the rear legs.

f) Lay out and cut two 1x4 cleats 7½ inches long. Tie the front and rear legs together at the top with these cleats, as shown in Fig. 8.

g) Nail the cleats to the legs at the top, holding the cleats flush with the top of the legs and spreading the legs to 2 feet 4 inches at the bottom. Use 6-penny coated

nails and clinch them on the inside.

2. Top Piece. The top is an important feature of the stepladder. It is not only important as the highest step of the ladder but also serves as a finishing member. Nailing should be done carefully to avoid splitting of the top piece.

a) On a piece of 1x8, lay off the top, 1 foot 10 inches in length. Cut off square on both ends.

b) Nail the top in place with 8-penny coated nails. The legs are set back 1¾ inches from the ends of the top piece, as shown in illustration at right, Fig. 8.

3. Steps. Study the front view of the ladder, Fig. 8. The length of the top piece is 22 inches and the legs are set in at the top 1¾ inches from each end. At the bottom the legs are spread to a measure of 2 feet. This difference in the spread of the legs at top and bottom makes it necessary to cut the four steps different lengths so they will conform to the shape of the ladder.

a) Set the legs to a spread of 2 feet at the bottom. Lay a piece of 1x4 in the notches cut for the lowest step. Mark the cutting lines for both ends of the step flush on the outside of the legs. This will insure the proper fit of the step to conform to the shape of the ladder. Cut off the length of the step along the marks and nail it into place with one nail to each leg.

b) Using the same method, cut

and fit each of the other steps into place, nailing them with one nail in each leg.

c) Cut the rear brace *(E)* the same length as the lowest step of the ladder and nail the brace in place with one nail in each rear leg.

d) After all the steps are in place, the stand of the ladder should be checked to make sure it stands plumb, not lopsided. Then nail all steps and the rear brace *(E)* securely, using 8-penny coated nails.

4. Braces.   There are five braces used in this type of stepladder, two at the back which are crossed as shown at *(C)*, Fig. 8, one at the bottom and rear, brace *(E)*, and two side braces near bottom, as shown at *(D)*, Fig. 8.

a) Cut and fit the 1x2 *(C)* braces and nail them in place as shown in the diagram, Fig. 8.

b) Before cutting and nailing the 1x2 *(D)* braces, check the leg spread at the bottom. This spread should be 2 feet 4 inches.

How to Make a Straightedge

The *straightedge*, a simple yet necessary device, is used in connection with a level for plumbing door jambs and corner posts, or for leveling work when spans greater than the length of the level are encountered, Fig. 9. Northern white pine, *Pinus strobus*, is a desirable wood to use for this purpose. When properly seasoned, white pine will not warp.

Accuracy in construction is all-essential. The edge *(1)* must be straight, true, and square with the surface. Edge *(2)* must be parallel with edge *(1)*. *Blocks (A)* must be of the same thickness. These blocks can be glued onto the main section or cut out from the main board, as desired. However, when finished, the ends of the straightedge must be *exactly* the same width. The *handhole* makes it convenient to grasp the device firmly while plumbing. There is on the market a two-glass leveling device which can be screwed to the face of the straightedge; this device does away with the need of the regular level.

The size of the straightedge varies with the needs of the job, but the dimensions shown in the diagram, Fig. 9, usually are accepted for average work. A makeshift emergency straightedge can be made

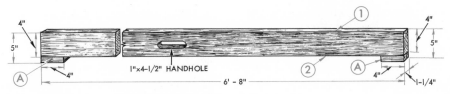

Fig. 9. Straightedge for plumbing door jambs and corner posts.

quickly by using a straight piece of 2x4 with blocks ⅞ of an inch in thickness nailed on each end similar to those shown in Fig. 9.

How to Make a Miter Box

It is difficult to make a perfect joint between two pieces which come together at an angle of ninety degrees to form a corner. There are a number of different methods of cutting these pieces to make such a joint. The simplest method is to cut off each piece at a bevel of forty-five degrees, so that the pieces will fit together at an angle of ninety degrees. A *miter box* is a convenient device used by carpenters for cutting pieces at the exact angle desired when mitering joints, Fig. 10. To miter moldings, the carpenter usually constructs a device on the job by nailing together lengthwise two pieces of 2x6, two or three feet in length. The desired angle cuts are laid out on this device, and saw cuts are made to serve as guides for cutting the angles on moldings.

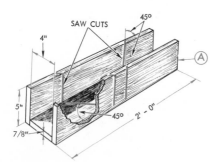

Fig. 10. Miter box.

A better looking and more permanent piece of equipment can be made by using hardwood boards, maple or birch, ⅞ of an inch in thickness with the sides glued or screwed on the bottom. Many woodworkers prefer a two-sided miter box which can be made easily by adding a second side as shown at (*A*), Fig. 10. For a simple miter box omit the side (*A*).

How to Make a Door Jack

Whenever it is necessary to fit a large number of doors, a carpenter finds it advisable to make a *door jack* to hold the doors while planing the edges and fitting the hinges. The door jack can be constructed easily out of materials found on any construction job. For the base use a 2x6 if available. However, a piece of 1x6 or even a 1x4 can be used for the base piece, shown at (*A*), Fig. 11. The 2x4 crosspiece (*B*), two feet in length, is nailed at right angles to (*A*), about 12 inches from one end of the base, which should be 6 feet long, see Fig. 11. The 1x6 piece (*C*), with a *V* cut in the upper end, holds any thickness of door and should be set at an angle great enough so that the *V* cut will be above the center of the door. Two 1x4 braces are required, one on each side of the *V* cut as indicated by (*D*) in Fig. 11. Though not essential the 1x6 shelf (*E*) is desirable as it provides additional stiffness to the jack and is also

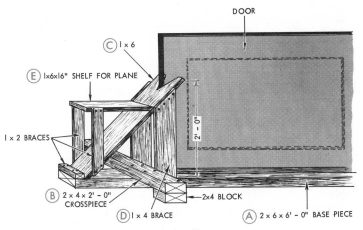

Fig. 11. Door jack for holding door while fitting it.

convenient for holding the plane when not in use. Note the 1x2 braces supporting the shelf, also the 1x2 brace on end of base. The crosspiece (*B*) is supported at each end by a 2x4 block. The distance between the upper end of the (*C*) piece and the base is 2 feet.

How to Make a Shoulder Box

The man who is skilful in the use of tools appreciates their value and takes good care of them. He has a place for every tool and keeps every tool in its place when it is not in use. Anyone who hopes to become a skilled mechanic should form this habit early, and when he buys tools he should also provide a place where they can be kept. The mechanic who works in a shop keeps his tools on the workbench, in the drawers of the

bench, or in a cabinet above the bench. However, the mechanic who moves about from job to job must provide himself with devices in which he can keep his tools. For this purpose he should have tool boxes which are convenient in size, and light enough in weight to carry around easily.

Every carpenter should provide himself with two toolboxes, a *shoulder box* and a *tool case*. The tool case will house the finer trim tools and keep them under lock and key. The shoulder box is for the framing or rough tools. Since it is not so large, it is more convenient to carry around on ladders or scaffolds while preparing the framework of a building.

The shoulder box should be made from materials which are light in weight but strong enough to withstand hard wear, Fig. 12. *Note:*

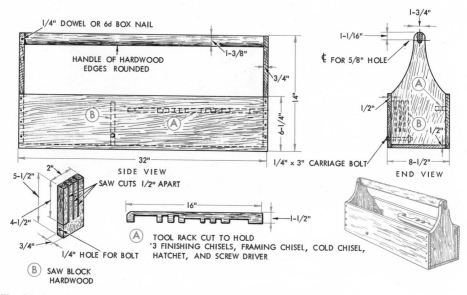

Fig. 12. Shoulder tool box: side view, end view, and thumbnail sketch.

Although not so specified here, the sides may be made of ¼-inch plywood; if available; however, the ends and bottom should be of solid boards which have better nail-holding qualities.

MATERIALS

Ends ....#1 soft lightweight wood, one piece 1″x8″ by 2′6″

Bottom and sides ....soft lightweight wood, one piece ½″x8″ by 8′6″

Handle and tool rack ......oak, birch, or maple, one piece ¾″x1½″ by 5′6″

Saw rack ....oak, birch, or maple, one piece ¾″x2″ by 6′

Hardware ......two #8x1½″ flathead screws; one ¼x3″ carriage bolt

PROCEDURE

1. End Pieces. It is assumed that the reader knows how to use the most important of the simple tools.

a) Saw the board intended for the end pieces into two equal lengths. Then square each board to ¾″x7½″x13½″. To square up a board it must first be cut to the correct length, width, and thickness; all faces should be planed smooth, true, and square with adjacent faces. The accuracy required depends upon where and how the board is to be used. For achieving a high degree of accuracy, the plane plays an important part; in less exacting cases, a good square cut with the saw might be sufficient.

b) For each end piece, measure off with the framing square 6¼ inches from one end. From this point draw a line square scross the board, then lay out the curves for the upper part which receives the handle, as illustrated in the end view, Fig. 12. Cut out the curves with a coping, or compass, saw. Smooth the edges with a spokeshave or woodfile, and finish with sandpaper. When finished, the width of the end piece at the top should be 1¾ inches.

c) Lay out the slot, ⅝"x1⅜" to receive the handle. Bore a ⅝-inch hole 1¹⁄₁₆ inches down from the top edge of the end piece, and cut out the remaining portion of wood with the saw, cutting on the waste side of the lines and leaving the bottom of the slot round in shape.

2. Bottom. Square up a piece of ½-inch lumber to ½"x7½"x32" for the bottom. Nail the bottom into place with four 6-penny coated nails on each end.

3. Sides. Square up two pieces to ½"x6¼"x32" for the sides and nail into place with four 6-penny coated nails on each end. *Note:* Quarter-inch fir or pine plywood, if available, is equally as strong as ½-inch solid wood and is lighter in weight.

4. The Handle. For the handle, select a piece of hardwood free from defects. Oak, birch, or maple will serve the purpose. The piece should be long enough to extend from outside to outside of the finished toolbox, as shown in Fig. 12.

a) Square up the handle piece to the required size—⅝"x1⅜"x32"—so it will fit tightly into the slots prepared for it in the two end pieces.

b) Chamfer the edges about ⅛ inch or just enough to give the handle a rounded shape.

c) Place the handle in position and bore a ¼-inch hole in each end for the *dowel pins,* or nail the handle in place with 6-penny box nails, Fig. 12.

5. Tool Rack for Holding Small Tools. The tool rack, indicated at (*A*), Fig. 12, should be cut from hardwood—oak, birch, or maple.

a) Square up this piece of hardwood to ¾"x1½"x16".

b) Select the tools which are to be kept in this rack and arrange them in order on the bench. Hold the board for the rack over the tools and mark the sides of the *cutouts.*

c) To make sure each tool will fit tightly into its place, indicate the depth of each cutout on the board with a marking gauge. *Note:* Both faces of the board should be so marked.

d) Make the cutouts with the saw and chisel, then remove the wood on the waste side, little by little.

e) Fasten the rack into place with two #8x1½-inch flathead screws. These should be screwed into the piece from the outside of the toolbox. *Note:* Bore pilot holes for the screws to prevent splitting of the wood.

6. Saw Block for Holding the Saws. The saw block, indicated at *B*, Fig. 12, should be made out of hardwood.

a) Square up a piece of hardwood to ¾"x2"x5½".

b) Lay out three *saw cuts*. The spaces between the cuts should be ½ inch in width. Saw on the lines indicated to within 1 inch from the other end of the block (*B*), Fig. 12.

c) Bore a ¼-inch hole through the block to receive a bolt.

d) Fasten the block into place in the box with a carriage bolt (¼x3 inches), as shown at (*B*), Fig. 12.

7. Painting. Two coats of paint on the outside of the box will help to preserve the wood and make the toolbox more durable. The paint will also improve the appearance of the box.

8. Tool Protection. Tools are exposed frequently to rain and snow. However, the tools can be protected to some extent by a piece of lightweight canvas 2'x2'8" spread over the shoulder box and tacked to the handle.

How to Make a Tool Case

Most mechanics favor a tool case which is not too heavy, yet is large enough to hold his most expensive equipment, Fig. 13. Such a case can be carried around by the mechanic while working, if it is suspended from his shoulder by a rope inserted through a short piece of garden hose and fastened to the two handles of the tool case. However, this case has the disadvantage of being too small to house the framing square which, therefore, must extend out through a hole in the cover, as shown in the side view of Fig. 13.

MATERIALS

Ends ....soft lightweight wood, one piece 1x10 by 1'8"

Bottom and partitions ....soft lightweight wood, two pieces ½"x10" by 2'9"

Top ....plywood, one piece ⅜"x10" by 2'8"

Sides ....plywood, two pieces ⅜"x9⅝" by 2'8"

Tray sides and bottom ....plywood, one piece ¼"x10" by 2'8"

Saw block ....oak, birch, or maple, one piece ¾"x2" by 7¼"

Hardware ....three hinges, one hasp, or trunk lock, and two handles

PROCEDURE

1. Ends of the Tool Case. When a box has a cover similar to that shown in Fig. 13, a better and easier fit of the cover can be obtained by building the box as a single unit, then making a saw cut through the box on a line 2½ inches below the top; the smaller piece becomes the cover.

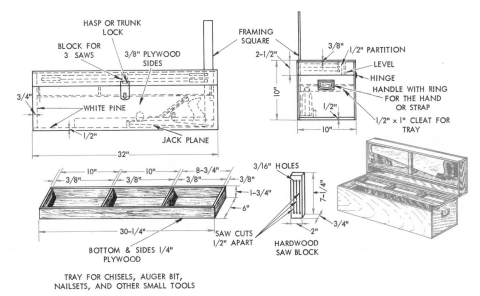

Fig. 13. Tool case: diagram showing construction and thumbnail sketch.

a) Square up two pieces of pine, spruce, or other soft lightweight wood to ¾"x9⅛"x9¼". *Note:* The grain of the wood should run with the 9¼-inch dimension as shown by the finished box in Fig. 13.

2. Bottom. Square up a piece of soft lightweight wood ½"x9¼"x32" for the bottom. Apply waterproof glue to the edges and nail onto the end pieces with 6-penny coated nails.

3. Sides. Square up two pieces of plywood to ⅜"x9⅝"x32". Glue and nail into place with 6-penny nails.

4. Top. Square up a piece of plywood to ⅜"x10"x32" for the top. After the bottom and side pieces have been nailed in position, apply waterproof glue to the edge of the top piece and nail it onto the two end pieces with 6-penny coated nails. Finally, apply waterproof glue to all the joints of the tool case.

5. Cover. In addition to serving its primary purpose as a cover, space is provided here for three saws and a level.

a) With a marking gauge, draw a line around the sides and ends of the box, 2½ inches down from the top and carefully saw the box apart along this line.

b) Fit the cover to the box by smoothing the sawed edges.

c) Prepare a piece of soft lightweight wood for the partition. Saw a piece ½"x10"x33" lengthwise into

299

four strips ½"x2½"x33". Square one piece to ½"x2¼"x30¼". Fit, glue, and nail the partition into place in the cover which will then hold the level and three saws. The size of the level governs the position of the partition. Two turn buttons fastened to this partition will hold the level in place.

d) Prepare a block to hold the saws and fasten it into place. The saw block should be made from a piece of hardwood which has been squared to ¾"x2"x7¼". Cut openings for the saws 3/16 of an inch in width and spaced ½ inch apart as shown in Fig. 13.

e) Cut a slot in the front right-hand corner of the cover for the tongue of the framing square, as shown in Fig. 13.

6. Finish. The tool case should be finished by smoothing the surface with sandpaper and applying paint. Finally, the hinges are added and the trunk lock, or hasp, is put in place to provide protection for the tools.

a) Sandpaper the entire box to a smooth surface, rounding the edges slightly.

b) Apply two coats of paint. The paint serves a twofold purpose, it improves the appearance of the box and also helps preserve the wood, hence prolonging the life of the box.

c) Fasten the cover to the box with three hinges. Then fasten in place the hasp or trunk lock. *Note:*

It is advisable to use flathead brass screws which can be cut off and riveted on the inside. Use flathead screws also for fastening the handles in place. See finished tool case at right in Fig. 13.

7. Inside Fittings. An important feature of the tool case is the inside tray. Tools that are used frequently can be kept in separate compartments. If kept in proper order these tools can be picked up easily when needed.

a) A tray of a size and arrangement that will carry chisels, bits, nail sets, and other small tools is shown in Fig. 13. The bottom and sides of such a tray can be made of ¼-inch plywood. However, it is advisable to use solid wood for the ends and partitions. The size and number of compartments should be arranged to suit the individual needs of the mechanic for whom the case is made. In the illustration given here, there are three compartments—one of 8¾ inches in length and the other two, each 10 inches long. The piece of plywood provided for the tray is 10 inches wide. This should be sawed into three lengthwise strips, one of which is 6 inches wide, the other two, each 2 inches wide. The 6-inch piece serves as the bottom of the tray, and the narrower pieces are for the sides. For the bottom, square a piece of plywood to ¼"x6"x30¼". The side pieces should be squared to ¼"x1½"x30¼". The end pieces and partitions, of soft lightweight wood, should be squared to $\frac{3}{8}"x1\frac{1}{2}"x5\frac{1}{2}"$. Fit and nail the sides and bottom piece to the two end pieces, then nail in the two partitions. The tray rests on two $\frac{1}{2}$x1-inch cleats fastened to the ends of the tool case, as shown in finished box at right, Fig. 13.

b) To protect the cutter of the jack plane, place a small block under the *toe* or *heel* of the plane. A partition one inch high will keep the plane in position. See side view at top, left, Fig. 13.

c) The balance of the storage space in the tool case may be occupied by other tools which are laid in without any special order or arrangement.

How to Make a Suitcase Tool Box

The suitcase toolbox, shown in Fig. 14, is preferred by many carpenters because its height is sufficient to completely house the framing square, and the tool capacity of this type of toolbox is considerably larger than that of the tool case shown in Fig. 13.

MATERIALS

Ends ....soft lightweight wood, one piece 1x8 by 4'0"
Reinforcing bar ....soft lightweight wood, one piece 1x2 by 2'8"
Top and bottom ......soft lightweight wood, two pieces $\frac{1}{2}"$x8" by 2'9"
Sides ....plywood, two pieces $\frac{1}{4}"$x18" by 2'9"
Tray ....plywood, one piece $\frac{1}{4}"$x8" by 2'8"
Saw block ....hardwood, one piece $\frac{3}{4}"$x2" by 0'6"
Strap ....leather, one piece 24"
Hardware ......three hinges, one hasp or trunk lock, two catches, and one suitcase handle

PROCEDURE

The peculiar L-shaped cover of the suitcase toolbox requires building the cover separate from the main part of the box. Otherwise the construction is similar to the case shown in Fig. 13.

1. Bottom or Lower Section. For the outside of this type of toolbox use lightweight wood and plywood.

a) Ends. Square up two pieces of white-pine boards to $\frac{3}{4}"$x6$\frac{1}{2}"$x14$\frac{3}{4}"$ *Note:* The grain of the wood should run up and down on the ends of the suitcase toolbox, as shown in thumbnail sketch Fig. 14, right.

b) Cutout. Lay out on the two end pieces the 2$\frac{3}{4}$x6$\frac{1}{4}$-inch cutout for the cover as shown in Fig. 14. Cut out this portion of each end piece and smooth the edges where the cut is made.

c) Bottom Piece. For the bottom piece square up a piece of white-pine board to $\frac{1}{2}"$x6$\frac{1}{2}"$x32". At the ends of this piece apply waterproof

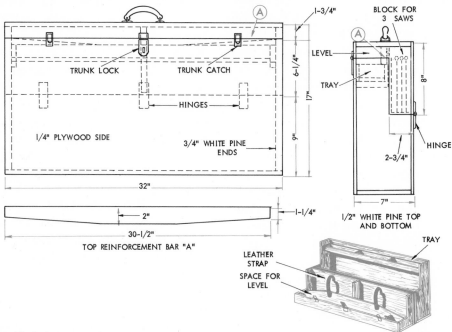

Fig. 14. Suitcase tool box: construction and thumbnail sketch.

glue where the bottom and end pieces meet. Then nail the bottom to the end pieces already prepared. Use 6-penny coated nails for this purpose.

d) Sides. For the side pieces square up two pieces of ¼-inch plywood. One piece should measure ¼"x9"x32"; the other piece should measure ¼"x15¼"x32". Apply waterproof glue where the sides meet the end pieces and the bottom piece. Then nail each side piece to the bottom and the end pieces with 6-penny coated nails.

2. Cover or Upper Section. For the outside of the cover use light-weight wood and plywood the same as that used for the lower section of the toolbox.

a) Ends. Square up two pieces of white-pine boards to ¾"x6½"x7½". The grain of the wood should run up and down.

b) Cutout. Lay out on the two end pieces of the cover the 3¾x6¼-inch cutout. This portion should be cut out so the cover will fit into the bottom section of the end pieces. See Fig. 14. Smooth edges of cut.

c) Top. Square up a piece of white-pine board to ½"x6½"x32". Apply waterproof glue to the outer edges of the ends. Then nail to the end pieces with 6-penny coated nails.

d) Sides. Square up two pieces of plywood for the two sides. One piece should measure 8x32 inches; the other piece should measure 1¾x32 inches. Apply waterproof glue where the sides meet the top and end pieces. Nail the sides into place with 6-penny coated nails.

3. Inside Fittings. The inside fittings of the suitcase toolbox include the reinforcing bar and saw block in the cover, and the small-tool tray fitted into the lower section.

a) Reinforcing Bar. For the reinforcing bar shown at *A* in Fig. 14, use lightweight wood. Square up and shape the bar as illustrated from ¾-inch material. The bar should measure 1¼ inches in width at the two ends and 2 inches in width at the center. The bar extends the full length of the toolbox or 32 inches. Apply waterproof glue to the bar where it meets the cover. Nail the bar into the middle of the cover as shown in Fig. 14. The purpose of the bar is to reinforce the cover and provide a place to fasten the handle.

b) Saw Block. Use a piece of hardwood for the saw block. Prepare the block similar to that shown in the illustration. The piece should measure ¾″x2″x6″. Apply waterproof glue to the block where it meets the cover and nail in place with 6-penny coated nails. To hold the saws in place nail two leather straps to the cover and reinforcing bar as shown in the illustration, Fig. 14. The straps should be about 12 inches in length.

c) Tray. Construct a tray from a piece of plywood. The measurements of the tray should be 3¾ inches in width and 30¼ inches in length. The height should be about 1¾ inches. For illustration see Fig. 14. If desired another tray of the same dimensions can be made to fit below the top tray. The tray can be divided into sections according to individual needs, by fitting in partitions.

4. Finish. After the box has been painted, the three hinges, lock, and catches can be fastened in place.

a) Sandpaper the entire box on the outside, and round the edges slightly.

b) Apply two coats of paint to the outside of the box.

c) After the paint has dried, fasten the hinges, lock, and catches in place with flat-headed brass screws. The screws can then be cut off and riveted on the inside. Finally, fasten the handle on securely with ⅛-inch bolts passed through the top and reinforcing bar.

Steel Square: Advanced Work

Some of the more advanced uses of the steel square are given in Appendix B. The use of the steel square rafter tables are covered for common rafters, hip and valley rafters, and jack rafters. Brace layouts and measurements are explained. The use of the 12th scale on the steel square is detailed.

How to Use Unit-Length Rafter Tables

When laying out rafters for a building, the skilled carpenter uses the unit-length rafter table stamped on the face side of the blade, or body, of the framing square, Fig. 1. This table gives the unit lengths of common rafters for 17 different rises, ranging from 2 inches to 18 inches. It also gives the unit length for hip rafters, difference in lengths of jack rafters set 16 inches on center (O.C.), jack rafters set 24 inches on center, and the side cuts for jack and hip rafters. When the carpenter once learns how to apply the information given in the tables, on the framing square, he finds them clever expedients as timesavers and quite simple. However, he must first understand the principles of roof framing and the laying out of the various rafters before attempting any short-cut methods, or undertaking to apply the information given in the tables. The following examples show how to find the different rafter lengths by means of the rafter tables given on the framing square.

EXAMPLES

For a building with a span of 10 feet and a unit rise of common rafter

Fig. 1. Unit-length rafter table on face of framing square.

LENGTH OF MAIN RAFTERS PER FOOT OF RUN	21.63	18.44	17.69
LENGTH OF HIP OR VALLEY RAFTERS PER FOOT OF RUN	24.74	22.00	21.38
DIFFERENCE IN LENGTH OF JACKS – 16 INCHES ON CENTERS	28.84	24.585	23.588
DIFFERENCES IN LENGTH OF JACKS – 2 FEET ON CENTERS	43.27	36.38	35.38
SIDE CUT OF JACKS	6–11/16	7–13/16	8–1/8
SIDE CUT OF HIP OR VALLEY	8–1/4	9–3/8	9–5/8

of 8 inches, by means of the tables given on the framing square, find:

1. Total length of the common rafter.

2. Total lengths for hip rafters and valley rafters.

3. Side cuts for hip rafters or valley rafters.

4. Common difference of lengths of jack rafters.

5. Side cuts for jack rafters.

1. Total Length of the Common Rafter. A *common rafter* extends from the plate to the ridge; the length of a common rafter is the shortest distance between the outer edge of the plate and a point on the center line of the ridge. The roof frame will not fit tightly together nor the structure be firmly braced unless the rafters are cut to just the right length. To insure correct cutting of rafter lengths by means of the rafter tables, proceed as follows.

PROCEDURE

a) First, find the rafter tables on the face of the blade of the framing square as shown in Fig. 1. Since the unit rise in this problem is 8 inches, locate the *8-inch* mark on the inch line along the outside edge of the rafter tables given on the square. This point is shown in (*A*), Fig. 2.

b) On the first line at the left end of the blade of the square is stamped *Length of main rafters per foot run*, Fig. 1. Follow this line until you come to the *8-inch* mark, shown at (*A*), Fig. 2. Under this mark you will find the number *14.42* on the first line. This means that when the unit rise per foot run is 8 inches the unit length of a main, or common, rafter will be 14.42 inches for every foot of run.

c) Since the span of the building in the example is 10 feet, the run of common rafter will be 5 feet (½ the width of the building). Multiply 14.42, the number of inches for every foot of run, by 5 feet, the number of feet in the run of the common rafter; this will equal 72.10 inches, or 72⅛ inches, equal to 6 feet and ⅛ inch, the total length of the common rafter, shown at (*B*), Fig. 2. This total length is laid out on the rafter

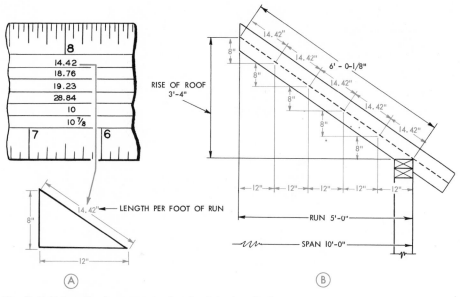

Fig. 2. Unit length of common rafter for 8 inch unit rise.

stock from the ridge cut at the top to the building line at the bottom.

2. Total Lengths for Hip Rafters and Valley Rafters. The *hip rafters* are the heavy rafters which slope up and back from the outside corners of a hip-roofed building to the ridge. The *valley rafters* are similar heavy rafters which also slope up from the outside wall to the ridge of the building, but occur at the intersection where adjacent roof slopes meet and form a valley.

PROCEDURE

a) On the second line at the left end of the blade of the square is stamped *Length of hip or valley rafters per foot run*, Fig. 1. Follow this line until you come to the *8*-inch mark shown at (*A*), Fig. 3. Under this mark you will find the number *18.76* on the second line. This means that when the unit rise per foot run is 8 inches, then for every foot of main, or common, rafter run, the length of the hip rafter will be 18.76 inches or 18¾ inches.

b) The unit length of hip rafter, 18.76 inches multiplied by the number of feet in the run of common rafter, 5 feet (½ the roof span) equals 93.80 inches or 93¹³⁄₁₆ inches which equals 7.81 feet, or 7 feet 9¹¹⁄₁₆ inches, the total length of the hip rafter or valley rafter (*B*), Fig. 3.

3. Side Cuts for Hip or Valley Rafters. Both hip and valley rafters must have an angle cut to fit

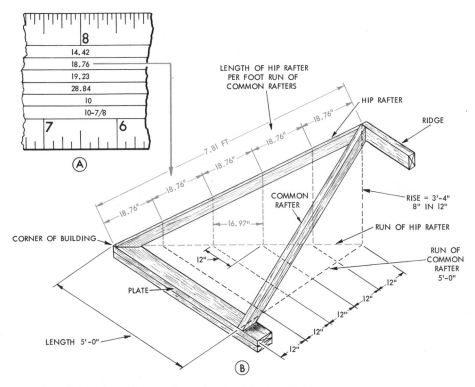

Fig. 3. Unit length of hip or valley rafter for 8 inch unit rise.

against the ridge or common rafter at the top. You will understand why accuracy is important in side cuts for hip and valley rafters when you begin practical construction work.

PROCEDURE

a) On the sixth line at the left end of the blade of the framing square, on the face side, is stamped *Side cut of hip or valley rafters*, Fig. 1. Follow this line to the 8-inch mark the same as you did in finding the lengths of the common and hip rafters. Under the figure *8* will find the number *10⅞* on the sixth line of the rafter table, shown at (*A*), Fig. 4.

b) On the rafter stock which is to be cut, lay the square in the position shown at (*B*), Fig. 4. Take the *12*-inch mark on the tongue and the *10⅞*-inch mark on the blade and hold the square in the position shown at (*B*), Fig. 4. Mark a line for cutting along the outside of the tongue on the 12-inch side of the square.

4. Common Difference of Lengths of Jack Rafters. In every roof containing a hip or a valley there

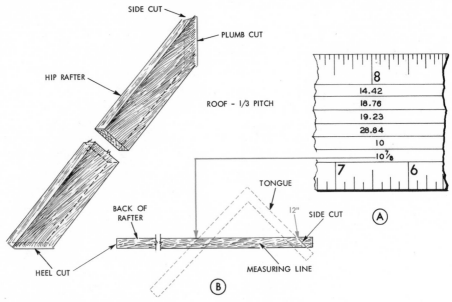

Fig. 4. Side cuts for hip and valley rafters, using figure shown in sixth line of table.

are some rafters known as *jack raft-ers* which are common rafters *cut off*, by the intersection of a hip or valley rafter, before reaching the full length from the plate to the ridge. Jack rafters are spaced the same distance apart as the common rafters, usually 12, 16, or 24 inches on center. Because the jack rafters fill a triangular-shaped space in the roof surface these rafters vary in length. Since they rest against the hip or valley rafters, equally spaced, the second jack rafter must be twice as long as the first one, the third jack rafter three times as long as the first one and so on. This establishes a common difference in jack rafters for various pitches. These dif-

ferences in lengths of jack rafters are given on the third and fourth lines of the rafter table found on the face side of the framing square, Fig. 1. The jack rafters have the same rise per foot run as the common rafters on the same slope of the roof, and the cuts where they rest against the wall plate or the ridge board are obtained in the same way as for common-rafter cuts, previously explained. Jack rafters differ from common rafters in length and in the side cut necessary to make them fit against the hip or valley rafter. When a roof slope has an 8-inch rise per foot run of common rafter and the jack rafters are spaced 16 inches on center, to find the common difference in lengths of these rafters proceed as follows.

PROCEDURE

a) On the third line at the left end of the blade of the framing square, on the face side, is stamped *Difference in length of jacks 16 inches centers.* Follow this line of the rafter table until you come to the 8-inch mark. Under this mark is the number *19.23.* This means that the difference in length of jack rafters or the length of the first and shortest jack rafter is 19.23 inches. To find the length of the third jack rafter multiply 19.23 by 3 which gives 57.69 inches, or 4 feet 9⅔ inches. When the spacing between the jack rafters is more than 24 inches the dimension is given in feet instead of inches.

b) On the fourth line at the left end of the blade of the square, on the face side, is stamped *Difference in lengths of jacks 2 feet conters,* Fig. 1. Follow along this line until you come to the 8-inch mark, Fig. 4. Under this figure, on the fourth line of the rafter table, you will find the number *28.84.* This means that the difference in length of jack rafters spaced 2 feet on center is 28.84 inches, or 2 feet 4.84 inches.

5. Side Cuts for Jack Rafters. Jack rafters must have an angle or side cut to fit against the hip or valley rafter. The angle of this cut can be found by again making use of the rafter table, on the face side, of the framing square.

PROCEDURE

a) On the fifth line of the rafter table at the left end of the framing square, on the face side, is stamped *Side cut of jacks.* Follow along this line to the 8-inch mark. Under this figure on the fifth line you will find the number *10,* Fig. 4.

b) On the stock which is to be used for jack rafters, lay the framing square in a position similar to that for side cuts of hip and valley rafters, shown at *(B),* Fig. 4. Since the number in the fifth line of the rafter table, under the 8-inch mark is *10,* locate this number on the blade of the square and *12* on the tongue of the square. Hold the square firmly in position at these two points while drawing the cutting line along the outside of the tongue of the square as shown at *(B),* Fig. 4. This will give the side cuts for the jack rafters on a roof that has a unit rise of 8 inches per foot of run of common rafter.

Study the diagrams and learn the locations of: *span, run, rise, pitch, common rafters, hip* and *valley rafters, jack rafters, plates,* and *the measuring line of the ridge.* With the illustrations at hand, study the procedures for working the various examples given in this chapter.

RULES

It would be to your advantage

later, if you would learn the following rules at this time.

Rule 1. The *total length of a common rafter* (Fig. 1) can be found by multiplying the length given in the rafter table under the figure representing the unit rise of the rafter by the number of feet of run.

Rule 2. The *total length for hip and valley rafters* (Fig. 3) can be found by multiplying the length given in the rafter table under the figure representing the unit rise of the rafter by the number of feet of run of the common rafter.

Rule 3. The *side cut for a hip or a valley rafter* can be found by taking the figure given in the rafter table, under the figure representing the unit rise of the rafter, on the blade of the square, and 12 inches on the tongue. Then draw a line along the tongue. This will give the cutting line for the side cut.

Rule 4. The *length of a jack rafter* can be found by multiplying the value given in the rafter table, under the figure representing the unit rise of the rafter, by the number indicating the position of that particular jack; that is, multiplying by 3 for the third jack.

Rule 5. The *side cuts for jack rafters* can be found by taking the figure shown in the table, under the figure representing the unit rise of the rafter, on the blade of the square and 12 inches on the tongue. Then

draw a line along the tongue for the side cut.

Brace Layout

1. The principles involved in laying out a brace are the same as those for laying out a common rafter. The common rafter represents the hypotenuse of a right triangle, while the run and rise of the rafter represent the other two sides of the triangle, as shown at (B), Fig. 3. Likewise, a brace represents the hypotenuse, while the run and rise of the brace represent the other two sides of a right triangle, 1—2—3, Fig. 5. Note that when cutting the brace to fit at the top (1) and at the bottom (3) the method used is the same as that for the common rafter. Also, the length for a long brace is stepped off in the same way as for a common rafter.

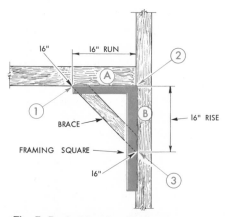

Fig. 5. Basic triangle of a brace.

PROCEDURE

a) When the run and rise of a brace are the same length, the brace represents the hypotenuse of a right triangle in which each of the acute angles is 45 degrees. The brace then is a 45-degree brace, Fig. 6.

b) For this type of brace, the angles for the cutting lines are laid out by taking the same figure on both the tongue and blade of the square. For example, if the run and rise are 16 inches or less in length, the brace can be laid out by taking the run on the tongue and the rise on the blade.

c) Draw a line along the tongue for the angle of the cut to fit against the top *(A)*, Fig. 5. Another line drawn along the blade will give the angle for the cut to fit against *(B)*, Fig. 5.

d) A line connecting points *(1)* and *(3)* will give the length of the outside of the brace as shown in Fig. 5.

e) For long braces, when the run and rise are the same length, the step method can be used to find the total length of the brace, as shown in Fig. 6. Here we assume the run and rise to be 48 inches, or 4 feet.

f) Lay the square in position near the right end of the piece of timber which is to be used for a brace. The 12-inch mark on both the blade and tongue should be exactly on the edge of the timber as shown in Fig. 6.

g) Holding the square firmly in this position, draw lines along the outside edge of both the blade and the tongue.

h) Next, move the square along the timber toward the left until the 12-inch mark on the blade coincides with the same point where the 12-inch mark of the tongue was in the previous position. Again draw lines along the outside of both blade and tongue. Continue this procedure until the four steps have been completed. The cutting lines of the brace at the points *(1)* and *(3)* will make an angle which fits at top and side. Care should be taken in using this method as a slight error will spoil the angle cut and cause an imperfect fit of the brace.

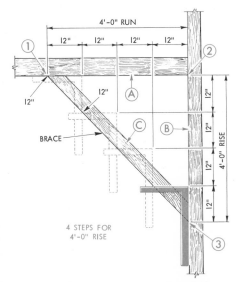

Fig. 6. Method of stepping off length of brace having equal run and rise.

2. For long braces when the total run is less than the total rise, to find the length of the brace and the angle cuts for the top and side, the total run is divided into as many units as there are feet in the rise. For example, if the total rise is 48 inches and the run 36 inches, since the rise contains four 12-inch units, then the run should be divided into four 9-inch units, as shown in Fig. 7.

PROCEDURE

a) Lay the square in position near the right end of the piece which is to be used for the brace, with the 9-inch mark of the tongue and the 12-inch mark of the blade exactly on the edge of the timber as shown in Fig. 7.

b) Draw lines along the outside edge of both blade and tongue. Then move the square to the left until the 12-inch mark of the blade coincides with the point where the 9-inch mark of the tongue was in the previous position.

c) Again draw lines along the outside edge of the blade and tongue of the square. Repeat this procedure until four positions of the square have been stepped off. This will give the length for a brace when the rise is 48 inches and the run 36 inches.

d) Cutting the timber on the lines indicated at each end will give the correct angle for fitting the brace at the top (*A*), and at the side (*B*), Fig. 7.

Brace Measure

Along the center of the back of the tongue of the framing square you will find a table which gives the lengths of common braces. This series of figures known as the *brace measure*, or the *brace rule*, is illustrated in Fig. 8.

The use of this table is somewhat limited since it is chiefly for 45-degree braces. For example, the figures of the table show that when the run and rise of the brace are both 36 inches, then the length of the brace will be 50.91 inches; or if the rise and run are both 24 inches, the length of the brace will be 33.94 inches. However, the last set of fig-

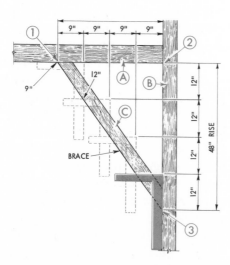

Fig. 7. Stepping off length of brace with unequal run and rise.

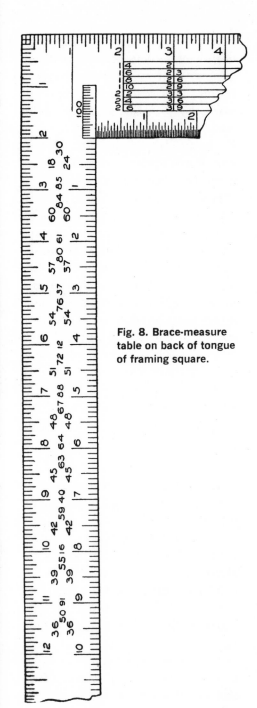

Fig. 8. Brace-measure table on back of tongue of framing square.

ures shown at the right end of the tongue is for braces which have the proportion of 18 inches of run to 24 inches of rise giving a brace of 30 inches in length.

Whenever possible to use it, the brace-measure table is convenient since it gives the total length of a brace, thus making it unnecessary to use the step-off method previously explained. Application of the table is illustrated in Fig. 9. Any multiple of the figures found in this table can also be used.

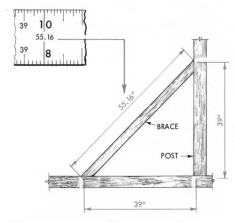

Fig. 9. Application of brace measure found on framing square.

EXAMPLE
Find the length of a brace with run and rise of 78 inches.

PROCEDURE
a) Since the figure 78 is not given on the table we use the multiple 39

313

which is one-half of 78. The table shows that when the run and rise of a brace are both 39 inches, then the length of the brace is 55.16 inches.

b) Since 39 inches is one-half of 78 inches, then twice 55.16 inches, or 110.32 inches, is the total length of the brace which has a run and rise of 78 inches.

The foregoing example shows that if you have a brace whose run and rise is longer than any run or rise shown in the brace-measure table, you can find the length of the brace by finding one-half the actual run or rise in the brace measure and then doubling the length given for it. Thus for a run and rise of 78 inches, you find $\frac{39}{39}$ *55.16* on the square and the length of the brace will be twice 55.16, which is 110.32 inches, or 9 feet 2.32 inches.

The 12th Scale on Framing Square

The 12th scale, with the inch divided into 12 parts instead of 16, is usually found on the back of the framing square along the outside edge. In this scale an inch represents one foot and each inch is divided into 12 parts; hence, each one of these parts or graduations equals 1 inch on the 12th scale. Thus, the 12th scale makes it possible to reduce layouts to $\frac{1}{12}$th of their regular size while still retaining the same proportions.

The 12th scale on the framing square can be put to many uses in roof framing. This scale is especially useful for solving basic right triangles, without mathematical computation. This scale also enables the workman to make a layout of his work for a building, or any part of it, one-twelfth ($\frac{1}{12}$th) of the regular size. If the layout is carefully made it can be relied upon to give reasonably accurate results. Many carpenters prefer to find rafter lengths by using the 12th scale instead of using the step method or the mathematical method. However, use of the 12th-scale method demands accuracy and unless the work is carefully done errors may occur. Use of the 12th scale is recommended for making an over-all check of rafter lengths when rafters are laid out by other methods.

Methods for using the 12th scale, given on the framing square, are explained by means of the following examples.

EXAMPLES

1. Find the total rise and total length of a rafter when total run and unit rise are given.

2. Find the unit rise of a rafter when the total rise and total run are given.

3. Find the theoretical length of a hip or valley rafter when the total run and the unit rise of the common rafter are given.

1. Find the Total Rise and Total Length of a Rafter When Total Run and Unit Rise Are Given. The total run of a rafter is 6 feet 7 inches and the unit rise is 8 inches. To find the total rise and total length.

PROCEDURE

a) Lay the framing square to the *cut* of the roof (*8* on the tongue and *12* on the blade) on a board with a sharp and straight edge, position (*1*), Fig. 10.

b) With a sharp pencil or a knife draw a line along the blade or run side of the square.

c) Slide the square, that is, move it to the right along this line until the figures $6\frac{7}{12}$ are directly over the lower edge of the board, position (*2*).

d) Hold the square to this line with the edge of the blade coinciding with the line and the tongue perpendicular to the line. Then read the figure on the tongue at the edge of the board. This figure should be *4* and *4½/12ths*, or 4 feet and 4½ inches, which will be the total rise of the rafter.

e) While the square is in this position (position 2), mark the edge

of the board on the tongue side of the square, as shown in Fig. 10.

f) Measure along the edge of the board with the 12th scale the distance between the line and the mark just made. This distance should read $7^{11}/_{12}ths$ or 7 feet and 11 inches, the total length of the rafter.

2. Find the Unit Rise of a Rafter When the Total Rise and Total Run Are Given. A rafter has a total run of 9 feet 6 inches and a total rise of 7 feet 11 inches. To find the unit rise.

PROCEDURE

a) Place the framing square as before on a board with a straight and smooth edge using $9^{6}/_{12}ths$ inches on the blade and $7^{11}/_{12}ths$ inches on the tongue, position (*1*), Fig. 11.

b) Mark along the blade with a sharp pencil or knife.

c) Slide the blade of the square along this line to the left so the figure *12* (unit run) is over the lower edge of the board, position (*2*), Fig. 11.

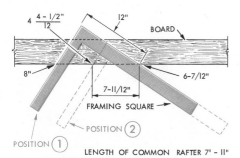

Fig. 10. Finding total rise and total length of common rafter on 12th scale.

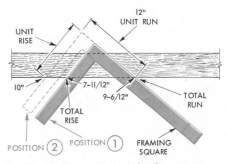

Fig. 11. Finding unit rise of rafter on 12th scale.

d) Read the figure on the tongue directly over the edge of the board. This should read *10* inches. Therefore, 10 inches is the unit rise for a rafter that has a total run of 9 feet 6 inches and a total rise of 7 feet 11 inches.

The 12th scale can also be used to find the theoretical length of the hip or valley rafters, as shown in the following example.

3. To Find the Theoretical Length of a Hip or Valley Rafter. The run of the common rafter of a roof is 6 feet 7 inches and the unit rise is 8 inches. Find the theoretical length of the hip or valley rafter.

PROCEDURE

a) Lay the framing square on a board with a straight and smooth edge, in the position shown in Fig. 12. Then take the figure *6⁷⁄₁₂ths* inches (run of the common rafter) on the blade and the same figures on the tongue. Make a mark along the blade and the tongue with a sharp pencil, as shown in Fig. 12.

b) The distance between these two marks will be *9⁴⁄₁₂ths* inches. Therefore, the total run of the hip or valley rafter will be 9 feet and 4 inches. The total run of the hip and valley rafter is the diagonal of a square whose sides are equal to the common rafter run, in this case 6 feet and 7 inches.

c) Find the total rise, 4 feet and 4 inches, by the method shown in Fig. 10.

d) Lay the square on the edge of the board, as shown in Fig. 13, taking *4⁴⁄₁₂ths* (total rise) on the tongue and 9⁴⁄₁₂ths (total run) on the blade. Mark with a sharp pencil on both sides of the square.

e) The distance between these two points will measure *10³⁄₁₂ths* inches. Therefore, the theoretical length of the hip or valley rafter will be 10 feet 3 inches.

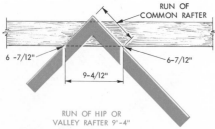

Fig. 12. Finding total run of hip or valley rafter on 12th scale.

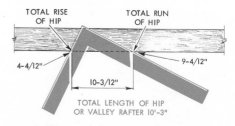

Fig. 13. Method of finding theoretical length of hip or valley rafter on 12th scale.

Softwood Lumber Standards

Lumber standards, both softwood and hardwood, are sponsored by the U.S. Department of Commerce, National Bureau of Standards, and voted on the affected lumber manufacturers, lumber mills, home builders, etc. When agreement is reached as to the acceptability of a proposed standard, it is adopted and adhered to by the industry. More than a majority acceptance, however, is needed before a lumber standard is adopted. The Department of Commerce requires that a *consensus* within the industry must be reached.

The Department of Commerce, in proposing new lumber standards, follows the recommendations of the American Lumber Standards Committee. This committee is composed of representatives from the lumber industry.

Recently a new standard for softwood lumber was adopted, (PS20-70). The major effect of the new softwood lumber standard is to reduce the *actual* sizes of lumber. For example, a nominal 2 inch dry dimension would have an actual size of 1½ inch in the proposed standard, as opposed to 1⅝ inch in the old standard. The new softwood standard also establishes the moisture content of *dry lumber* at a maximum of 19 percent.

The following tables present information on lumber sizes based on the new American Softwood Lumber Standard, PS20-70.

TABLE 1. NOMINAL AND MINIMUM DRESSED DRY SIZES OF FINISH, FLOORING, CEILING, PARTITION, AND STEPPING AT 19 PERCENT MAXIMUM MOISTURE CONTENT.

(The thicknesses apply to all widths and all widths to all thicknesses except as modified.)

Item	Thicknesses		Face Widths	
	Nominal [1] Inches	Minimum Dressed Inches	Nominal Inches	Minimum Dressed Inches
Finish	3/8	5/16	2	1-1/2
	1/2	7/16	3	2-1/2
	5/8	9/16	4	3-1/2
	3/4	5/8	5	4-1/2
	1	3/4	6	5-1/2
	1-1/4	1	7	6-1/2
	1-1/2	1-1/4	8	7-1/4
	1-3/4	1-3/8	9	8-1/4
	2	1-1/2	10	9-1/4
	2-1/2	2	11	10-1/4
	3	2-1/2	12	11-1/4
	3-1/2	3	14	13-1/4
	4	3-1/2	16	15-1/4
Flooring[2]	3/8	5/16	2	1-1/8
	1/2	7/16	3	2-1/8
	5/8	9/16	4	3-1/8
	1	3/4	5	4-1/8
	1-1/4	1	6	5-1/8
	1-1/2	1-1/4		
Ceiling[2]	3/8	5/16	3	2-1/8
	1/2	7/16	4	3-1/8
	5/8	9/16	5	4-1/8
	3/4	11/16	6	5-1/8
Partition[2]	1	23/32	3	2-1/8
			4	3-1/8
			5	4-1/8
			6	5-1/8
Stepping[2]	1	3/4	8	7-1/4
	1-1/4	1	10	9-1/4
	1-1/2	1-1/4	12	11-1/4
	2	1-1/2		

[1]/ For nominal thicknesses under 1 inch, the board measure count is based on the nominal surface dimensions (width by length). With the exception of nominal thicknesses under 1 inch, the nominal thicknesses and widths in this table are the same as the board measure or count sizes.

[2]/ In tongued-and-grooved flooring and in tongued-and-grooved and shiplapped ceiling of 5/16 inch, 7/16 inch, and 9/16 inch dressed thicknesses, the tongue or lap shall be 3/16 inch wide, with the overall widths 3/16 inch wider than the face widths shown in the table above. In all other worked lumber of dressed thicknesses of 5/8 inch to 1-1/4 inch, the tongue shall be 1/4 inch wide or wider in tongued-and-grooved lumber, and the lap 3/8 inch wide or wider in shiplapped lumber, and the overall widths shall be not less than the dressed face widths shown in the above table plus the width of the tongue or lap.

TABLE 2. NOMINAL AND MINIMUM DRESSED DRY SIZES OF SIDING AT 19 PERCENT MAXIMUM MOISTURE CONTENT.

(The thicknesses apply to all widths and all widths to all thicknesses.)

Item	Thicknesses		Face Widths	
	Nominal [1] Inches	Minimum Dressed Inches	Nominal Inches	Minimum Dressed Inches
Bevel Siding	1/2 9/16 5/8 3/4 1	7/16 butt, 3/16 tip 15/32 butt, 3/16 tip 9/16 butt, 3/16 tip 11/16 butt, 3/16 tip 3/4 butt, 3/16 tip	4 5 6 8 10 12	3-1/2 4-1/2 5-1/2 7-1/4 9-1/4 11-1/4
Bungalow Siding	3/4	11/16 butt, 3/16 tip	8 10 12	7-1/4 9-1/4 11-1/4
Rustic and Drop Siding (shiplapped, 3/8-in. lap)	5/8 1	9/16 23/32	4 5 6	3 4 5
Rustic and Drop Siding (shiplapped, 1/2-in. lap)	5/8 1	9/16 23/32	4 5 6 8 10 12	2-7/8 3-7/8 4-7/8 6-5/8 8-5/8 10-5/8
Rustic and Drop Siding (dressed and matched)	5/8 1	9/16 23/32	4 5 6 8 10	3-1/8 4-1/8 5-1/8 6-7/8 8-7/8

1/ For nominal thicknesses under 1 inch, the board measure count is based on the nominal surface dimensions (width by length). With the exception of nominal thicknesses under 1 inch, the nominal thicknesses and widths in this table are the same as the board measure or count sizes.

TABLE 3. NOMINAL AND MINIMUM DRESSED SIZES OF BOARDS, DIMENSION, AND TIMBERS.

(The thicknesses apply to all widths and all widths to all thicknesses.)

ITEM	Thicknesses			Face Widths		
		Minimum Dressed			Minimum Dressed	
	Nominal	Dry[1]	Green[1]	Nominal	Dry[1]	Green[1]
Boards[2]	1 1-1/4 1-1/2	3/4 1 1-1/4	25/32 1-1/32 1-9/32	2 3 4 5 6 7 8 9 10 11 12 14 16	1-1/2 2-1/2 3-1/2 4-1/2 5-1/2 6-1/2 7-1/4 8-1/4 9-1/4 10-1/4 11-1/4 13-1/4 15-1/4	1-9/16 2-9/16 3-9/16 4-5/8 5-5/8 6-5/8 7-1/2 8-1/2 9-1/2 10-1/2 11-1/2 13-1/2 15-1/2
Dimension	2 2-1/2 3 3-1/2	1-1/2 2 2-1/2 3	1-9/16 2-1/16 2-9/16 3-1/16	2 3 4 5 6 8 10 12 14 16	1-1/2 2-1/2 3-1/2 4-1/2 5-1/2 7-1/4 9-1/4 11-1/4 13-1/4 15-1/4	1-9/16 2-9/16 3-9/16 4-5/8 5-5/8 7-1/2 9-1/2 11-1/2 13-1/2 15-1/2
Dimension	4 4-1/2	3-1/2 4	3-9/16 4-1/16	2 3 4 5 6 8 10 12 14 16	1-1/2 2-1/2 3-1/2 4-1/2 5-1/2 7-1/4 9-1/4 11-1/4	1-9/16 2-9/16 3-9/16 4-5/8 5-5/8 7-1/2 9-1/2 11-1/2 13-1/2 15-1/2
Timbers	5 and thicker	1/2 off		5 and thicker	1/2 off	

[1] Dry Lumber. For the purposes of this standard, dry lumber is defined as lumber which has been seasoned or dried to a moisture content of 19 percent or less.

Green Lumber. For the purpose of this standard, green lumber is defined as lumber having a moisture content in excess of 19 percent.

[2] Boards less than the minimum thickness for 1 inch nominal but 5/8 inch or greater thickness dry (11/16 inch green) may be regarded as American Standard Lumber, but such boards shall be marked to show the size and condition of seasoning at the time of dressing. They shall also be distinguished from 1 inch boards on invoices and certificates.

TABLE 4. NOMINAL AND MINIMUM DRESSED SIZES OF (2-inch and under) SHIPLAP, CENTERMATCH AND D & M.

(The thicknesses apply to all widths and all widths to all thicknesses)

Item	Thicknesses			Face Widths		
		Minimum Dressed			Minimum Dressed	
	Nominal Inches	Dry[1] Inches	Green[1] Inches	Nominal Inches	Dry[1] Inches	Green[1] Inches
Shiplap . . . . . 3/8-inch lap	1	3/4	25/32	4 6 8 10 12 14 16	3-1/8 5-1/8 6-7/8 8-7/8 10-7/8 12-7/8 14-7/8	3-3/16 5-1/4 7-1/8 9-1/8 11-1/8 13-1/8 15-1/8
Shiplap . . . . . 1/2-inch lap	1	3/4	25/32	4 6 8 10 12 14 16	3 5 6-3/4 8-3/4 10-3/4 12-3/4 14-3/4	3-1/16 5-1/8 7 9 11 13 15
Centermatch . . . 1/4 -inch tongue	1 1-1/4 1-1/2	3/4 1 1-1/4	25/32 1-1/32 1-9/32	4 5 6 8 10 12	3-1/8 4-1/8 5-1/8 6-7/8 8-7/8 10-7/8	3-3/16 4-1/4 5-1/4 7-1/8 9-1/8 11-1/8
2" D & M 3/8-inch tongue	2	1-1/2	1-9/16	4 6 8 10 12	3 5 6-3/4 8-3/4 10-3/4	3-1/16 5-1/8 7 9 11
2" Shiplap 1/2-inch lap	2	1-1/2	1-9/16	4 6 8 10 12	3 5 6-3/4 8-3/4 10-3/4	3-1/16 5-1/8 7 9 11

1/ Dry Lumber. For the purposes of this standard, dry lumber is defined as lumber which has been seasoned or dried to a moisture content of 19 percent or less.

Green Lumber. For the purpose of this standard, green lumber is defined as lumber having a moisture content in excess of 19 percent.

TABLE 5. WORKED LUMBER, SUCH AS FACTORY FLOORING, HEAVY ROOFING
DECKING, AND SHEET PILING.

(The thicknesses apply to all widths and all widths to all thicknesses.)
See "NOTE"

THICKNESSES[1]			FACE WIDTHS		
NOMINAL	MINIMUM DRESSED		NOMINAL	MINIMUM DRESSED	
	Inches			Inches	
TONGUE AND GROOVED					
	Dry	Green		Dry	Green
2-1/2	2	2-1/16	4	3	3-1/16
3	2-1/2	2-9/16	6	5	5-1/8
3-1/2	3	3-1/16	8	6-3/4	7
4	3-1/2	3-9/16	10	8-3/4	9
4-1/2	4	4-1/16	12	10-3/4	11
SHIPLAP					
	Dry	Green		Dry	Green
2-1/2	2	2-1/16	4	3	3-1/16
3	2-1/2	2-9/16	6	5	5-1/8
3-1/2	3	3-1/16	8	6-3/4	7
4	3-1/2	3-9/16	10	8-3/4	9
4-1/2	4	4-1/16	12	10-3/4	11
GROOVED-FOR-SPLINES					
	Dry	Green		Dry	Green
2-1/2	2	2-1/16	4	3-1/2	3-9/16
3	2-1/2	2-9/16	6	5-1/2	5-5/8
3-1/2	3	3-1/16	8	7-1/4	7-1/2
4	3-1/2	3-9/16	10	9-1/4	9-1/2
4-1/2	4	4-1/16	12	11-1/4	11-1/2

NOTE: In worked lumber of nominal thicknesses of 2 inch and over, the tongue shall be 3/8
inch wide in tongued-and-grooved lumber and the lap 1/2 inch wide in shiplapped
lumber, with the overall widths 3/8 inch and 1/2 inch wider, respectively, than
the face widths shown in the above table. Double tongued-and-grooved decking may be
manufactured with a 5/16-inch tongue.

[1] See Table 3 for information on 2 inch dimension.

First Aid Equipment

A carpenter's equipment is not complete without a few essential first-aid supplies. These supplies should include at least antiseptics, bandages, and first aid for burns. Such provisions will help to prevent infection after minor skin injuries, bruises, and burns. Tweezers for removing splinters will also be useful. Provision should be made also to avoid excessive loss of blood, heat exhaustion, and eye injuries. A minimum supply of first-aid provisions should include the following materials:

Antiseptic. A small bottle of an antiseptic with applicator of either mercurochrome or metaphan.

Bandages. Four compresses, three inches square, sealed in wax paper; a small roll of 1-inch gauze; a five-yard roll of ½-inch adhesive tape; and a package of band aids.

First Aid for Burns. One tube of Butesin Picrate or Sulfa Diazine.

Heat Exhaustion. One bottle of 50 sodium chloride (common table salt) tablets. There are two kinds of sodium chloride tablets — the plain and the enteric coated. The enteric coated do not dissolve until they reach the intestines. This avoids stomach disturbances.

Eye Protection. Every tool kit should contain a good pair of goggles for eye protection when drilling holes or when using abrasive tools or papers.

Instruction. The physical well-being of the carpenter is of equal or greater importance than his skill or knowledge of the trade. The carpenter must be physically fit in order to do his work properly. He must not only keep himself physically fit but he must be safety conscious also in order to protect himself and his fellow workers against accidents and the consequent loss of time on the job. Although the carpenter may be safety conscious and take every precaution possible to prevent accidents, nevertheless, he should be able to administer simple first aid to an injured worker when accidents occur. A reliable instruction book on first aid should have a place in his tool kit. The *American Red Cross First Aid Book* is recommended.

Accidents are all too frequent in the construction industry, yet the severity of these accidents is not as great as in many other industries. Large construction organizations have their safety engineers, doctors, nurses, and hospital facilities. However, the smaller organizations, unfortunately, cannot provide these aids. Therefore, the carpenter in the small organization must be his own safety engineer and be prepared to administer first aid to an injured worker. It is of prime importance then that every mechanic become safety conscious, thinking in terms of safety for himself and others while performing every operation in the process of erecting a building. Since safety instruction becomes most effective when given as the situation or need arises, such instruction is given throughout this book in connection with the various construction operations.

It is not within the scope of this text to deal with first aid, hence this information must be obtained from another source such as the textbook issued by the American Red Cross. However, a few suggestions are advisable here.

1. The carpenter should develop safety consciousness, since "an ounce of prevention is worth a pound of cure."

2. He should protect his eyes with goggles when working near flying objects.

3. Slight cuts, bruises, or skin breaks should be treated immediately with an antiseptic and protected with a bandage to prevent infection. *Note:* Never put adhesive tape directly on a wound.

4. Air, dust, and dirt should be excluded from burns with butesin picrate or sulfa diazine, then covered with a bandage immediately.

5. To avoid heat exhaustion, a construction worker should drink plenty of water and take salt tables to replace the salt lost from the body through perspiration.

6. Before moving an injured worker, always examine him for broken bones. This precaution may prevent compound fractures.

7. In case of serious injuries, always call or see a doctor as quickly as possible.

Buildings are designed by architects and building designers who must be trained in many aspects of structural engineering as well as in artistic fields.

The architect puts his ideas on a drawing which is then duplicated many times by means of blueprints. These blueprints are the source of information to the various building tradesmen as to where, what kinds, and how they will perform the work of their trade. The blueprints are working drawings that each building tradesman must follow if the building is to be built correctly.

Every carpenter must know how to read and interpret blueprints. He is responsible for following the blueprints as they are drawn, or referring to them with the contractor or architect.

This information is not intended to teach you to read blueprints. You should have had a course in blueprint reading before using this text or you should have instruction in blueprint reading along with the explanations given in this chapter. This information should serve to refresh your memory or to emphasize the major points that you, as a carpenter, will need to know most.

Scale

Because of the large size of a house, full-sized drawings would be inconvenient, expensive, and impractical. Therefore, the drawings are made to *scale;* that is, reduced proportionately to a size which can be made and handled conveniently. House drawings usually are drawn to a one-fourth inch scale, indicated as ¼″=1′0″. This means that every ¼″ on the drawing will equal one foot on the building, or the building will be 48 times larger than the drawing. To reduce the size of the drawings for larger buildings, the ⅛″ scale (⅛″=1′0″) is frequently used. Some parts of a building are more complicated than others and to show the details better these parts are drawn to a larger scale, ½″=1′0″, or ¾″=1′0″, or 1½″=1′0″. Certain complicated details are sometimes drawn full size; for example, the plaster cornice and head of the entrance.

By using these various scales, Fig. 1, the architect makes it possible for the builder to use his own rule to make scaled measurements on draw-

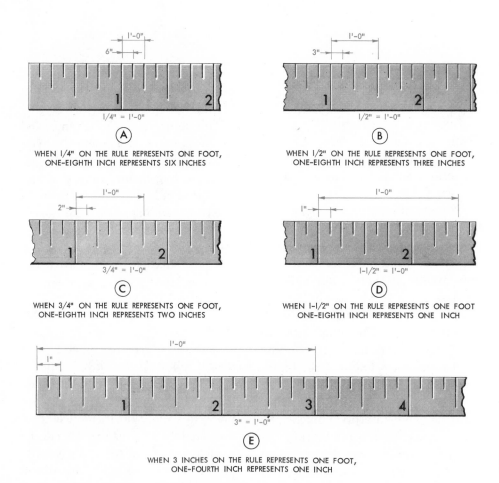

WHEN 1/4" ON THE RULE REPRESENTS ONE FOOT,
ONE-EIGHTH INCH REPRESENTS SIX INCHES

WHEN 1/2" ON THE RULE REPRESENTS ONE FOOT,
ONE-EIGHTH INCH REPRESENTS THREE INCHES

WHEN 3/4" ON THE RULE REPRESENTS ONE FOOT,
ONE-EIGHTH INCH REPRESENTS TWO INCHES

WHEN 1-1/2" ON THE RULE REPRESENTS ONE FOOT
ONE-EIGHTH INCH REPRESENTS ONE INCH

WHEN 3 INCHES ON THE RULE REPRESENTS ONE FOOT,
ONE-FOURTH INCH REPRESENTS ONE INCH

Fig. 1. Scales showing method of reducing dimensions on architectural drawings.

ings. Therefore, it is essential that the carpenter find out the scale to which the drawings are made before he begins taking any measurements with his rule. Scale is almost always indicated on the blueprint just below the drawing. *Example:* ¾″=1′0″.

Types of Lines

Full or Visible Lines. Border lines and the outline, or visible parts, of the house are always represented by *full*, or *visible lines*, Fig. 2.

Hidden Lines. The outline of hidden, or invisible, parts of a house are shown by *dash lines*. These represent the outline of parts which may be hidden under floors, within walls, or occur beyond or behind elevations.

Center Lines. Fine, alternate long and short lines used to show the center of the axis of an object are called *center lines*. The center of a round object is shown by two intersecting center lines.

Extension Lines. Fine lines which show the extreme limits of a dimension are called *extension lines*.

Dimension Lines. Fine solid lines, terminated by arrowheads and used to indicate distances between points and lines, are called *dimension lines*, Fig. 2. The radius of a circle is indicated by a dimension line drawn from the center of the circle and terminating with an arrow at the circumference of the circle. The length of the radius is expressed by the dimension and the letter R; that is, ¾″R means the center of the

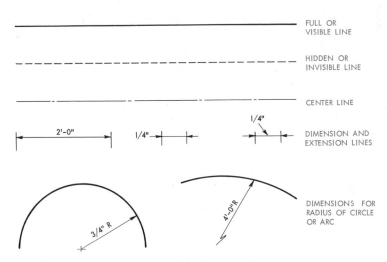

Fig. 2. Various types of lines used on architectural drawings.

circle is three-fourths of an inch from the circumference.

The *ceiling lines* and *floor lines* are shown as heavy, alternate long and short lines in the elevation drawings. (The elevation in Fig. 4 illustrates ceiling lines and floor lines.)

Working Drawings

Every construction job except the very smallest cabins and garages has a set of *working drawings*. These are copies made from the original set of architectural drawings done by the architect. Generally a number of sets of working drawings are made so that each building craft can have a set for its own use. The working drawings include all the information necessary to construct the building. They are supplemented with a set of *specifications* which contains, in written form, information that is not shown on the drawings. Thus a blueprint will show where a wooden beam is to be installed and its size, but the specification will state what kind of wood, grade, and finish that must be used.

The blueprints will show dimension, location of openings and floors, electrical work, plumbing, heating, millwork, masonry, painting, etc., as well as carpentry information. The purpose of these drawings is to furnish definite information to every one concerned as to just what the building is to be like. The drawings, and specifications that go with them, let the contractor, owner, material dealers, and tradesmen understand just what has been decided by the architect and owner for the building. A well-drawn set of drawings and well-written specifications will prevent disagreements and misunderstanding.

For practice in blueprint reading the carpenter should study *Building Trades Blueprint Reading, Part I* by Elmer W. Sundberg. This gives detailed instructions on interpreting and understanding blueprints. Only a representative selection of working drawings is included here. The full set of working drawings for this house may be found in *Fundamentals of Carpentry, Vol. II* by Durbahn and Sundberg.

Floor Plans

Drawings for construction may be divided into four groups: *plans, elevations, sections,* and *details:* The drawings for a building often are called *the plans.* However, this is incorrect as the *plan view* is that part of the drawings which shows the plan views *looking directly down on the flat surface of any particular*

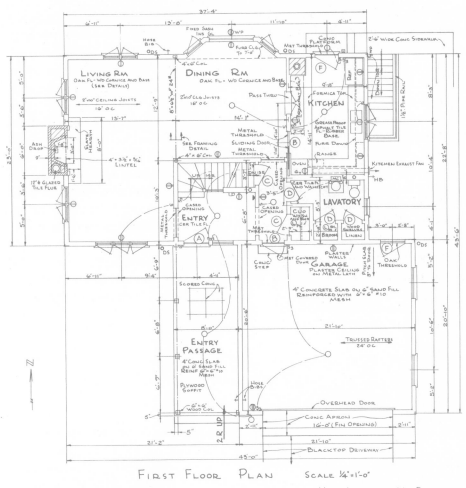

FIRST FLOOR PLAN   SCALE ¼"=1'-0"

PUBLISHER'S NOTE: THIS DRAWING WAS
ORIGINALLY DRAWN TO THE SCALE SHOWN.
THE DRAWING WAS REDUCED TO FIT THE
PAGE AND CAN NO LONGER BE SCALED.

NOTE: ALL EXTERIOR WALL DIMENSIONS
ARE TO OUTSIDE FACE OF STUDS
AND CENTERLINES OF WINDOWS
AND DOORS. INTERIOR DIMENSIONS
ARE TO CENTERLINES OF PARTITIONS.

Fig. 3. A typical floor plan.

floor or foundation. The terms *plan view* and *floor plan* are used interchangeably by architects and builders.

A *plan view* shows the room arrangement, chimneys, fireplaces, stairs, and closets. The plan view also shows the location of various devices, such as plumbing fixtures, lighting outlets, heating apparatus, and other mechanical appliances. The average set of drawings for a

329

house has three floor plans—basement with footing, a first-floor, and a second-floor plan. Sometimes, in addition, a *plot plan* is furnished to show lot lines, location of the house on the lot, trees, and the contour of the grounds. For complicated buildings, special plans are shown of the footings, joists, and rafter layouts. Fig. 3 illustrates a typical first floor plan for a house. In a full set of floor plans for this house a basement plan and a second floor plan would also be included. (The full set of working drawings for this house may be consulted in *Fundamentals of Carpentry, Vol. II.*)

Elevations

Elevation drawings show the outside of the building in true proportion. When the architect designs a house he thinks of the elevations in terms of the location of the house on the lot. Therefore, he names them the *south, east, north,* and *west elevation.* Sometimes the front of the building is known as the *front elevation.* As one observes the house from the front, the side to the right of the observer is called the *right elevation;* the side to the left, *left elevation;* and the one showing the back of the house, the *rear elevation.* A typical elevation is illustrated in Fig. 4.

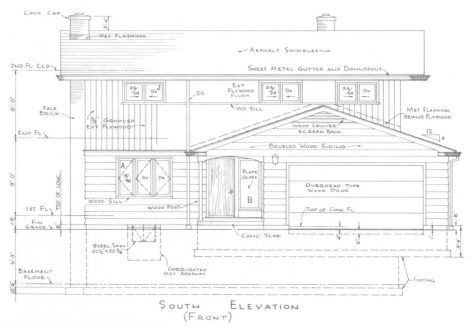

Fig. 4. A typical elevation view.

Elevation drawings also show the floor levels and grade lines, story and window heights, and the various materials to be used.

Sections

A *section view* is one in which a part of the building or object has been cut away, exposing the construction, size, and shape of materials which need further clarification. An example of a sectional view for a wall section is shown in Fig. 5. A detailed drawing for a fireplace is shown in Fig. 6.

Construction details of the wall sections show size of joists, studs, and rafters; sills, headers, plates, window cornice, floor construction, and other important details. Such detailed sectional views are impor-

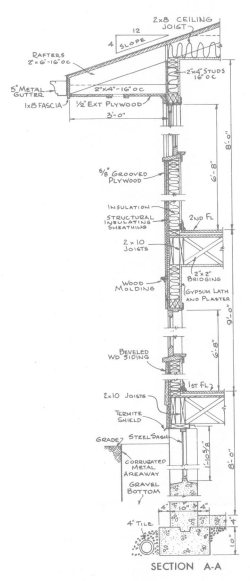

Fig. 5. Typical wall section.

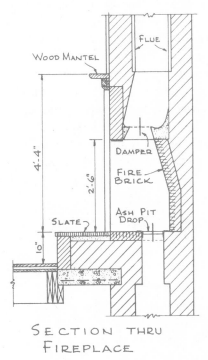

Fig. 6. Typical section through a fireplace.

tant as an aid to the carpenter in framing the building. A vertical section provides more information than can be given on floor plans. Details of the stairs and of doors, detailed vertical sections of the bay window, porch beams, and interior trim; and detailed vertical sections and elevations of the entrance doorways may also be shown.

Details

The plans and elevations are usually drawn to a scale which is too small to show accurately the character or construction of certain parts. To show these parts more clearly, larger scale drawings are made, as in Fig. 7. Details are also made of parts of elevations, floor plans, sections, etc. Figs. 8A and 8B show some typical details that may go on the working drawings. Fig. 6, which is a section, is also a detail drawing; it contributes more information.

Molding and various interior-trim members usually are shown in full-size to bring out intricate lines more

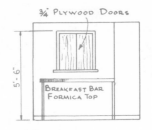

Fig. 8A. Kitchen elevation details.

clearly. See Fig. 9. These detailed drawings often are spread around on different plan views or elevations wherever the architect can find room to show the section view. Sometimes all the details are grouped together on one or more sheets called *detail sheets*. Notes on the plans refer the workman to the detail sheets. Example: See Sheet #4, Cabinet Details.

Fig. 7. Beam framing detail.

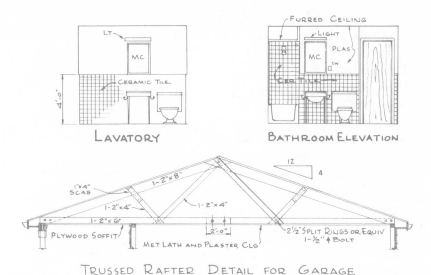

Fig. 8B. Lavatory, bathroom and trussed rafter details.

Fig. 9. Detail of typical trim (full size).

Transverse or Longitudinal Sections

Transverse or longitudinal sections sometimes are shown. These elevation sections show the interior of a building along a certain line. The transverse section is across the building while the longitudinal section is lengthwise through the building. Different floor levels and interior views of stairs can be illustrated more clearly with this type of sectional view.

333

Schedules

Separate schedules for doors and windows are shown with the first-floor plans. References to window openings are sometimes indicated by numbers and references to doors by letters. This practice helps to keep the drawings from becoming cluttered with too many details which often make the instructions difficult to read. Fig. 10, illustrates a typical door schedule.

Door Schedule for Entire House			
MARK	SIZE	AMT REQ'D	REMARKS
A	3'-0" x 6'-8" x 1¾"	1	Exterior Flush Door
B	2'-8" x 6'-8" x 1¾"	7	Flush Doors 1-Sliding 1-Metal Covered
C	2'-6" x 6'-8" x 1⅜"	4	Flush Door
C₁	2'-6" x 6'-8" x 1⅜"	2	Louvered
D	2'-4" x 6'-8" x 1⅜"	4	Flush Door
D₁	2'-4" x 6'-8" x 1⅜"	1	Louvered
E	1'-3" x 6'-8" x 1⅜"	1	Bi-Fold Louvered
F	2'-10" x 6'-8" x 1¾"	2	Exterior 2 Lights
G	2'-8" - 6'-8" x 1¾"	1	Exterior 2 Lights

Fig. 10. Typical door schedule.

Symbols

Because floor plans are proportionately so small, it is not possible to show all details exactly as they will appear in full size. For example, walls contain many parts and it would be impossible to show all of the parts on such a small scale. Hence, we use symbols; each symbol having a definite meaning either as to structure, or material, or both.

Drawings are simplified by the use of symbols. Various materials, such as wood, stone, brick, and concrete, are represented by certain symbols. Examples of material symbols commonly used in the building trade are shown in Fig. 11. Mechanical devices also are represented by symbols which indicate where heating, lighting, and plumbing appliances are to be installed in a new building. Mechanical symbols commonly used are shown in Figs. 12 and 13. The elevation of windows and their common plan symbols and the elevation of doors and their plan symbols are shown in Fig. 14. Fig. 15 illustrates the four symbols used to designate a frame wall indicating a wall and the swing of the door. The standard wall convention is shown by symbol 1. Symbols 2 and 3 are occasionally used by architects. Symbol 4 would be used on plans drawn to a very small scale.

Miscellaneous structural symbols are shown in Figs. 16 and 17. Although the symbols used by the carpentry trade are standardized to some extent and can be readily understood by any tradesman, regardless of the language he speaks, there still is a possibility of slight variations in the use of symbols. To avoid misunderstanding of instructions, architects usually provide a *key* on the drawings as an aid in reading the symbols used for any particular job.

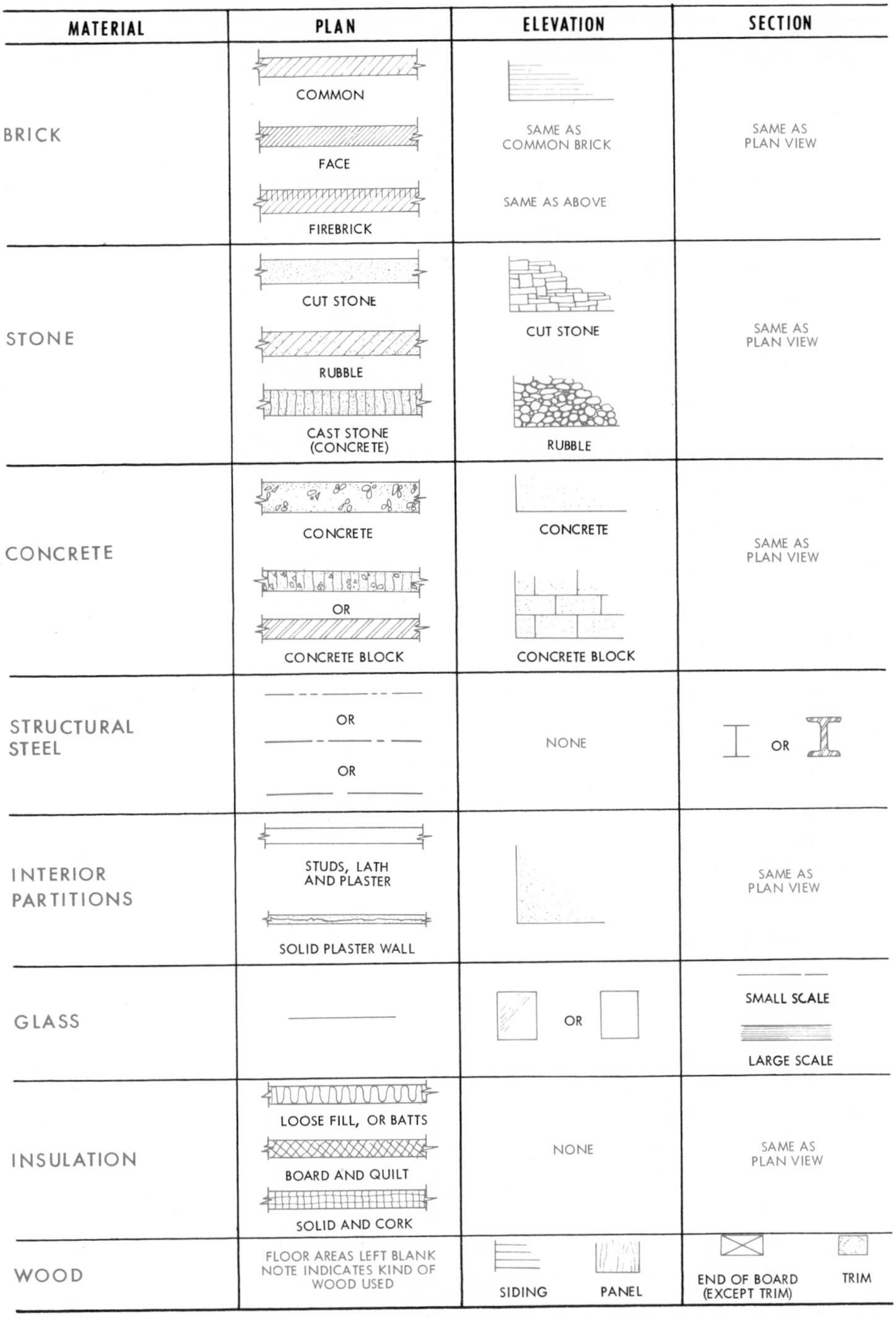

MATERIAL	PLAN	ELEVATION	SECTION
BRICK	COMMON / FACE / FIREBRICK	SAME AS COMMON BRICK / SAME AS ABOVE	SAME AS PLAN VIEW
STONE	CUT STONE / RUBBLE / CAST STONE (CONCRETE)	CUT STONE / RUBBLE	SAME AS PLAN VIEW
CONCRETE	CONCRETE / OR / CONCRETE BLOCK	CONCRETE / CONCRETE BLOCK	SAME AS PLAN VIEW
STRUCTURAL STEEL	OR / OR	NONE	I OR I
INTERIOR PARTITIONS	STUDS, LATH AND PLASTER / SOLID PLASTER WALL		SAME AS PLAN VIEW
GLASS		OR	SMALL SCALE / LARGE SCALE
INSULATION	LOOSE FILL, OR BATTS / BOARD AND QUILT / SOLID AND CORK	NONE	SAME AS PLAN VIEW
WOOD	FLOOR AREAS LEFT BLANK NOTE INDICATES KIND OF WOOD USED	SIDING PANEL	END OF BOARD (EXCEPT TRIM) TRIM

Fig. 11. Symbols used for common materials shown on blueprints.

335

Fundamentals of Carpentry

MATERIAL	PLAN	ELEVATION	SECTION
SHEET METAL FLASHING	INDICATE BY NOTE		HEAVY LINE SHAPED TO CONFORM
EARTH	NONE	NONE	
ROCK	NONE	NONE	
SAND	NONE	NONE	
GRAVEL OR CINDERS	NONE	NONE	
FLOOR AND WALL TILE			
SOUNDPROOF WALL		NONE	NONE
PLASTERED ARCH		DESIGN VARIES	SAME AS ELEVATION VIEW
GLASS BLOCK IN BRICK WALL			SAME AS ELEVATION VIEW
BRICK VENEER	OR / ON FRAME / ON CONCRETE BLOCK	SAME AS BRICK	SAME AS PLAN VIEW
CUT STONE VENEER	OR / ON FRAME / ON BRICK / ON CONCRETE BLOCK	SAME AS CUT STONE	SAME AS PLAN VIEW
RUBBLE STONE VENEER	OR / ON FRAME / ON BRICK / ON CONCRETE BLOCK	SAME AS RUBBLE	SAME AS PLAN VIEW

Fig. 11. Continued.

336

Review of Working Drawings, Conventions and Symbols

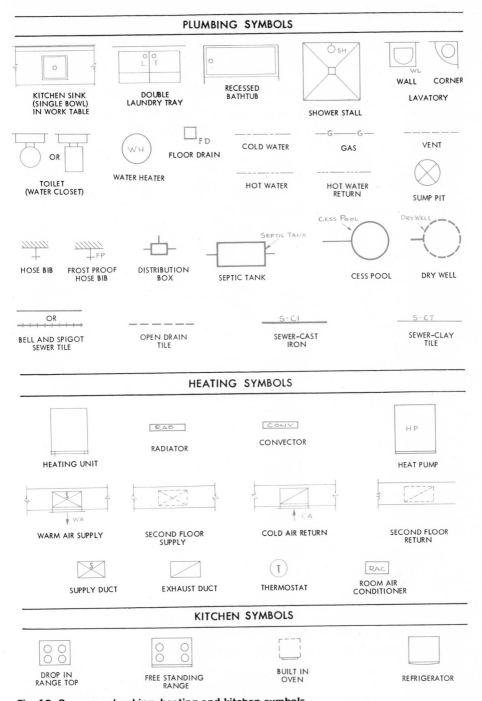

Fig. 12. Common plumbing, heating and kitchen symbols.

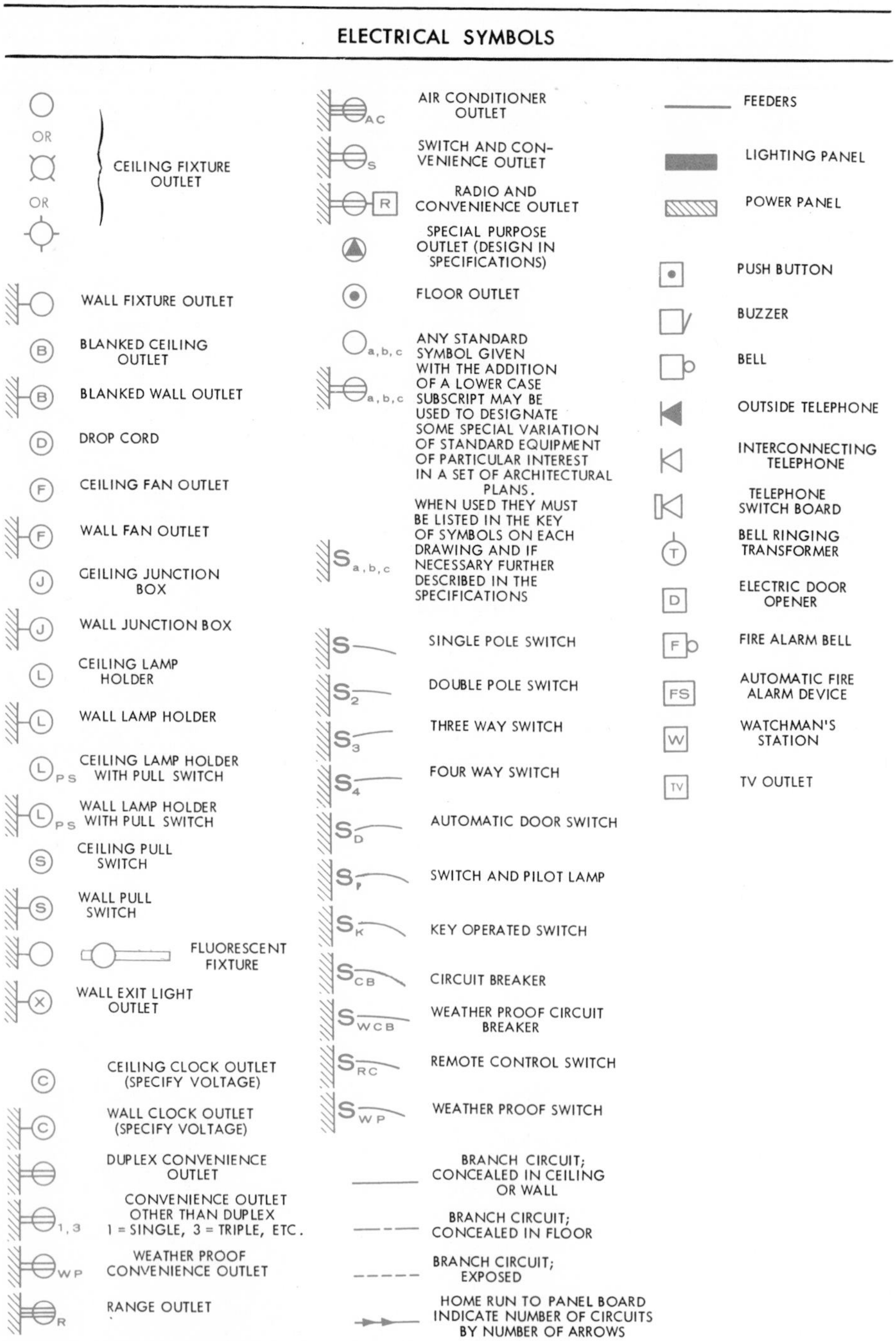
ELECTRICAL SYMBOLS
OR
OR
CEILING FIXTURE OUTLET
WALL FIXTURE OUTLET
B
BLANKED CEILING OUTLET
B
BLANKED WALL OUTLET
D
DROP CORD
F
CEILING FAN OUTLET
F
WALL FAN OUTLET
J
CEILING JUNCTION BOX
J
WALL JUNCTION BOX
L
CEILING LAMP HOLDER
L
WALL LAMP HOLDER
L PS
CEILING LAMP HOLDER WITH PULL SWITCH
L PS
WALL LAMP HOLDER WITH PULL SWITCH
S
CEILING PULL SWITCH
S
WALL PULL SWITCH
FLUORESCENT FIXTURE
WALL EXIT LIGHT OUTLET
C
CEILING CLOCK OUTLET (SPECIFY VOLTAGE)
C
WALL CLOCK OUTLET (SPECIFY VOLTAGE)
DUPLEX CONVENIENCE OUTLET
1, 3
CONVENIENCE OUTLET OTHER THAN DUPLEX 1 = SINGLE, 3 = TRIPLE, ETC.
WP
WEATHER PROOF CONVENIENCE OUTLET
R
RANGE OUTLET
AC
AIR CONDITIONER OUTLET
S
SWITCH AND CONVENIENCE OUTLET
R
RADIO AND CONVENIENCE OUTLET
SPECIAL PURPOSE OUTLET (DESIGN IN SPECIFICATIONS)
FLOOR OUTLET
a, b, c
a, b, c
S a, b, c
ANY STANDARD SYMBOL GIVEN WITH THE ADDITION OF A LOWER CASE SUBSCRIPT MAY BE USED TO DESIGNATE SOME SPECIAL VARIATION OF STANDARD EQUIPMENT OF PARTICULAR INTEREST IN A SET OF ARCHITECTURAL PLANS. WHEN USED THEY MUST BE LISTED IN THE KEY OF SYMBOLS ON EACH DRAWING AND IF NECESSARY FURTHER DESCRIBED IN THE SPECIFICATIONS
S
SINGLE POLE SWITCH
S2
DOUBLE POLE SWITCH
S3
THREE WAY SWITCH
S4
FOUR WAY SWITCH
SD
AUTOMATIC DOOR SWITCH
SP
SWITCH AND PILOT LAMP
SK
KEY OPERATED SWITCH
SCB
CIRCUIT BREAKER
SWCB
WEATHER PROOF CIRCUIT BREAKER
SRC
REMOTE CONTROL SWITCH
SWP
WEATHER PROOF SWITCH
BRANCH CIRCUIT; CONCEALED IN CEILING OR WALL
BRANCH CIRCUIT; CONCEALED IN FLOOR
BRANCH CIRCUIT; EXPOSED
HOME RUN TO PANEL BOARD INDICATE NUMBER OF CIRCUITS BY NUMBER OF ARROWS
FEEDERS
LIGHTING PANEL
POWER PANEL
PUSH BUTTON
BUZZER
BELL
OUTSIDE TELEPHONE
INTERCONNECTING TELEPHONE
TELEPHONE SWITCH BOARD
T
BELL RINGING TRANSFORMER
D
ELECTRIC DOOR OPENER
F
FIRE ALARM BELL
FS
AUTOMATIC FIRE ALARM DEVICE
W
WATCHMAN'S STATION
TV
TV OUTLET

Fig. 13. Common electrical symbols.

Review of Working Drawings, Conventions and Symbols

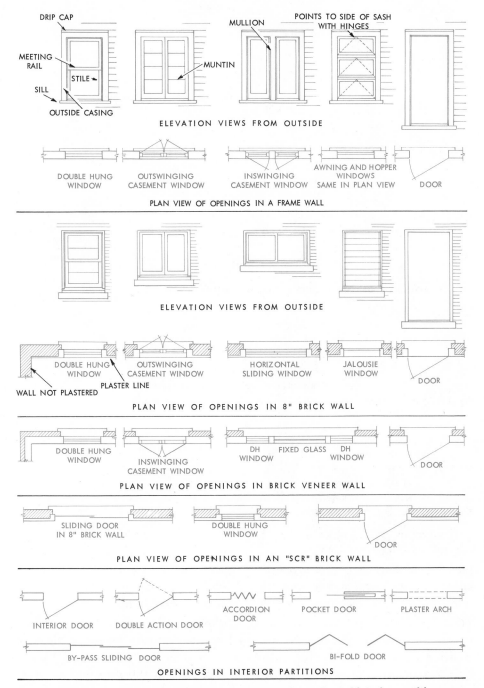

Fig. 14. Symbols commonly used for openings in exterior walls and interior partitions.

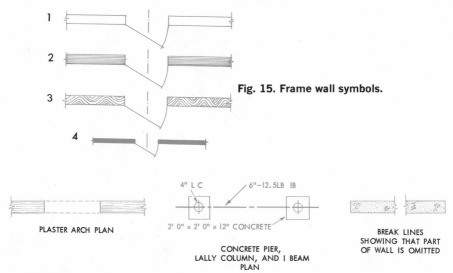

Fig. 15. Frame wall symbols.

PLASTER ARCH PLAN

4" L C   6"–12.5LB IB

2' 0" × 2' 0" × 12" CONCRETE

CONCRETE PIER,
LALLY COLUMN, AND I BEAM
PLAN

BREAK LINES
SHOWING THAT PART
OF WALL IS OMITTED

Fig. 16. Miscellaneous construction symbols on working drawings.

BEAM   WF BEAM   CHANNEL IRON   ANGLE IRON   PLATE

Fig. 17. Structural steel sections.

Carpentry Specifications

It is impossible to show every detail on drawings, so additional explanations are given in the *carpentry specifications* which supplement the drawings. These specifications are written, telling in words what cannot be shown graphically on the drawings. The information furnished by the specifications include grades of lumber and other materials, and detailed instructions as to how the work is to be performed. These specifications may be defined as *instructions to the builder*, and as such they must be simple and complete. The primary aim of the written specifications is to make perfectly clear to the builder every item that cannot be shown on the *drawings* or *blueprints*.

In addition to their primary purpose, specifications have other important uses. Estimators, including general contractors, subcontractors, manufacturers, and material dealers make use of building specifications as well as the working drawings when calculating cost of materials and labor. If carefully written, specifications make it possible for estimators to price material and labor exactly. The specifications also serve as a guide to all the trades in carrying out their specific parts of a construction job. Well-prepared specifications save time, reduce waste in both material and labor, and assure better workmanship. They also serve as a guide in the purchase of all types and qualities of fixtures, especially millwork and built-in furnishings. Another important use of specifications is the preventing of disputes between the owner and the general contractor, also between the general contractor and the subcontractor. If all necessary items are amply covered by the specifications, there can be no grounds for a dispute. Contracts are made in accordance with specifications. During the process of constructing a new house, whenever the information in the specifications appears to conflict with the instructions shown on the drawings, the carpenter or contractor should consult the architect in order to find out exactly what is wanted before proceeding with his work.

Building specifications also give general information regarding building permits for various trades, contract payments, insurance, liabilities, provisions for changes from original plans, drawings, or specifications, and supervision of construction work. However, in this text, we are interested only in the carpentry phase of the work.

Glossary of Trade Terms

A

abutment: That part of a pier or wall from which an arch is suspended; specifically the support at either end of an arch, beam, or bridge which resists the pressure due to a load.

acoustical materials: Sound-absorbing materials for covering walls and ceilings; a term applied to special plasters, tile, or any other material for wall coverings composed of mineral, wood, or vegetable fibers; also, cork or metal used to control or deaden sound.

acoustical tile: Any tile composed of materials having the property of absorbing sound waves, hence reducing the reflection and reverberation of sound; any tile designed and constructed to absorb sound waves.

adhesives: New glues and mastics for construction are being rapidly developed by the industry. The new compounds make it possible to bond almost any like, or unlike, rigid, and some flexible, materials together, for various construction purposes. Improvements are evident in labor and weight saving, economy, strength, and suitability for construction conditions.

adjustable clamp: Any type of clamping device that can be adjusted to suit the work being done, but particularly clamps used for holding column forms while concrete is poured.

aggregate: A collection of granulated particles of different substances into a compound, or conglomerate mass. In mixing concrete, the stone, or gravel, used as a part of the mix is commonly called the *coarse aggregate,* while the sand is called the *fine aggregate.*

air conditioning: The process of heating or cooling, cleaning, humidifying or dehumidifying, and circulating air throughout the various rooms of a house or public building.

air-dried lumber: Any lumber which is seasoned by drying in the air instead of being dried in a kiln or oven.

air space: A cavity or space in walls or between various structural members.

anchor blocks: Blocks of wood built into masonry walls, to which partitions and fixtures may be secured.

anchor bolts: Large bolts used for fastening or anchoring a wooden sill to a masonry foundation, floor, or wall. See Fig. 9. Also, any of several types of metal fasteners used to secure wood construction to masonry.

anchors: In building construction, devices used to give stability to one part of a structure by securing it to another part; metal ties, such as concrete inserts or toggle bolts, used to fasten any structural wood member to a concrete or masonry wall.

angle iron: A section of a strip of structural iron bent to form a right angle.

annual ring: The arrangement of the wood of a tree in concentric rings, or layers, due to the fact that it is formed gradually, one ring being added each year. For this reason the rings are called *annual rings*. The rings can easily be counted in cross section of a tree trunk. If a tree is cut close to the ground, the age of the tree can be estimated by the number of annual growth rings.

apron: A plain or molded finish piece below the stool of a window; put on to cover the rough edge of the plastering.

arc: Any part of the *circumference* of a circle.

arch: A curved or pointed structural member supported at the sides or ends. An *arch* is used to bridge or span an opening, usually a passageway or open spaces. See Figs. 15 and 20. An arch may also be used to sustain weight, as the arch of a bridge.

architect: One who designs and oversees the construction of a building; anyone skilled in methods of construction and in planning buildings; a professional student of architecture.

archway: The passageway under an arch.

area: An uncovered space, such as an open court; also, a sunken space around the basement of a building, providing access and natural lighting and ventilation. Same as *areaway*. See Fig. 1.

area drain: A drain set in the floor of a basement areaway, any depressed entryway, a loading platform, or a cemented

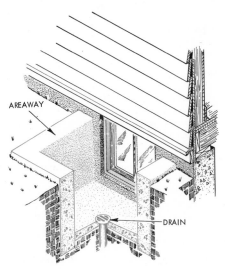

Fig. 1. Areaway.

driveway which cannot be drained otherwise. See Fig. 1.

areaway: An open subsurface space around a basement window or doorway, adjacent to the foundation walls. An *areaway* provides a means of admitting light and air for ventilation, and also affords access to the basement or cellar. See Fig. 1.

armored concrete: Concrete which has been strengthened by reinforcing with steel rods or steel plates. See *reinforced concrete*.

arris: An edge or ridge where two surfaces meet. The sharp edge formed where two moldings meet is commonly called an arris.

artificial stone: A special kind of manufactured product resembling a natural stone. A common type is made from pulverized quarry refuse mixed with Portland cement (sometimes colored) and water. After being pressed into molds, the mixture is allowed to dry out, and then is seasoned in the open air for several months before being used.

artisan: A skilled craftsman; an artist; one trained in a special mechanical art or trade; a handicraftsman who manufactures articles of wood or other material.

asbestos cement: A fire-resisting, water-proofing material made by combining Portland cement with asbestos fibers.

asbestos shingles: A type of shingle made for fireproof purposes. The principal composition of these shingles is *asbestos,* which is incombustible, nonconducting, and chemically resistant to fire. This makes *asbestos shingles* highly desirable for roof covering.

ashlar: One of the studs or uprights between floor beams and rafters in a garret. A short stud cutting off the angle between floor and roof in an attic, thus affording a wall of some height; also, squared stone used in foundations and for facing of certain types of masonry walls. See Fig. 2.

ashlar brick: A brick that has been rough-hackled on the face to make it resemble stone.

ashlar masonry: Masonry work of sawed, dressed, tooled, or quarry-faced stone with proper bond. See Fig. 2.

asphalt cement: A cement prepared by refining petroleum until it is free from water and all foreign material, except the mineral matter naturally contained in the asphalt. It should contain less than one per cent of ash.

attic: A garret; the room or space directly below the roof of a building. In modern buildings the *attic* is the space between the roof and the ceiling of the upper story. In classical structures the *attic* is the space, or low room, above the entablature or main cornice of a building.

auger: A wood-boring tool used by the carpenter for boring holes larger than can be made with a gimlet. The handle of an *auger* is attached at right angles to the tool line. There are several different types of augers made for various purposes.

auger bit: An auger without a handle to be used in a brace. Such a bit has square tapered shanks made to fit in the socket of a common brace. This combination tool is known as a *brace and bit.*

awning window: A type of window in which each light opens outward on its own hinges, which are placed at its upper edge. Such windows are often used as ventilators in connection with fixed picture windows.

B

back filling: Coarse dirt, broken stone, or other material used to build up the ground level around the basement or foundation walls of a house to provide a slope for drainage of water away from the foundation.

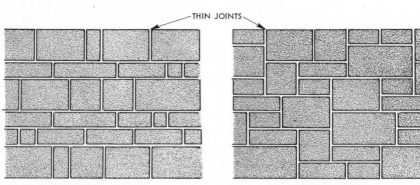

Fig. 2. Ashlar. COURSED ASHLAR   RANDOM ASHLAR

backing hip rafter: The beveling arris as at corners of hip rafters to tie up with adjacent roof surfaces.

backing of a joist or rafter: The blocking used to bring a narrow joist up to the height of the regular width joists. The widths of joists or rafters may vary, and in order to assure even floors or roofs some of the joists or rafters must be blocked up until all the upper surfaces are of the same level.

backing of a wall: The rough inner face of a wall; the material which is used to fill in behind a retaining wall.

backing tier: In masonry, the tier of rough brickwork which backs up the *face tier* of an exterior wall for a residence or other well-built brick structure. This part of a brick wall is often of a cheaper grade of brick than that used for the face tier. See Fig. 3.

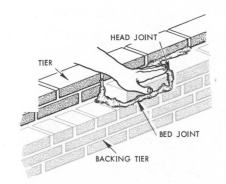

HEAD JOINT

TIER

BED JOINT

BACKING TIER

Fig. 3. Backing brick.

back plastering: The application of a ⅜″ thick mortar coat on the back of the facing tier for purposes of moisture-proofing and air-proofing; also called *parging.* See Fig. 22.

backsaw: Any saw with its blade stiffened by an additional metal strip along the back. The *backsaw* is commonly used in cabinet work as a bench saw.

balloon framing: A type of building construction in which the studs extend in one piece from the foundation to the roof; in addition to being supported by a ribbon or ledger board, the second-floor joists are nailed to the studs. See Fig. 4.

ball peen hammer: A hammer having a peen which is hemispherical in shape; used especially by metal workers and stonemasons.

baluster: One of a series of small pillars, or units, of a balustrade; an upright support of the railing for a stairway. See *closed-string stair,* Fig. 28.

balustrade: A railing consisting of a series of small columns connected at the top by a coping; a row of balusters surmounted by a rail.

banister: The balustrade of a staircase; a corruption of the word *baluster.*

bar clamp: A device consisting of a long bar and two clamping jaws, used by woodworkers for clamping large work.

bargeboard: The decorative board covering the projected portion of a gable roof; the same as a *verge board;* during the late part of the nineteenth century, bargeboards frequently were extremely ornate.

barge course: A part of the tiling which usually projects beyond the principal rafters or *bargeboards,* along the sloping edge of a *gable roof;* also, a course of brick laid on edge to form the coping of a wall. See *bargeboard.*

bark pocket: A patch of bark nearly, or wholly, enclosed in the wood is known as a *bark pocket.*

base: The lowest part of a wall, pier, monument, or column; the lower part of a complete architectural design.

baseboard: A board forming the base of something; the finishing board covering the edge of the plastered wall where the wall and floor meet; a line of boarding around the interior walls of a room, next to the floor.

base course: A footing course, as the lowest course of masonry of a wall or pier; the foundation course on which the remainder rests.

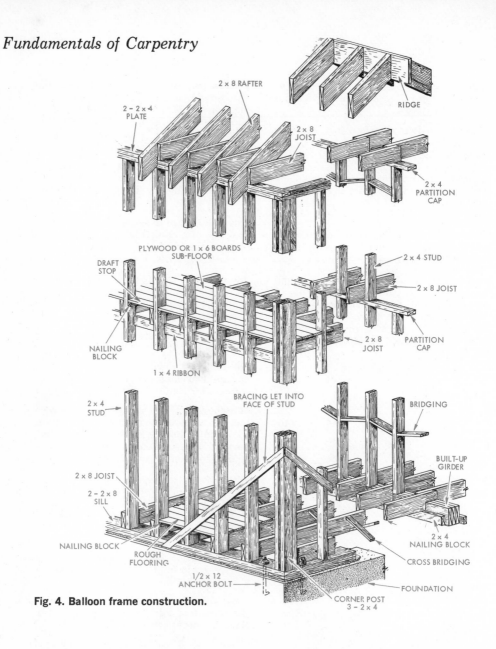

2 x 8 RAFTER

RIDGE

2 – 2 x 4 PLATE

2 x 8 JOIST

2 x 4 PARTITION CAP

PLYWOOD OR 1 x 6 BOARDS SUB-FLOOR

DRAFT STOP

2 x 4 STUD

2 x 8 JOIST

NAILING BLOCK

2 x 8 JOIST

PARTITION CAP

1 x 4 RIBBON

2 x 4 STUD

BRACING LET INTO FACE OF STUD

BRIDGING

2 x 8 JOIST

2 – 2 x 8 SILL

BUILT-UP GIRDER

NAILING BLOCK

ROUGH FLOORING

2 x 4 NAILING BLOCK

CROSS BRIDGING

1/2 x 12 ANCHOR BOLT

FOUNDATION

CORNER POST 3 – 2 x 4

Fig. 4. Balloon frame construction.

basement: The story of a building next below the main floor; a story partly or wholly below the ground level; the finished portion of a building below the main floor, or section; also, the lowest division of the walls of a building.

base molding: The molding above the plinth of a wall, pillar, or pedestal; the part between the shaft and the pedestal,

or if there is no pedestal, the part between the shaft and the plinth.

base trim: The finish at the base of a piece of work, as a board or molding used for finishing the lower part of an inside wall, such as a *baseboard;* the lower part of a column which may consist of several decorative features, including various members which make up the base as a whole;

these may include an ornate pedestal and other decorative parts.

batten: A thin, narrow strip of board used for various purposes; a piece of wood nailed across the surface of one or more boards to prevent warping; a narrow strip of board used to cover cracks between boards; a small molding used for covering joints between sheathing boards to keep out moisture. When sheathing is placed on walls in a vertical position and the joints covered by battens, a type of siding is formed known as *boards and battens*. A cleat is sometimes called a *batten*. Squared timbers of a special size used for flooring are also known as *battens*. These usually measure 7 inches in width, 2½ inches in thickness, and 6 feet, or more, in length.

batten door: A door made of sheathing boards reinforced with strips of boards nailed crossways and the nails clinched on the opposite side.

batter: A receding upward slope; the backward inclination of a timber or wall which is out of plumb; the upward and backward slope of a retaining wall which inclines away from a person who is standing facing it. A wall is sometimes constructed with a sloping outer face while the inner surface is perpendicular; thus the thickness of the wall diminishes toward the top.

batter board: Usually, one of two horizontal boards nailed to a post set up near the proposed corner of an excavation for a new building. The builder cuts notches or drives nails in the boards to hold the stretched building cord which marks the outline of the structure. The boards and strings are used for relocating the exact corner of the building at the bottom of the finished excavation. See Fig. 5.

batt insulation: A type of small-sized blanket insulating material, usually composed of mineral fibers and made in relatively small units for convenience in handling and applying. Sometimes spelled *bat*.

bead: A circular or semicircular molding; a beaded molding is known as *beading;* when the beads are flush with the surface and separated by grooves, this type of molding is called *quirk bead*.

beam: Any large piece of timber, stone, iron, or other material, used to support a load over an opening, or from post to post; one of the principal horizontal timbers, relatively long, used for supporting the floors of a building.

beam ceiling: A type of construction in which the beams of the ceiling, usually placed in a horizontal position, are exposed to view. The beams may be either true or false, but if properly constructed

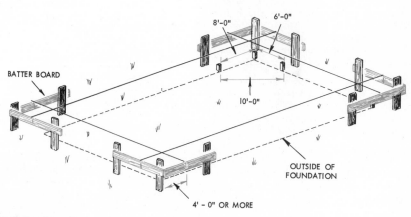

Fig. 5. Batter board.

the appearance of the ceiling will be the same, whether the beams are false or true.

beam fill: Masonry or concrete used to fill the spaces between joists; also, between a basement or foundation wall and the framework of a structure, to provide fire stops in outside walls for checking fires which start in the basement of a building.

bearing: That portion of a beam or truss which rests upon a support; that part of any member of a building that rests upon its supports.

bearing plate: A plate placed under a heavily loaded truss beam, girder, or column, to distribute the load so the pressure of its weight will not exceed the bearing strength of the supporting member.

bearing wall or partition: A wall which supports the floors and roof in a building; a partition that carries the floor joists and other partitions above it.

bed: In masonry, a layer of cement or mortar in which the stone or brick is embedded, or against which it bears; either of the horizontal surfaces of a stone in position, as the *upper* and *lower beds;* the lower surface of a brick, slate, or tile.

bed joint: In brickwork, the horizontal joint upon which the bricks rest (Fig. 3); also, the radiating joints of an arch.

bed molding: Finish molding used where the eaves of a building meet the top of the outside walls; the moldings, in any architectural order, used as a finish immediately beneath the corona and above the frieze; any molding in an angle, as between the projection of the overhanging eaves of a building and the sidewalls.

bed of a stone: The under surface of a stone; when the upper surface is prepared to receive another stone, it is called the *top bed,* and the natural stratification of the stone is called the *natural bed.*

bedplate: A foundation plate used as a support for some structural part; a metal plate used as a bed, or rest, for a machine; a foundation framing forming the bottom of a furnace.

belt courses: A layer of stone or molded work carried at the same level across or

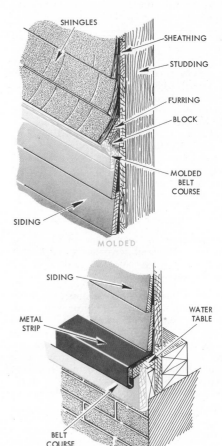

Fig. 6. Belt courses.

around a building. Also, a decorative feature, as a horizontal band around a building, or around a column. Two types of belt courses are shown in Fig. 6.

bench hook: A hook-shaped device used to prevent a piece of work from slipping on the bench during certain operations; a flat timber or board with cleats nailed on each side and one on each end to hold a piece of work in position and to prevent slipping which might cause injury to the top of the workbench.

bench marks: A basis for computing elevations by means of identification marks or symbols on stone, metal, or other durable matter, permanently fixed in the ground, and from which differences of elevations are measured.

bench plane: Any plane used constantly and kept handy on the bench; a plane used on the bench as a jack plane, a truing plane, or a smoothing plane.

bench stop: An adjustable metal device, usually notched, attached near one end of a workbench, to hold a piece of work while it is being planed.

bench table: A course of projecting stones forming a stone seat running around the walls at the base of a building such as a large church; a projecting course around the base of a pillar sufficient to form a seat.

bent: A framework transverse to the length of a structure usually designed to carry lateral as well as vertical loads.

bevel: One side of a solid body which is inclined in respect to another side with the angle between the two sides being either greater or less than a right angle; a sloping edge.

bevel siding: A board used for wall covering, as the shingle, which is thicker along one edge. When placed on the wall the thicker edge overlaps the thinner edge of the siding below to shed water. The face width of the bevel siding is from 3½″ to 11¼″ wide.

bib: In plumbing, a faucet or tap. A water faucet threaded so a hose may be attached to carry water. Also spelled *bibb*.

bid: An offer to furnish, at a specified price, supplies or equipment for performing a designated piece of work; an offer to pay a specified sum for goods sold at auction.

blade: The longer of the two extending arms of the *framing square,* usually 24 inches long and 2 inches wide. The *tongue* of the square forms a right angle with the *blade. Rafter framing tables* and *essex board measure tables* appear on the faces of the blade of the square. Also called *body.*

blank flue: If the space on one side of a fireplace is not needed for a flue, a chamber is built in and closed off at the top in order to conserve material and labor, and to balance the weight.

bleeder tile: The pipe placed in the foundation walls of a building, to allow the surface water accumulated by the outside tile drain to pass into the drain provided on the inside of the foundation wall. Sometimes called bleeder pipe. See Fig. 7.

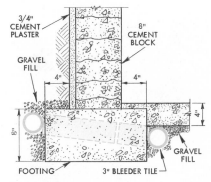

3/4″ CEMENT PLASTER
8″ CEMENT BLOCK
GRAVEL FILL
4″
4″
4″
8″
GRAVEL FILL
FOOTING
3″ BLEEDER TILE

Fig. 7. Bleeder tile.

blemish: Any imperfection which mars the appearance of wood.

blind header: In masonry work, stones or bricks having the appearance of headers; they really are only short blocks of stone or the ends of bricks.

block: In building construction, a small piece of wood glued into the interior angle of a joint to strengthen and stiffen the joint; a piece of wood placed back of a wainscot for support and to hold it away from the wall; a building unit of terra cotta or cement which differs from brick in being larger and sometimes hollow; also, a small piece of stone which has been cut down, usually for attaching a rope for lifting purposes.

STRETCHER BOND

ENGLISH CROSS BOND

COMMON BOND

FLEMISH BOND

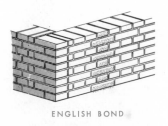

ENGLISH BOND

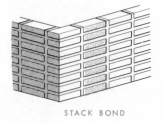

STACK BOND

Fig. 8. Typical brick bonds.

block-in-course: A kind of masonry used for heavy engineering construction, in which the stones are carefully squared and finished to make close joints, and the faces are dressed with a hammer.

bloom: An efflorescence which sometimes appears on masonry walls, especially on a brick wall. Also a defect on a varnished surface usually caused by a damp atmosphere.

blueprint: A working plan used by tradesmen on a construction job; an architectural drawing made by draftsmen, then transferred to chemically treated paper by exposure to sunlight, or strong artificial light. The sensitized paper, to which the drawing is transferred, turns blue when exposed to light.

blue stain: A discoloration of lumber due to a fungus growth in the unseasoned wood. Although *blue stain* mars the appearance of lumber, it does not seriously affect the strength of the timber.

board measure: A system of measurement for lumber. The unit of measure being one board foot which is represented by a piece of lumber 1 foot square and 1 inch thick. Quantities of lumber are designated and prices determined in terms of *board feet.*

board rule: A measuring device with various scales for finding the number of board feet in a quantity of lumber without calculation; a graduated scale used in checking lumber to find the cubic contents of a board without mathematical calculation.

body: Same as the *blade* of a *framing square.*

bolster: A crosspiece on an arch centering, running from rib to rib; the bearing place of a truss bridge upon a pier; a top piece on a post used to lengthen the bearing of a beam.

bond: In masonry and bricklaying, the arrangement of brick or stone in a wall by lapping them upon one another, to prevent vertical joints falling over each other. As the building goes up, an inseparable mass is formed by tying the face and backing together. Various types of bond are shown in Fig. 8.

bondstones: In masonry, stones running through the thickness of a wall at right angles to its base to bind the wall together.

bossage: In masonry, stones which are roughly dressed, such as corbels and quoins, built in so as to project, and then finish-dressed in position.

Boston hip roof: A method of shingling used to cover the joint, or hip, of a hip roof. To insure a watertight job, a double row of shingles or slate is laid lengthwise along the hip.

boulder wall: In masonry, a type of rustic wall composed of boulders, usually undressed, and mortar.

bow: Any part of a building which projects in the form of an arc or of a polygon.

box column: A type of built-up hollow column used in porch construction; it is usually square in form.

box frame: A window frame containing boxes for holding the sash weights.

box sill: A header nailed on the ends of joists and resting on a wall plate. It is used in frame-building construction. See Fig. 9.

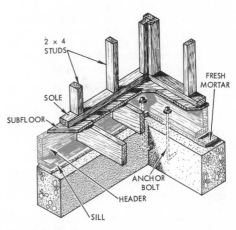

Fig. 9. Box sill.

brace: A piece of wood or other material used to resist weight or pressure of loads; an inclined piece of timber used as a support to stiffen some part of a structure; a support used to help hold parts of furniture in place, giving strength and durability to the entire piece. A term also applied to a tool with which *auger bits* are turned for boring holes in wood.

brace frame: A type of framework for a building in which the corner posts are braced to sills and plates.

brace measure: A table which appears on the *tongue* of a *framing square*. This table gives the lengths of common 45° braces plus the length of a brace with a run of 18″ to 24″ of rise. Limited in use to braces conforming to these specifications.

bracing: The ties and rods used for supporting and strengthening the various parts of a building.

bracket: A projection from the face of a wall used as a support for a cornice, or some ornamental feature; a support for a shelf.

brad: A thin, usually small, nail made of wire with a uniform thickness throughout and a small head.

break: A lapse in continuity; in building, any projection from the general surface of a wall; an abrupt change in direction as in a wall.

breaking of joints: A staggering of joints to prevent a straight line of vertical joints. The arrangement of boards so as not to allow vertical joints to come immediately over each other.

break iron: An iron fastened to the top of the bit of a plane. The purpose of the iron to to curl and break the shavings.

breastsummer: A heavy timber, or summer, placed horizontally over a large opening; a beam flush with a wall or partition which it supports; a lintel over a large window of a store, or shop, where the lintel must support the superstructure above it.

breezeway: A covered passage, open at each end, which passes through a house or between two structures, increasing ventilation and adding an outdoor living effect.

brick: Block of material used for building or paving purposes. The brick are made from clay or a clay mixture molded into blocks which are then hardened by drying in the sun or baking in a kiln. American-made brick average 2½ x 4 x 8 inches in size.

brick beam: A lintel made of brick, with iron straps.

brick cement: A waterproofed masonry cement employed for every kind of brick, concrete brick, tile, or stone masonry, and also in stucco work.

brick facing: The same as *brick veneer*.

bricklayer's hammer: A tool used by bricklayers for dressing brick. It has both a sharpened peen and a hammer head. See Fig. 10.

Fig. 10. Brick hammer.

brick nogging: In a wood-framed wall or partition, brickwork used to fill in the spaces between studs or timbers; also called brick-and-stud work.

brick pier: A detached mass of masonry which serves as a support.

brick set: In masonry, a tool used to cut bricks when exact surfaces are required. The *bricklayer's hammer* is used to force the chisel-like brick set into the brick.

brick trimmer: An arch built of brick between trimmers in the thickness of an upper floor to support a hearth and to guard against fire.

brick trowel: In masonry, a flat triangular-shaped trowel used by bricklayers for picking up mortar and spreading it on a wall. See *buttering trowel.*

brick veneer: A brick facing applied to the surface of the walls of a frame structure, or other types of structures.

bridging: An arrangement of small wooden pieces between timbers, such as joists, to stiffen them and hold them in place; a method of bracing partition studding and floor joists by the use of short strips of wood; cross bridging used between floor joists; usually a piece of 1x3, 2x2, or 2x4. See Fig. 4. Solid bridging used between partition studs is the same size as the studding.

British thermal unit: The quantity of heat required to raise the temperature of one pound of pure water one degree Fahrenheit at or near the temperature of maximum density of water 39 degrees Fahrenheit. Abbreviation B.t.u.

brush or spray coat: A waterproofing application of one or more coats of asphalt, or a commercial waterproofing on the exterior of the foundation, below grade line, with a brush, trowel, or by spraying. May be used where subgrade moisture problems are not severe.

builders' tape: Steel measuring tape usually 50 or 100 feet in length, contained in a circular case. *Builders' tape* is made sometimes of fabricated materials.

building: A structure used especially for a dwelling, barn, factory, store, shop, or warehouse; the art, or work, of assembling materials and putting them together in the form of a structure; the act of one who or that which builds.

building block: Any hollow rectangular block of burned clay, terra cotta, concrete, cement, or glass, manufactured for use as building material.

building line: The line, or limit, on a city lot beyond which the law forbids the erection of a building; also, a second line on a building site within which the walls of the building must be confined; that is, the outside face of the wall of the building must coincide with this line.

building paper: A form of heavy paper prepared especially for construction work. It is used between rough and finish floors, and between sheathing and siding, as an insulation and to keep out vermin. It is used, also, as an undercovering on roofs as a protection against weather.

building stone: An architectural term applied in general to any kind of stone which may be used in the construction of a building, such as limestone, sandstone, granite, marble, or others.

bulkhead: In building construction, a box-like structure which rises above a roof or floor to cover a stairway or an elevator shaft.

bull header: In masonry, a brick having one rounded corner, usually laid with the short face exposed to form and brick sill under and beyond a window frame; also used as a *quoin* or around doorways.

bull nose: An exterior angle which is rounded to eliminate a sharp or square corner. In masonry, a brick having one rounded corner; in carpentry; a stair step with a rounded end used as a starting step. Also called *bull's nose.*

burl: An abnormal growth on the trunks of many trees; an excrescence often in the form of a flattened hemisphere; veneer made from these excrescences, an especially beautiful *burl* veneer is cut from the stumps of walnut trees.

Burnett's process: The infusion of timber with chloride of zinc as a preservative.

burnisher: A tool, of hardened steel, used for finishing and polishing metal work by friction. The *burnisher* is held against the revolving metal piece which receives a smooth polished surface due to the compression of the outer layer of the metal. This tool is used, also, to turn the edge of a scraper.

buttering: In masonry, the process of spreading mortar on the edges of a brick before laying it.

buttering trowel: In masonry, a flat tool similar to, but smaller than, the brick trowel; used for spreading mortar on a brick before it is placed in position.

butt hinge: A hinge secured to the edge of a door and the face of the jamb it meets when the door is closed, as distinguished from the strap hinge. Usually mortised into the door and jamb.

butt joint: Any joint made by fastening two parts together end to end without overlapping.

buttress: A projecting structure built against a wall or building to give it greater strength and stability.

buzz saw: A circular saw.

C

cabinet: A piece of furniture, fitted with shelves or drawers, sometimes both, and enclosed with doors, as a *kitchen cabinet* for holding small kitchen equipment; a case with shelves or drawers used as a depository for various articles, such as jewels or precious stones. The doors for such cases are often made of glass, especially when the cases are used for display purposes.

cabinet latch: A name applied to various kinds of catches. These range from the type of catch used on refrigerator doors to the horizontal spring-and-bolt latch operated by turning a knob, as on kitchen cabinets.

cabinet scraper: A tool, made of a flat piece of steel, designed with an edge in such a shape that when the implement is drawn over a surface of wood any irregularities, or uneven places, will be removed, leaving the surface clean and smooth. The *cabinet scraper* is used for final smoothing of surfaces before sandpapering.

cabinetwork: The work of one who makes fine furniture, or beautifully finished woodwork of any kind.

cabin hook: A type of fastener, consisting of a small hook and eye, used on the doors of cabinets.

caisson: A deeply recessed panel sunk in a ceiling or soffit; also, a watertight box used for surrounding work involved in laying a foundation of any structure below water.

caisson pile: A type of pile which has been made watertight by surrounding it with concrete.

calking: The process of driving tarred oakum or other material into the seams between planks to make the joints watertight, airtight, or steam tight; to fill seams of a ship to prevent leaking; to fill or close seams or crevices with rust cement.

calking tool: A tool used for driving tarred oakum, cotton, and other materials into seams and crevices to make joints watertight and airtight. The *calking tool* is made of steel and in appearance somewhat resembles a chisel.

camber: A slight arching or convexity of a timber, or beam; the amount of upward curve given to an arched bar, beam, or girder to prevent the member from becoming concave due to its own weight or the weight of the load it must carry.

canopy: A rooflike structure projecting from a wall or supported on pillars, as an ornamental feature.

cant: To incline at an angle; to tilt; to set up on a slant, or at an angle; also a molding formed of plain surfaces and angles rather than curves.

cant hook: A stout wooden lever with an adjustable steel, or iron, hook near the lever end. The *cant hook* is used for rolling logs and telephone, or telegraph, poles.

cantilever: A projecting beam supported only at one end; a large bracket, usually ornamental, for supporting a balcony or cornice; two bracketlike arms projecting toward each other from opposite piers or banks to form the span of a bridge making what is known as a *cantilever bridge*.

canting strip: A projecting molding near the bottom of a wall to direct rain water away from the foundation wall; in frame buildings, the same as a *water table*.

cap: The top parts of columns, doors, and moldings; the coping of a wall; a cornice over a door; the lintel over a door or window; a top piece.

capping: The uppermost part on top of a piece of work; a crowning, or topping part.

carpenter: A craftsman who builds with wood; a worker who builds with the heavier forms of wood, as with lumber in the structural work of a building.

carpenter's finish: A term applied to practically all finish work performed by a carpenter, except that classed as *rough finish*. It includes casings, laying finish flooring, building stairs, fitting and hanging doors, fitting and setting windows, putting on baseboards, and installing all other similar finish material.

carpentry: Work which is performed by a craftsman in cutting, framing, and joining pieces of timber in the construction of ships, houses, and other structures of a similar character.

carriage: The support for the steps of a wooden stairway; these supports may be either of wood or steel.

casement window: Windows with sash that open on hinges; a window sash made to open by turning on hinges attached to its vertical edge.

casing: The framework around a window or door.

catch basin: A cistern, or depression, at the point where a gutter discharges into a sewer to catch any object which would not readily pass through the sewers; a reservoir to catch and retain surface drainage; a receptacle at an opening into a sewer to retain any matter which would not easily pass through the sewer; a trap to catch and hold fats, grease, and oil from kitchen sinks to prevent them from passing into the sewer.

caul: A tool used in forming veneer to the shape of a curved surface.

cavil: In masonry, a kind of heavy sledge hammer, having one blunt end and one pointed end, used for rough dressing of stone at the quarry; a term also applied to a small stone working ax.

cavity wall: A hollow wall, usually consisting of two brick walls erected a few inches apart and joined together with ties of metal or brick. Such walls increase thermal resistance and prevent rain from driving through to the inner face. Also called *hollow wall*. See Fig. 21.

cellar: A room, or set of rooms, below the surface of the ground, used especially for keeping provisions and other stores; a room beneath the main portion of a building. In modern homes, the heating plant is usually located in the *cellar*.

cement: In building, a material for binding other material or articles together; usually plastic at the time of application but hardens when in place; any substance which causes bodies to adhere to one another, such as Portland cement, stucco, and natural cements; also mortar or plaster of Paris.

cement colors: A special mineral pigment used for coloring cement for floors. In addition to the natural coloring pigment obtained from mineral oxides, there are manufactured pigments produced especially for cement work.

cementing trowel: A trowel similar to the plasterer's trowel, but often of a heavier gauge stock.

cement joggle: In masonry construction, a key which is formed between adjacent stones by running mortar into a square-section channel which is cut equally into each of the adjoining faces, thus preventing relative movement of the faces.

cement mortar: A building material composed of Portland cement, sand, and water.

centering: The frame on which a brick or stone arch is turned; the false work over which an arch is formed. In concrete work the *centering* is known as the *frames*.

center line: A broken line, usually indicated by a dot and dash, showing the center of an object and providing a convenient line from which to lay off measurements.

centerpiece: An ornament placed in the middle of a ceiling.

center to center: In taking measurements, a term meaning *on center* as in the spacing of joists, studding, or other structural parts.

ceramic tile: A thin, flat piece of fired clay, usually square. These pieces of clay are attached to walls, floors, or counter tops, with cement or other adhesives, creating durable, decorative, and dirt-resistant surfaces. Tiles may be plastic process (formed while clay is wet) or dust-pressed process (compressed clay powder). They may be glazed vitrified coating); unglazed (natural surface); non-vitrified; semivitrified, and vitreous (porous, semiporous, or relatively nonporous).

chamfer: A groove, or channel, as in a piece of wood; a bevel edge; an oblique surface formed by cutting away an edge or corner of a piece of timber, or stone. Any piece of work that is cut off at the edges at a 45 degree angle so that two faces meeting form a right angle are said to be *chamfered.*

channel: A concave groove cut in a surface as a decorative feature; a grooved molding used for ornamental purposes; a decorative concave groove on parts of furniture.

channel iron: A rolled iron bar with the sides turned upward forming a rim, making the *channel iron* appear like a channel-shaped trough. In sectional form, the *channel iron* appears like a rectangular box with the top and two ends omitted.

chase: In masonry, a groove or channel cut in the face of a brick wall to allow space for receiving pipes; in building, a trench dug to accommodate a drainpipe; also, a recess in a masonry wall to provide space for pipes and ducts.

chasing: The decorative features produced by grooving or indenting metal.

check: An ornamental design composed of inlaid squares; a blemish in wood caused by the separation of wood tissues.

checking of wood: Blemishes or cracks in timber due to uneven seasoning.

check rail: The middle horizontal member of a double-hung window, forming the lower rail of the top sash and the top rail of the lower sash.

chimney: That part of a building which contains the flues for drawing off smoke or fumes from stoves, furnaces, fireplaces, or some other source of smoke and gas.

chimney breast: That part of a chimney which projects from a wall where the chimney passes through a room. When the chimney is a part of a fireplace, the breast of the chimney is usually built much wider than the chimney itself to provide for a mantel or to improve the appearance of the room.

chimney lining: Rectangular or round tiles placed within a chimney for protective purpose. The glazed surface of the tile provides resistance to the deteriorating effects of smoke and gas fumes.

chipping: The process of cutting off small pieces of metal or wood with a chisel and a hammer.

cinder blocks: Building blocks in which the principal materials are cement and cinders.

cinder concrete: A type of concrete made from Portland cement mixed with clean, well-burned coal cinders which are used as coarse aggregate.

circular and angular measure: A standard measure expressed in degrees, minutes, and seconds, as follows:

60 seconds (″)	=	1 minute (′)
60 minutes	=	1 degree (°)
90 degrees	=	1 quadrant
4 quadrants	=	1 circle or circumference

circular saw: A saw with teeth spaced around the edge of a circular plate, or disk, which is rotated at high speed upon a central axis, or spindle, used for cutting lumber or sawing logs.

circumference: The perimeter of a circle; a line that bounds a circular plane surface.

circumscribe: The process of drawing a line to enclose certain portions of an object, figure, or plane; to encircle; to draw boundary lines; to enclose within certain limits.

clamp: A device for holding portions of work together, either wood or metal; an appliance with opposing sides or parts that may be screwed together to hold objects or parts of objects together firmly.

clapboard: A long thin board, graduating in thickness from one end to the other, used for siding, the thick end overlapping the thin portion of the board.

cleat: A strip of wood or metal fastened across a door or other object to give it additional strength; a strip of wood or other material nailed to a wall usually for the purpose of supporting some object or article fastened to it.

clinch: The process of securing a driven nail by bending down the point; to fasten firmly by bending down the ends of protruding nails.

clockwise: Moving in the same direction as the rotation of the hands of a clock; with a right-hand motion.

closed cornice: A cornice which is entirely enclosed by the *roof, fascia,* and the *plancher;* also called a *boxed cornice.* See Fig. 11.

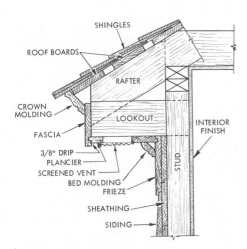

SHINGLES

ROOF BOARDS

RAFTER

CROWN MOLDING

LOOKOUT

INTERIOR FINISH

FASCIA

3/8" DRIP

PLANCIER

SCREENED VENT

BED MOLDING

FRIEZE

STUD

SHEATHING

SIDING

Fig. 11. Closed cornice.

closer: In constructing a masonry wall, any portion of a brick used to close up the bond next to the end brick of a course; the last stone, if smaller than the others, in a horizontal course, or a piece of brick which finishes a course; also, a piece of brick in each alternate course to enable a bond to be formed by preventing two headers from exactly superimposing oh a stretcher; same as *closure.*

coarse aggregate: Crushed stone or gravel used to reinforce concrete; the size is regulated by building codes.

code: Any systematic collection or set of rules pertaining to one particular subject, and devised for the purpose of securing uniformity in work or for maintaining proper standards of procedure, as a *building code.*

coffer: An ornamental sunken panel in a ceiling, or soffit; a deeply recessed panel in a dome.

cofferdam: A watertight enclosure usually built of piles or clay, within which excavating is done for foundations; also, a watertight enclosure fixed to the side of a ship for making repairs below the water line.

collar: In carpentry, an encircling band resembling a *collar;* a molding extending around a leg of furniture.

collar beam: A horizontal tie beam, in a roof truss, connecting two opposite rafters at a level considerably above the wall plate.

column: A pillar usually round; a vertical shaft which receives pressure in the direction of its longitudinal axis; the parts of a column are: the *base* on which the shaft rests, the body, or *shaft,* and the head known as the *capital.*

column footings: Concrete footings, reinforced with steel rods; used as supports for columns which in turn carry the load of I beams which serve as supports for the superstructure of a building.

combination square: A tool which combines in handy compact form the equivalent of several tools, including an inside try square, outside try square, mitre square, plumb, level, depth gauge, marking gauge, straight edge, bevel protractor, and center head in addition to square head.

common bond: In masonry, a form of bond in which every sixth course is a header course, and the intervening courses are stretcher courses. Sometimes varied, so a header bond is used every fourth or fifth course. See *typical bonds,* Fig. 8.

common brick: Any brick commonly used for construction purposes; primarily made for building and not especially treated for texture or color, but including clinker and overburned brick.

common rafter: A *rafter* which extends at right angles from the plate line to the *ridge* or *purlin* of a roof.

concrete: In masonry, a mixture of cement, sand, and gravel, with water in varying proportions according to the use which is to be made of the finished product.

concrete blocks: In masonry, precast, hollow, or solid blocks of concrete used in the construction of buildings.

concrete paint: A specially prepared thin paint, consisting of a mixture of cement and water, applied to the surface of a concrete wall to give it a uniform finish, and to protect the joints against weathering by rain or snow.

concrete wall: In building construction, any wall made of reinforced concrete, such as a basement wall.

conduit: A natural or artificial channel for carrying fluids, as water pipes, canals, and aqueducts; a tube, or trough, for receiving and protecting electric wires.

construction: The process of assembling material and building a structure; also, that which is built; style of building, as of wood, iron, or steel *construction.*

continuous beam: A timber that rests on more than two supporting members of a structure.

continuous header: The top plate is replaced by 2x6's turned on edge and running around the entire house. This header

is strong enough to act as a lintel over all wall openings, eliminating some cutting and fitting of stud lengths and separate headers over openings. This development is especially important because of the new emphasis on one-story, open-planning houses.

contour: The outline of a figure, as the profile of a molding.

contractor: One who agrees to supply materials and perform certain types of work for a specified sum of money, as a *building contractor* who erects a structure according to a written agreement, or *contract.*

coped joint: The seam, or juncture, between molded pieces in which a portion of one piece is cut away to receive the molded part of the other piece.

coping: A covering or top for brick walls. Usually, the coping is made of glazed tile. The cap or top course of a wall. The coping frequently is projected out from the wall to afford a decorative as well as protective feature. See Fig. 16.

corbel: A short piece of wood or stone projecting from the face of a wall to form a support for a timber, or other weight; a bracketlike support; a stepping out of courses in a wall to form a ledge; any supporting projection of wood or stone on the face of a wall.

corbel out: The building of one, or more, courses of masonry out from the face of a wall to form a support for timbers.

corbel table: A horizontal row of corbels supporting lintels or small arches; a projecting course, as of masonry, which is supported by a series of corbels; a cornice supported by corbels.

cord: Wood cut in four-feet lengths, usually for firewood. A pile of wood measuring four feet in width, four feet in height, and eight feet in length.

corner bead: A small projecting molding, or bead, built into plastered corners to prevent accidental breaking of the plaster; such a *bead* usually is of metal.

cornice: Projection at the top of a wall; a term applied to construction under the eaves, or where the roof and side walls meet; the top course, or courses, of a wall when treated as a crowning member. See Fig. 11.

counterbracing: Diagonal bracing which transmits a strain in an opposite direction from the main bracing; in a truss or girder, bracing used to give additional support to the beam and to relieve it of transverse stress.

counterclockwise: Motion in the direction opposite to the rotation of the hands of a clock.

countersink: To make a depression in wood or metal for the reception of a plate of iron, the head of a screw, or for a bolt, so that the plate, screw, or bolt will not project beyond the surface of the work; to form a flaring cavity around the top of a hole for receiving the head of a screw or bolt.

course: A continuous level range or row of brick or masonry throughout the face or faces of a building; to arrange in a row. A row of bricks, when laid in a wall, is called a *course*. See Fig. 12.

coursed ashlar: In masonry, a type of ashlar construction in which the various blocks of structural material have been arranged, according to height, to form regular courses in the face of walls. See Fig. 2.

court: An open space surrounded partly or entirely by a building; an open area partly or wholly enclosed by buildings or walls.

cove: A concave molding; an architectural member, as a ceiling, which is curved or arched at its junction with the side walls: also, a large, hollow cornice; a niche.

cove bracketing: The lumber skeleton, or framing for a cove; a term applied chiefly to the *bracketing* of a cove ceiling.

cove ceiling: A ceiling which rises from the walls with a concave curve.

cove molding: A molding called the *cavetto;* a quarter round, or concave molding.

crawl space: In cases where houses have no basements, the space between the first floor and the ground is made large enough for a man to crawl through for repairs and installation of utilities.

cresting: An ornamental finish of the wall or ridge of a building. The *cresting* of shingle roofs is generally of sheet metal.

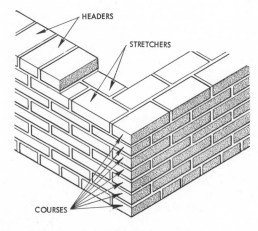

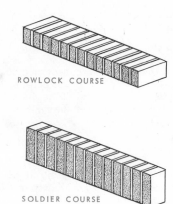

Fig. 12. Courses in brickwork.

crib: A cratelike framing used as a support for a structure above; any of various frameworks, as of logs or timbers, used in construction work; the wooden lining on the inside of a shaft; openwork of horizontally, cross-piled squared timbers, or beams, used as a retaining wall.

cripple: In building construction, any part of a frame which is cut less than full size, as a *cripple studding* over a door or window opening.

cripple jack rafter: A *jack rafter* that is cut in between a hip and valley rafter. A *cripple jack* touches neither the ridge nor the plate, but extends from a valley rafter to a hip rafter.

cripple rafter: A rafter extending from a hip to a valley rafter.

cripple studding: In framing, a studding which is less than full length, as a studding cut short to be used over a door or window opening.

cripple timbers: In building construction, timbers which are shortened for some reason, as the *cripple rafters* in a hip roof.

cross bridging: Bridging especially in floors consisting of transverse rows of small diagonal braces or struts set in pairs, and crossing each other between the timbers. See Fig. 4.

crosscut saw: A saw made to cut transversely, as across the grain of wood.

cross grain: A section of wood cut at right right angles to the longitudinal fiber.

crosslap: A joint where two pieces of timber cross each other. This type of joint is formed by cutting away half the thickness of each piece at the place of joining, so that one piece will fit into the other and both pieces will lie on the same plane.

cross section: A transverse section cut at right angles to the longitudinal axis of a piece of wood, drawing, or other work.

crown molding: A molding at the top of the cornice and immediately beneath the roof.

cup shake: A defect in wood where annual rings separate from each other, thus forming a semicircular flaw. Such flaws may occur between two or more concentric layers of wood. Because of their appearance, such defects are known as *cup shake,* but, since they are caused by the wind, they are also known as *windshake.*

curb roof: The mansard roof which takes its name from the architect who designed it. This type of roof has a double slope on each side, with the lower slope almost vertical. Frequently the lower slope contains dormer windows, which make possible the addition of another story to the house.

curl: A spiral or curved marking in the grain of wood; a feather-form mark in wood.

curtain wall: A thin wall, supported by the structural steel or concrete frame of the building, independent of the wall below.

cushion head: In foundation construction, a capping to protect the head of a pile which is to be sunk into the ground with a *pile driver.* Such a cushion usually consists of a castiron cap.

cut nails: Iron nails cut by machines from sheet metal, as distinguished from the more common wire nails now in general use.

D

damper: A device used for regulating the draft in the flue of a furnace; also, a device for checking vibrations.

damp-proofing: The special preparation of a wall to prevent moisture from oozing through it; material used for this purpose must be impervious to moisture.

deadening: The use of insulating materials, made for the purpose, to prevent sounds passing through walls and floors.

dead level: An emphatic statement used to indicate an absolute level.

dead load: A permanent, inert load whose pressure on a building or other structure is steady and constant, due to the weight of its structural members and the fixed loads they carry, imposing definite stresses and strains upon it. See *live loads.*

decimal: A fractional part of a number, proceeding by tenths, each unit being ten times the unit next smaller.

decimal equivalent: The value of a fraction expressed as a decimal, as ¼ equals .25.

defect: In lumber, an irregularity occurring in or on wood that will tend to impair its strength, durability, or utility value.

deflection: A deviation, or turning aside, from a straight line; bending of a beam or any part of a structure under an applied load.

deformation: Act of deforming or changing the shape; alteration in form which a structure undergoes when subjected to the action of a weight, or load.

degree: One 360th part of a circumference of a circle, or of a round angle.

derrick: Any hoisting device used for lifting or moving heavy weights; also, a structure consisting of an upright or fixed framework, with a hinged arm which can be raised and lowered and usually swings around to different positions for handling loads.

design: A drawing showing the plan, elevations, sections, and other features necessary in the construction of a new building. As used by architects, the term *plan* is restricted to the horizontal projection, while *elevation* applies to the vertical, or exterior, views.

detail: A term in architecture applied to the small parts into which any structure or machine is divided. It is applied generally to moldings or other decorative features and to drawings showing a special feature of construction.

detail drawing: A separate drawing showing a small part of a machine or structure in detail; a drawing showing the separate parts of a machine or other object with complete tabular data, such as dimensions, materials used, number of pieces, and operations to be performed; also, a drawing showing the position of the parts of a machine or tool and the manner in which the various parts are placed in assembling them.

detailer: One who prepares small drawings for shop use; a draftsman who makes detailed drawings.

diagonal bond: In masonry, a form of bond sometimes used in unusually thick walls, or for strengthening the bond in footings carrying heavy loads. The bricks are laid diagonally across the wall, with successive courses crossing each other in respect to rake.

diagram: A figure which gives the outline or general features of an object; a line drawing, as a chart or graph used for scientific purposes; a graphic representation of some feature of a structure.

diameter: A straight line passing through the center of a circle or sphere and terminating in the circumference.

dimension lumber: Lumber as it comes from the saws, commonly called *dimension stuff*, 2 inches thick and from 4 to 12 inches wide. See *scantlings* and *planks;* also, lumber cut to standard sizes or to sizes ordered.

dimension shingles: Shingles cut to a uniform size as distinguished from *random shingles.*

door check: A device used to retard the movement of a closing door and to guard against its slamming, or banging, but also insures the closing of the door.

doorframe: The case which surrounds a door and into which the door closes and out of which it opens. The frame consists of two upright pieces called *jambs* and the *lintel* or horizontal piece over the opening for the door.

doorhead: The upper part of the frame of a door.

doorstop: A device used to hold a door open to any desired position; a device usually attached near the bottom of a door to hold it open and operated by the pressure of the foot. The *doorstop* may or may not be attached to the door. The strip against which a door closes on the inside face of a door frame is also known as a *doorstop.*

dormer window: A vertical window in a projection built out from a sloping roof; a

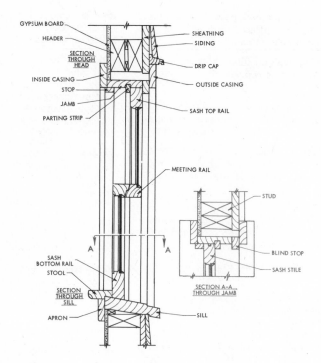

Fig. 13. Double-hung window.

small window projecting from the slope of a roof.

double-acting hinge: A hinge which permits motion in two directions, as on a swinging door, or on folding screens.

double Flemish bond: A bond in which both the inner and outer faces of an exposed masonry wall are laid in *Flemish bond,* with all headers *true* or *full headers.*

double-hung window: A window with upper and lower movable sashes. See Fig. 13.

double-pole switch: A switch to connect or break two sides of an electric circuit.

dovetail: In carpentry, an interlocking joint; a joint made by cutting two boards or timbers to fit into each other. A common type of joint used in making boxes or cases.

dovetail cramps: A device, usually of iron bent at the ends, or of dovetail form, used to hold structural timbers or stone together.

dovetail-halved joint: A joint which is halved by cuts narrowed at the heel, as in a dovetail joint.

dovetailing: A method of fastening boards or timbers together by fitting one piece into the other as with dovetail joints.

dowel: A pin of wood or metal used to hold or strengthen two pieces of timber where they join; a pin or tenon fitting into a corresponding hole and serving to fasten two pieces of wood together.

downspout: Any connector, such as a pipe, for carrying rain water from the roof of a building to the ground or to a sewer connection. Also called a *leader.*

draftsman: One who draws plans or sketches; usually a term applied to one who uses mechanical aids or instruments for preparing drawings for tradesmen.

draftsman's scale: A measuring scale used by draftsmen, usually triangular in shape but sometimes flat. One edge is graduated in $\frac{1}{16}$, $\frac{1}{8}$, $\frac{1}{4}$, $\frac{1}{2}$ and so on, as on a standard scale. Other edges are divided into fractional parts to facilitate reducing measurements.

draft stop or **fire stop:** Any obstruction placed in air passages to block the passing of flames or air currents upward or across a building. See Fig. 4.

drawknife: A woodworking tool with a blade and a handle at each end. The handles are at right angles to the blade which is long and narrow. It is used to smooth a surface by drawing the knife over it.

D & M: An abbreviation for the term *dressed and matched.* Boards or planks which have been machined in such a manner that there is a groove on one edge and a corresponding tongue on the other edge. Same as *tongue-and-groove* material.

D4S: A symbol used on building plans meaning *dressed on four sides.*

dressed size: The size of lumber after it is planed and seasoned from the unfinished (nominal) size.

dressing: Any decorative finish, as molding around a door; also, in masonry, all those stone or brick parts distinguished from the plain wall of a building, such as ornamental columns, jambs, arches, entablatures, copings, quoins, and string courses. The process of smoothing and squaring lumber or stone for use in a building.

drip: A construction member, wood or metal, which projects to throw off rain water.

drip cap: A molding placed above the top of a window or door casing so as to cause the water to run off. See Fig. 13.

drop siding: A special type of weatherboarding used on the exterior surface of frame structures.

dry kiln: An ovenlike chamber in which wood is seasoned artificially, thus hastening the process of drying.

dry rot: Various types of decay in timber, all of which reduces the wood to a fine powder.

dry-wall construction: A type of construction where the finish material used is other than plaster, such as gypsum panels, wood paneling, plywood, or wallboard.

ducts: In building construction, metal pipes, usually round or rectangular in shape, for distributing warm air from the heating plant to the various rooms, or for conveying air from air-conditioning devices. In electricity, a space in an underground conduit to hold a cable or conductor.

E

easement: In architecture, a curved member used to prevent abrupt changes in direction as in a baseboard or handrail. In stairway construction, a triangular piece to match the inside string and the wall base where these join at the bottom of the stairs.

eaves: That part of a roof which projects over the side wall; a margin, or lower part of a roof hanging over the wall; the edges of the roof which extend beyond the wall.

eaves trough: A gutter at the eaves of a roof for carrying off rain water.

elevation: A geometrical drawing or projection on a vertical plane showing the external upright parts of a building.

ell: An addition to a building at right angles to one end, or an extension of a building at right angles to the length of the main section.

encased knot: A defect in a piece of wood, where the growth rings of the knot are not intergrown and homogeneous with the growth rings of the piece in which the knot is encased.

end-grain: In woodworking, the face of a piece of timber which is exposed when the fibers are cut transversely.

end-lap joint: A joint formed at a corner where two boards lap. The boards are cut away to half their thickness so that they fit into each other. They are halved to a distance equal to their width, and, when fitted together, the outer surfaces are flush.

English bond: In brickwork, a form of bond in which one course is composed entirely of *headers* and the next course is composed entirely of *stretchers,* the header and stretcher courses alternating throughout the wall; a type of bond especially popular for use in a building intended for residential purposes. See *typical bonds,* Fig. 8.

English cross bond: A form of bond similar to Old English bond. It is used where strength and beauty are required. Same as *Dutch bond.* See *typical bonds,* Fig. 8.

erecting: Raising and setting in an upright position, as the final putting together in perpendicular form the structural parts of a building.

essex board measure: A method of rapid calculation for finding board feet; the essex board-measure table usually is found on the framing square conveniently located for the carpenter's use.

estimating: A process of judging or calculating the amount of material required for a given piece of work, also the amount of labor necessary to do the work, and finally an approximate evaluation of the finished product.

excavation: A cavity or hole made by digging out of earth to provide room for engineering improvements.

expansion joint: In masonry, a bituminous fiber strip used to separate blocks or units of concrete to prevent cracking due to expansion as a result of temperature changes. See Fig. 14.

exterior finish: In building construction, the outside finish which is intended primarily to serve as a protection for the interior of the building and for decorative purposes. It includes the cornice trim, gutters, roof covering, door and window frames, water tables, corner boards, belt courses, and wall covering.

F

facade: The entire exterior side of a building, especially the front; the face of a structure; the front elevation, or exterior face, of a building.

facebrick: The better quality of brick such as is used on exposed parts of a building, especially those parts which are prominent in view.

face hammer: A heavy hammer having flat faces, with one blunt end and one cutting end; used for rough dressing of blocks of quarried stone.

face of arch: In building, the exposed vertical surface of an arch. See Fig. 15.

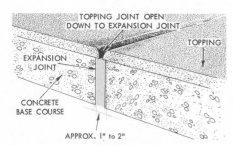

Fig. 14. Expansion joint.

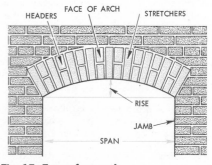

Fig. 15. Face of an arch.

facing hammer: In masonry, a special type of stone hammer used for dressing the surface of stone or cast-concrete slabs.

false header: In masonry, a half brick that is sometimes used in *Flemish bond;* in framing, a short piece of timber fitted between two floor joists.

false rafter: A short extension added to a main rafter over a cornice, especially where there is a change in the roof line.

falsework: Framework, usually temporary, such as bracing and supports used as an aid in construction but removed when the building is completed.

fascia: The flat outside horizontal member of a cornice placed in a vertical position. See Fig. 11.

felt papers: Sheathing papers used on roofs and side walls of buildings as protection against dampness, also as insulation against heat, cold, and wind. *Felt papers* applied to roofs are often infused with tar, asphalt, or chemical compounds.

fenestration: The arrangement of windows and doors in a building; in an architectural composition, the design and proportion of windows as a decorative feature.

ferroconcrete: Concrete work reinforced by steel bars or steel mesh, embedded in the material before it sets, to provide increased strength.

fiberboard: A type of building board made by reducing fibrous material, such as wood, cane, or other vegetable fibers, to a pulp, then reassembling the fibers into large sheets or boards; used extensively for insulating buildings against heat or cold.

field tile: A type of porous tile which is placed around the outside of a foundation wall of a building, to absorb excess water and prevent seepage through the foundation.

figure: In carpentry, mottled, streaked, or wavy grain in wood.

file: A tool, with teeth, used principally for finishing wood or metal surfaces. Common files are from 4 to 14 inches in length.

The width and thickness are in proportion to the length. In cross section the *file* may be rectangular, round, square, half round, triangular, diamond shaped, or oval. Single-cut files have parallel lines of teeth running diagonally across the face of the file. The double-cut files have two sets of parallel lines crossing each other. Single-cut files have four graduations—rough, bastard, second cut, and smooth; double-cut files have an added finer cut known as *dead smooth.*

fillet: A narrow concave strip connecting two surfaces meeting at an angle. It adds strength and beauty of design by avoiding sharp angles.

fillister: A plane used for cutting grooves; also, a rabbet, or groove, as the groove on a window sash for holding the putty and glass; in mechanical work, the rounded head of a cap screw slotted to receive a screw driver.

finished string: In architecture and building, the end string of a stair fastened to the rough carriage. It is cut, mitered, dressed, and often finished with a molding or bead.

finish floor: A floor, usually of high-grade material, laid over the subfloor. The *finish floor* is not laid until all plastering and other finishing work is completed. Also called *finished floor.*

finish hardware: All of the exposed hardware in a house, such as door knobs, door hinges, locks, and clothes hooks.

finishing: The final perfecting of workmanship on a building, as the adding of casings, baseboards, and ornamental moldings.

finishing tools: In masonry and cement work, tools designed especially for shaping curved section which must be made smooth and true.

Fink truss: A type of roof truss commonly used for short spans because of the shortness of its struts which makes it economical and prevents waste. Also called a *W-truss.*

firebrick: Any brick which is especially made to withstand the effects of high heat

365

without fusion; usually made of *fire clay* or other highly siliceous material.

fire clay: Clay which is capable of being subjected to high temperatures without fusing or softening perceptibly. It is used extensively for laying *firebrick*.

fire-division wall: A solid masonry wall for subdividing a building to prevent the spread of fire, but one not necessarily extending continuously from the foundation through all the stories and through the roof; also, a wall of reinforced concrete which is more or less fire-resistant, tending to restrict the spread of fire in a building.

fireplace unit: A prefabricated metal form usually covered by fireplace facing; usually includes: heating chamber, firebox, damper, wind shelf, and smoke chamber.

fireproof: To build with incombustible materials in order to reduce fire hazards: to cover or treat with an incombustible material; anything constructed of a minimum amount of combustible material.

fire-resisting: In building construction, a term applied to any structural material which is relatively immune to the effect of exposure to fire which has a maximum severity for an anticipated duration of time. Same as *fire-resistive.*

fire-resistive: In the absence of a specific ruling by the authority having jurisdiction, the term *fire-resistive* is applied to all building materials which are not combustible in temperatures of ordinary fires and will withstand such fires without serious impairment of their usefulness for at least one hour.

fire stops: Blocking, of incombustible material, used to fill air passages through which flames might travel in case the structure were to catch fire; any form of blocking of air passages to prevent the spread of fire through a building. See Fig. 4.

firmer tools: In woodworking, the tools commonly used on the workbench, such as the ordinary chisels and gouges.

fished joint: A joint commonly used when a structural piece must be lengthened.

The joint is made by placing a second piece end to end with the first one, then covering the juncture with two additional pieces which are nailed or bolted on opposite sides of the joint. These pieces are called *fish plates,* and may be wood or metal.

flagstone: A kind of stone that splits easily into flags, or slabs; also, a term applied to irregular pieces of such stone split into slabs from 1 to 3 inches thick and used for walks or terraces. A pavement made of stone slabs is known as *flagging.*

flange: A projecting edge, or rib. Some types of insulation materials are provided with *flanges* for nailing purposes.

flank: In architecture, the side of an arch.

flashing: Piece of lead, tin, or sheet metal, either copper or galvanized iron, used around dormers, chimneys, or any rising

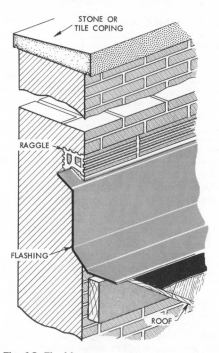

Fig. 16. Flashing.

projection, such as window heads, cornices, and angles between different members, or any place where there is danger of leakage from rain water or snow. These metal pieces are worked in with shingles of the roof or other construction materials used. See Fig. 16.

flat grain: Lumber sawn parallel with the pith of the log and approximately at right angles to the growth rings.

flat molding: A thin, flat molding used only for finishing work.

flat roof: A roof with just enough pitch to provide for drainage of rain water, or melting snow.

Flemish bond: A bond consisting of *headers* and *stretchers,* alternating in every course, so laid as always to break joints, each header being placed in the middle of the stretchers in courses above and below. See *typical bonds,* Fig. 8.

flexible insulation: A type of insulation which may be made of fluffy mineral wool, fibrous slag, glass, rock or processed vegetable or animal fibers. One-surface asphalt-impregnated paper can serve as a vapor barrier.

flight of stairs: A series of steps between floors of a building; a single flight of stairs may be broken into two flights by means of a landing.

flitch girder: A combination beam composed of two or more joists which have between them steel plates 1/4 inch or more in thickness. Bolts are used to hold the joists and steel plates together.

float coat: In cement work, a term frequently applied to the mortar-setting bed which is put on with a float; also, a term applied to a coat of finishing cement, sometimes called *float finish,* which is also put on with a float.

floater: A tool used to smooth and finish cement work.

floating: The process of spreading plastering, stucco, or cement on the surface of walls to an equal thickness by the use of a board called a *float.*

floating foundation: In building construction, a special type of foundation made to carry the weight of a superstructure which is to be erected on swampy land, or on unstable soil. Such a foundation consists of a large raftlike slab composed of concrete, reinforced with steel rods or mesh.

floatstone: In masonry, a type of stone used by bricklayers to smooth gauged brickwork.

floor: In architecture and building, different stories of structure are frequently referred to as floors, for example, the *ground floor,* the *second floor,* and the *basement floor;* also, that portion of a building or room on which one walks.

floor drain: A plumbing fixture used to drain water from floors into the plumbing system. Such drains are usually located in the laundry and near the furnace and are fitted with a deep seal trap.

floor framing: In building construction, the framework for a floor, consisting of sills and joists; also, the method used in constructing the frame for a floor, including the joists, sills, and any floor openings.

floor plan: An architectural drawing showing the length and breadth of a building and the location of the rooms which the building contains. Each floor has a separate plan.

flue: An enclosed passageway, such as a pipe, or chimney, for carrying off smoke, gases, or air.

flue lining: Fire clay or terra-cotta pipe, either round or square, usually obtainable in all ordinary flue sizes and in two-foot lengths. It is used for the inner lining of chimneys with brick or masonry work around the outside. Flue lining should run from the concrete footing to the top of the chimney cap.

flush: The continued surface of two contiguous masses in the same plane; that is, surfaces on the same level.

flush door: A door of any size, not paneled, having two flat faces, frequently of hollow core construction.

folding stair: A stairway which folds into the ceiling, used for access to areas of a building not in general use. Such a stairway uses, only limited space while in use. It is fixed by means of hinges at its uppermost end, while the lower end is provided with any of various catches which fasten the stairway when folded. Quite often the underside of such stairways is finished so as to match the ceiling area into which they are folded.

footing: A foundation as for a column; spreading courses under a foundation wall; an enlargement at the bottom of a wall to distribute the weight of the superstructure over a greater area and thus prevent settling. *Footings* are usually made of cement and are used under chimneys and columns as well as under foundation walls. See Fig. 7.

footing forms: Forms made of wood for shaping and holding concrete for footings of columns which support beams and girders.

footing stop: In concrete work, a term applied to a device consisting of a plank nailed to a 4x4, placed in the forms to hold the concrete at the close of a day's pouring. See Fig. 17.

forms: In building construction, an enclosure made of either boards or metal for holding green concrete to the desired shape until it has set and thoroughly dried.

form stop: In concrete work, a term applied to a device consisting of a plank nailed to a 4x4 placed in the forms at the end of a day's pouring. See Fig. 17.

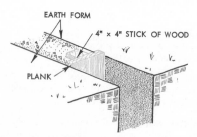

EARTH FORM
4" x 4" STICK OF WOOD
PLANK

Fig. 17. Form stop.

foundation: The lowest division of a wall for a structure intended for permanent use; that part of a wall on which the building is erected; usually that part of a building which is below the surface of the ground and on which the superstructure rests. See Fig. 4.

foundation bolt: Any bolt or device used to anchor the structural parts of a building to the foundation on which it rests; any bolt used to hold machinery in position on its foundation.

four-way switch: A switch used in house wiring when a light (or lights) is to be turned on or off at more than two places. Thus, for three places, use two three-way and one four-way switches; for four places, use two three-way and two four-way switches — an additional four-way switch for each additional place of control.

frame: In carpentry, the timber work supporting the various structural parts, such as windows, doors, floors, and roofs; the woodwork of doors, windows, and the entire lumber work supporting the floors, walls, roofs, and partitions.

frame of a house: The framework of a house which includes the joists, studs, plates, sills, partitions, and roofing; that is, all parts which together make up the skeleton of the building.

framework: The frame of a building: the various supporting parts of a building fitted together into a skeleton form.

framing: The process of putting together the skeleton parts for a building; the rough lumber work on a house, such as flooring, roofing, and partitions.

framing square: An instrument having at least one right angle and two or more straight edges, used for testing and laying out work for trueness. A good *framing square* will have the following tables stamped on it for the use of the carpenter in laying out his work: *unit length rafter tables; essex board measure; brace measure; octagon scale;* and, a *twelfths scale*. Also called *square* or *steel square*.

free end: The end of a beam which is unsupported, as that end of a cantilever which is not fixed.

friction catch: A device consisting of a spring and plunger contained in a casing, used on small doors or articles of furniture to keep them tightly closed but not locked.

furred: The providing of air space between the walls and plastering or subfloor and finish floor by use of wood strips, such as lath or 1x2's nailed to the walls in a vertical position. Walls or floors prepared in this manner are said to be *furred*.

furring: The process of leveling up part of a wall, ceiling, or floor by the use of wood strips; also, a term applied to the strips used to provide air space between a wall and the lath or dry wall. See Fig. 18.

furring strips: Flat pieces of lumber used to build up an irregular framing to an even surface, either the leveling of a part of a wall or ceiling. The term *furring strips* or *furrings* is also applied to strips placed against a brick wall for nailing lath, to provide air space between the wall and plastering to avoid dampness. See Fig. 18.

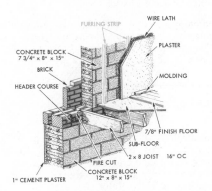

Fig. 18. Furring strips.

gable: The end of a building as distinguished from the front or rear side; the triangular end of an exterior wall above the eaves; the end of a ridged roof which at its extremity is not returned on itself but is cut off in a vertical plane which above the eaves is triangular in shape due to the slope of the roof.

G

gable molding: The molding used as a finish for the gable end of a roof.

gable roof: A ridged roof which terminates either at one end or both ends in a gable.

gain: The notch or mortise where a piece of wood is cut out to receive the end of another piece of wood.

gambrel roof: A type of roof which has its slope broken by an obtuse angle, so that the lower slope is steeper than the upper slope; a roof with two pitches.

girder: A large, supporting, built-up, horizontal member used to support walls or joists; a beam, either timber or steel, used for supporting a superstructure.

girt: The same as girth; the circumference of of round timber.

girt strip: A board attached to studding to carry floor joists; a ledger board.

glass block: A hollow glass building brick having the advantage of admitting light with privacy, insulating against the passage of sound, but not safe to use in a load-bearing wall. Sometimes called *glass brick*.

glazed: Equipped with window panes; the process of placing glass in windows, doors, and mirrors is known as *glazing*.

glazed brick: Building brick prepared by fusing on the surface a glazing material; brick having a glassy surface.

glazed tile: A type of masonry tile which has a glassy or glossy surface.

glazing: Placing glass in windows, doors, and mirrors; the filling up of interstices in the surface of a grindstone or emery wheel with minute abraded particles detached in grinding.

grade: In building trades the term used when referring to the ground level around a building.

grade line: The level of the ground at the building line.

grading: Filling in around a building with rubble and earth, so the ground will slope downward from the foundation, at an angle sufficient to carry off rain water.

grain: In woodworking, a term applied to the arrangement of wood fibers; working a piece of wood longitudinally may be either with or against the grain; a cross-section, or transverse, cut of wood is spoken of as cross grain.

grating: A framework, or gratelike arrangement of bars either parallel or crossed, used to cover an opening.

gravel fill: Crushed rock, pebbles, or gravel, deposited in a layer of any desired thickness at the bottom of an excavation, the purpose of which is to insure adequate drainage of any water. See Fig. 7.

green wood: A term used by woodworkers when referring to timbers which still contain the moisture, or sap, of the tree from which the wood was cut. Lumber is said to be *seasoned* when the sap has been removed by natural processes of drying or by artificial drying in a kiln.

grille: A grating or open barrier, usually of metal but sometimes of wood, used to cover an opening, or as a protection over the glass of a window or door. A *grille* may be plain but often it is of an ornamental or decorative character.

ground: One of the pieces of wood flush with the plastering of a room, to which moldings and other similar finish material are nailed. The *ground* acts as a straight edge and thickness gauge to which the plasterer works to insure a straight plaster surface of proper thickness.

ground course: A horizontal course, usually of masonry, next to the ground.

ground floor: Usually the main floor of a building; the floor of a house most nearly on a level with the ground; that is, the first floor above the ground level.

ground joist: A joist which is blocked up from the ground.

ground wall: In building, the foundation wall; the wall on which a superstructure rests.

grout: A mortar made so thin by the addition of water it will run into joints and cavities of masonry; a fluid cement mixture used to fill crevices.

gusset: A brace or angle bracket used to stiffen a corner or angular piece of work.

gutter: A channel of wood or metal at the eaves or on the roof of a building for carrying off rain water and water from melting snow.

gypsum: A mineral, hydrous sulphate of calcium. In the pure state gypsum is colorless. When part of the water is removed by a slow heating process the product becomes what is known as *plaster of Paris,* used extensively for decorative purposes.

H

half story: An attic in a pitched-roof structure having a finished ceiling and floor and some side wall.

half-timbered: A term applied to any building constructed of a timber frame with the spaces filled in, either with masonry or with plaster on laths.

hammer: A tool used for driving nails, pounding metal, or for other purposes. Though there are various types of hammers, used for a variety of purposes, all hammers are similar in having a solid head set crosswise on a handle.

hand drill: A hand-operated tool used for drilling holes.

handrail: Any railing which serves as a guard; a rail which is intended to be grasped by the hand to serve as a support, as on a stair or along the edge of a gallery. See Fig. 28.

handsaw: Any ordinary saw operated with one hand; that is, a one-handled saw, either a ripsaw or a crosscut saw, used by woodworkers.

hanger: A drop support, made of strap iron or steel, attached to the end of a joist or beam used to support another joist or beam. See *stirrup.*

hanger bolt: A bolt used for attaching hangers to woodwork; it consists of a lag screw at one end with a machinebolt screw and nut at the other end.

hanging stile: That part of a door to which the hinges are attached; the vertical part of a door or casement window to which the hinges are fixed.

hardboard: A board material manufactured from wood fiber; the wood is broken down into its individual fibers and compressed by hot presses. Lignin, a natural wood substance, bonds the fibers together.

hardwood: The botanical group of broad-leaved trees, such as oak, maple, basswood, poplar, and others. The term has no reference to the actual hardness of the wood. *Angiosperms* is the botanical name for hardwoods.

hardware: In building construction, fastenings which permit movement of parts, even when these parts are held together securely. Fastenings, commonly known as *builders' hardware,* include hinges, catches, lifts, locks, and similar devices.

H beam: An H-shaped beam.

header: In building, a brick or stone laid with the end toward the face of the wall. See Fig. 12. One or more pieces of lumber used generally around openings to support free ends of floor joists, studs, or rafters and transfer their load to other parallel joists, studs, or rafters. See Fig. 13.

header joist: In carpentry, the large beam or timber into which the common joists are fitted when framing around openings for stairs, chimneys, or any openings in a floor or roof; placed so as to fit between two long beams and support the ends of short timbers. See Fig. 9.

head room: The vertical space in a doorway; also, the clear space in height between a stair tread and the ceiling or stairs above.

hearth: The floor of a fireplace; also the portion of the floor immediately in front of the fireplace.

heartwood: The wood at the center of a log or tree surrounding the *pith.* The heartwood is surrounded by the *sapwood.*

heavy joist: In woodworking, a timber measuring between 4 and 6 inches in thickness and 8 inches or over in width.

heel: That part of a timber, beam, rafter, or joist which rests on the wall plate.

height: In reference to an arch, the perpendicular distance between the middle point of the chord and the intrados. Sometimes called the *rise.* See Fig. 15.

helve: The handle of a tool, such as a hammer, hatchet, or ax.

hewing: Dealing cutting blows with an ax or other sharp instrument for the purpose of dressing a timber to a desired form or shape.

hip rafters: Rafters which form the hip of a roof as distinguished from the common rafters. A *hip rafter* extends diagonally from the corner of the plate to the ridge, and is located at the apex of the outer angle formed by the meeting of two sloping sides of a roof whose wall plates meet at a right angle. See Fig. 26.

hip roof: A roof which rises by inclined planes from all four sides of a building.

hips: Those pieces of timber or lumber placed in an inclined position at the corners or angles of a hip roof. See Fig. 26.

hollow concrete blocks: A type of precast concrete building block having a hollow core.

hollow core door or wall: A faced door or wall with a space between the facings which is occupied by a structure consisting of air or insulation filled cells; made of wood, plastic, or other suitable material. Hollow core constructions have special fire, temperature, and sound insulating properties, as well as being light weight and strong.

hollow masonry unit. A masonry unit whose cross-sectional area in any given plane parallel to the bearing surface is less than 75 per cent of its gross cross-sectional area measured in the same plane.

hollow wall: In masonry, a wall constructed of brick, stone, or other materials, having an air space between the outside and inside faces of the wall. Also called *cavity wall.*

hollow tile: Tile made in a variety of forms and sizes; used extensively as a building material for both exterior walls and partitions. When used for outside walls the tiles usually are covered with stucco.

honeycomb: A cell-like structure. Concrete that is poorly mixed and not adequately puddled having voids or open spaces is known to be *honeycombed.*

honeycomb core: A structure of air cells, resembling a honeycomb, often made of paper, which is placed between plywood panels, sometimes replacing studs. This type of wall construction provides lighter prefabricated walls with excellent insulating properties. See *hollow core door or wall.*

hopper windows: A window in which each sash opens inward on hinges placed at the bottom of each sash.

horizontal: On a level; in a direction parallel to the horizon. For example, the surface of a still body of water is *horizontal,* or level.

horse: In building and woodworking, a trestle; one of the slanting supports of a set of steps to which the treads and risers of a stair are attached; a kind of stool, usually a horizontal piece to which three or four legs are attached, used as a support for work; a braced framework of timbers used to carry a load.

hose bib: A water faucet which is threaded so a hose may be attached; a *sill cock.*

housed string: A stair string with horizontal and vertical grooves cut on the inside to receive the ends of the risers and treads. Wedges covered with glue often are used to hold the risers and treads in place in the grooves.

I

I beam: A steel beam whose cross section resembles a letter I, used in structural work.

inclined plane: A surface inclined to the plane of the horizon; the angle it makes

with the horizontal line is known as the *angle of inclination.*

insulated: Any part of a building separated from other parts of the structure, to prevent the transfer of heat or electricity, is said to be *insulated.*

insulation: Any material used in building construction for the reduction of fire hazard or for protection from heat or cold. Insulation also prevents transfer of electricity.

interior finish: A term applied to the total effect produced by the inside finishing of a building, including not only the materials used but also the manner in which the trim and decorative features have been handled.

J

jack rafter: A short rafter of which there are three kinds: (1) those between the plate and a hip rafter; (2) those between the hip and valley rafters; (3) those between the valley rafters and the ridge board. *Jack rafters* are used especially in hip roofs. See Fig. 26.

jalousie window: A window consisting of narrow pieces of glass opening outward to admit air but exclude rain. The window appears similar to a venetian blind.

jamb: In building, the lining of an opening, such as the vertical side posts used in the framing of a doorway or window. See Figs. 13 and 25.

jig saw: In woodworking, a type of saw with a thin, narrow blade to which an up-and-down motion is imparted either by foot power or by mechanical means.

joinery: A term used by woodworkers when referring to the various types of joints used in woodworking.

joint: In carpentry, the place where two or more surfaces meet; also, to form, or unite, two pieces into a *joint;* to provide with a *joint* by preparing the edges of two pieces so they will fit together properly when joined.

jointing: In masonry, the operation of making and finishing the exterior surface

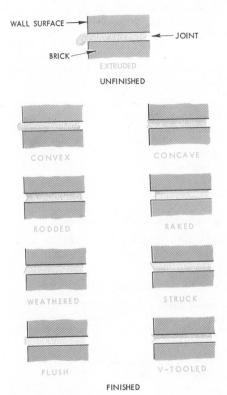

Fig. 19. Jointing.

key: In building, a wedge for splitting a tenon in a mortise to tighten its hold; a strip of wood inserted in a piece of timber across the grain to prevent casting; also a wedge of metal used to make a dovetail joint in a stone; a hollow in a tile to hold mortar or cement; a groove made in cement footings for tying in the cement foundation of a structure. A footing key is shown in Fig. 31.

keystone: The wedge-shaped piece at the top of an arch which is regarded as the most important member because it binds, or locks, all the other members together. The position of a keystone is shown in Fig. 20.

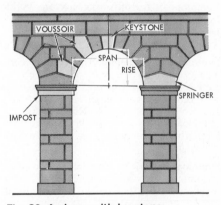

Fig. 20. Archway with keystone.

of mortar joints between courses of bricks or stones. See Fig. 19.

joist: A heavy piece of horizontal timber to which the boards of a floor, or the lath of a ceiling, are nailed. Joists are laid edgewise to form the floor support. See Fig. 4.

K

kerf: A cut made with a saw.

kerfing: The process of cutting grooves or kerfs across a board so as to make it flexible for bending. *Kerfs* are cut down to about two-thirds of the thickness of the piece to be bent. An example is found in the bullnose of a stair which frequently is bent by the process of kerfing.

kick plate: A metal plate, or strip, placed along the lower edge of a door, to prevent the marring of the finish by shoe marks.

kiln: A large oven or heated chamber for the purpose of baking, drying, or hardening, as a *kiln* for drying lumber; a *kiln* for baking brick; a lime *kiln* for burning lime.

kiln-dried lumber: Lumber which has been dried in kilns or ovens instead of through the natural process known as *air drying* or *seasoning.*

373

king post: In a roof truss, the central upright piece against which the rafters abut, and which supports the tie beam.

kraft paper: A type of strong brown paper used extensively for wrapping purposes, and as a building paper.

L

lag screw: A heavy wood screw with a square head. Since there is no slot in the head, the screw must be tightened down with a wrench.

laid to the weather: The amount of shingle or siding exposed to the weather.

lally column: A cylindrically shaped steel member, sometimes filled with concrete, used as a support for girders or other beams.

laminate: In furniture making, the building up with layers of wood, each layer being a lamination or ply; also, the construction of plywood.

laminated construction: Any type of construction where the work is built up by thin layers to secure maximum strength with minimum weight. In pattern making this method is especially desirable since it eliminates cross-grain wood and provides strength, particularly on thin curved members.

laminated rafter: A rafter built up of plies or laminations which are joined and held together with glue, or with mechanical fastenings.

laminated wood: An assembly of pieces of wood with the fibers or grain in each piece parallel to the fibers of the other pieces. The wood is built up of plies or laminations and joined together with glue or with some mechanical fastenings. This is in contrast to plywood where the grain of the various layers alternate crosswise, with the grain on the two exposed faces parallel.

landing: In stair construction, a platform introduced at some point to change the direction of the stairway, or to break the run.

landing newel: A post at the landing point of a stair supporting the handrail.

landing tread: In building, a term used when referring to the front end of a stair landing. The method of construction usually provides the front edge with a thickness and finish of a stair tread while the back has the same thickness as the flooring of the landing.

lap joint: The overlapping of two pieces of wood or metal. In woodworking, such a uniting of two pieces of board is produced by cutting away one-half the thickness of each piece. When joined, the two pieces fit into each other so that the outer faces are flush.

lathe: In shopwork, a mechanical device used in the process of producing circular work, for wood or metal turning.

lathing: In architecture, the nailing of lath in position; also a term used for the material itself.

leader: The same as a downspout.

lean-to roof: The sloping roof of a room having its rafters, or supports, pitched against and leaning on the adjoining wall of a building.

ledge: In architecture, any shelflike projection from a wall.

ledger board: In building, the same as a ribbon strip; a support attached to studding for carrying joists; horizontal member of a scaffold.

level: A device (also known as a *spirit level*) consisting of a glass tube nearly filled with alcohol or ether, leaving a movable air bubble. This device, protected by a metal or wood casing, is used for determining a point, or adjusting an object, in a line or plane perpendicular to the direction of the force of gravity. When centered, the bubble indicates the line of sight to be truly horizontal. A slight tilting of the *level* at either end will cause the bubble to move away from center, indicating a line which is not horizontal.

leveling instrument: A leveling device consisting of a spirit level attached to a sighting tube and the whole mounted on a tripod; used for leveling a surface to a horizontal plane. When the bubble in the level is in the center the line of sight is horizontal.

leveling rod or **leveling staff:** A rod, or staff, with graduated marks for measuring heights, or vertical distances, between given points and the line of sight of a *leveling instrument.* The different types of leveling rods in common use are the *target rods* read only by the rodman and the *self-reading rods,* which are read directly by the men who do the leveling.

level man: The surveyor who has charge of the leveling instrument.

light: A window pane; a section of a window sash for a single pane of glass.

lineal foot: Pertaining to a line one foot in length as distinguished from a square foot or a cubic foot.

linear: Resembling a line, or thread; narrow and elongated; involving measurement in one direction; pertaining to length.

linear measure: A system of measurement in length; also known as *long measure:*

12 inches (in.)	=	1 foot (ft.)
3 feet	=	1 yard (yd.)
16½ feet	=	1 rod (rd.)
320 rods	=	1 mile (mi.)
5280 feet	=	1 mile

lintel: A piece of wood, stone, or steel placed horizontally across the top of door and window openings to support the walls immediately above the openings.

live load: The moving or variable weight to which a building is subjected, due to the weight of the people who occupy it; the furnishings and other movable objects as distinct from the *dead load* or weight of the structural members and other fixed loads.

load-bearing walls: Any wall which bears its own weight as well as other weight; same as a supporting wall. Also called *bearing wall.*

locking stile: The vertical section of a door to which the lock is fastened.

longitudinal section: In shopwork and drawing, a lengthwise cut of any portion of a structure; also, pertaining to a measurement along the axis of a body.

lookouts: Short wooden brackets which support an overhanging portion of a roof (see Fig. 11); also, a place from which observations are made, as from a watchtower.

loose knot: In woodworking, a term applied to a knot which is not held in position firmly by the surrounding wood fibers; such a knot is a severe blemish in a piece of lumber making the board unfit for first-class work.

louver: An opening for ventilating closed attics or other used spaces; a lantern or turret on a roof for ventilating or lighting purposes, commonly used in medieval buildings; also, a louver board. A slatted opening for ventilation in which the slats are so placed as to exclude rain, light, or vision.

louver boards: In architecture, a series of overlapping sloping boards or slats in an opening so arranged as to admit air but keep out rain or snow.

lumber: Any material, such as boards, planks, or beams cut from timber to a size and form suitable for marketing.

M

mansard roof: A roof with two slopes on all four sides, the lower slope very steep, the upper slope almost flat; frequently used as a convenient method of adding another story to a building.

mantel: The ornamental facing around a fireplace, including the shelf which is usually attached to the breast of the chimney above the fireplace.

mason: A workman skilled in laying brick or stone, as a *bricklayer,* a *stonemason.*

masonry: A term applied to anything constructed of stone, brick, tiles, cement, concrete, and similar materials; also, the work done by a mason who works in stone, brick, cement, tiles, or concrete.

masonry arches: Arches, usually curved, thrown across openings in masonry walls for providing support for the superimposed structure. The arches may be constructed of such material as stone blocks or brick put together in a particular arrangement, so a completed masonry arch will resist the pressure of the load it carries by balancing of certain thrusts and counterthrusts.

masonry nail: A hardened-steel nail of specialized design, used for fastening wood, etc., to masonry work.

masonry saw: Portable, electrically powered hand saw, similar to all-purpose electric hand saw. Designed specifically for cutting masonry, this saw has a variety of masonry blade choices, including diamond blades and abrasive blades.

masonry wall: Any wall constructed of such material as stone, brick, tile, cement blocks, or concrete, put in place by a mason.

matched boards: Boards which have been finished so as to hold a tongue-and-groove joint securely in place; also boards finished with a rebated edge for close fitting.

maul: A heavy hammer or club used for driving stakes or piles; also, a heavy mallet or mace; any of various types of heavy hammers used for driving wedges, piles, or stakes.

meeting rail: The strip of wood or metal forming the horizontal bar which separates the upper and lower sash of a window.

mensuration: The process of measuring, especially that branch of mathematics which deals with the determining of length, area, and volume; that is, finding

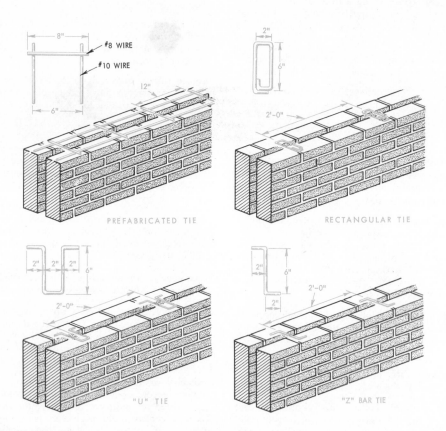

Fig. 21. Metal ties.

the length of a line, the area of a surface, and the volume of a solid.

metal strip: A term sometimes applied to metal flashing; used on water tables or around chimneys to prevent water seeping into the roof or walls. See *belt course,* Fig. 6.

metal ties: In masonry, a type of steel tie which is coated with Portland cement, and used to bond two separate wall sections together in cavity-type walls. Typical metal ties, commonly used, are shown in Fig. 21.

millwork: In woodworking, any work which has been finished, machined, and partly assembled at the mill.

millwright: A workman who designs and sets up mills or mill machinery; also, a mechanic who installs machinery in a mill or workshop.

miter: In carpentry, the ends of any two pieces of board of corresponding form, cut off at an angle and fitted together in an angular shape.

miter box: A device used by a carpenter for guiding a handsaw at the proper angle for cutting a miter joint in wood. The carpenter usually makes his own *miter box* on the job.

miter cut: In carpentry, a cut made at an angle for joining two pieces of board so cut that they will form an angle.

mitering: The joining of two pieces of board at an evenly divided angle; joining two boards by using a miter joint.

miter-saw or **miter-sawing board:** A device used to guide a saw at a desired angle.

modular brick: Brick which are designed for use in walls built in accordance with the modular dimensional standards. These brick include four basic sizes, known as *economy brick, oversize brick, standard brick,* and *twin brick.*

modular construction: Any building construction in which the size of the building materials used is based upon a common unit of measure, known as the *modular dimensional standards.* Also called *modular design.*

modular dimensional standards: Dimensional standards approved by the American Standards Association for all building material and equipment, based upon a common unit of measure of 4 inches, known as the *module.* This module is used as a basis for the *grid* which is essential for dimensional co-ordination of two or more different materials.

modular masonry: Masonry construction in which the size of the building material used, such as brick or tile, is based upon common units of measure, known as the *modular dimensional standards.*

module: A unit of measure used as a basis for dimensional coordination in the design of a structure.

moisture barrier: A waterproofed material used to retard passage of vapor or moisture through an insulator placed on the warm side.

moisture content in wood: The amount of moisture in wood, usually expressed as percentage of the dry weight of wood.

moisture proofing: A term applied to the process of making a material resistant to change in moisture content, especially to the entrance or absorption of moisture or vapor.

molding: A strip of material, either plane or curved, formed into long regular channels or projections; used for finishing and decorative purposes. *Molding* can be bought in many different sizes and shapes.

monolithic: Pertaining to a hollow foundation piece constructed of masonry, with a number of open wells passing through it. The wells are finally filled with concrete to form a solid foundation; a term applied to any concrete structure made of a continuous mass of material or cast as a single piece.

mortar: In masonry, a pasty building material, compose of sand and lime, or cement mixed with water, which gradually hardens when exposed to the air. *Mortar* is used as a joining medium in brick and stone construction.

mortar bed: A thick layer of plastic mortar in which is seated any structural member, the purpose of which is to provide a sound, contour-formed base.

mortar board: In masonry, a small square board, with a handle underneath, on which a mason holds his mortar. Same as *hawk.*

mortar joints: Joints which represent a wide range of types in finishing the mortar in stone or brickwork. See Fig. 19.

mortise: In woodworking, a cavity cut in a piece of wood, or timber, to receive a tenon, or tongue, projecting from another piece; for example, a mortise-and-tenon joint.

mudsill: The lowest sill of a structure, as a foundation timber placed directly on the ground, or foundation.

mullion: The slender bars between the lights or panes of windows.

muntin: Small strips of wood, or metal, which separate the glass in a window frame; vertical separators between pancls in a panel door.

N

nail: A slender piece of metal pointed at one end for driving into wood, and flat or rounded at the other end for striking with a hammer; used as a wood fastener by carpenters and other construction workers. The sizes of nails are indicated by the term *penny,* which originally indicated the price per hundred, but now refers to the length. Although the sizes of nails may vary as much as $1/8''$ to $1/4''$ from that indicated, the approximate lengths as sold on the market are:

$$4\text{-penny nail} = 1\tfrac{1}{4}''$$
$$6\text{-penny nail} = 2''$$
$$8\text{-penny nail} = 2\tfrac{1}{2}''$$
$$10\text{-penny nail} = 3''$$
$$20\text{-penny nail} = 4''$$
$$60\text{-penny nail} = 6''$$

nailing block: A nailing base for material, usually a small block of wood.

nail puller: Any small punch bar suitable for prying purposes, with a V-shaped, or forked, end which can be slipped under the head of a nail for prying it loose from the wood; also, a mechanical device provided with two jaws, one of which serves as a leverage heel for gripping a nail and prying it loose from a board.

nail set: A tool usually made from a solid bar of high-grade tool steel, measuring about 4 inches in length, used to set the heads of nails below the surface of wood. One end of the tool is drawn to a taper and the head is so shaped there is slight possibility of the device slipping off the head of a nail. Both ends are polished, body machine knurled.

nest of saws: A set of saw blades intended for use in the same handle, which is detachable. Such a collection of thin, narrow-bladed saws usually consists of one or more compass saws and a keyhole saw designed primarily for cutting out small holes, such as keyholes.

newel: In architecture, an upright post supporting the handrail at the top and bottom of a stairway, or at the turn on a landing; also, the main post about which a circular staircase winds; sometimes called the *newel post.* See Fig. 28.

nominal size: The unfinished size of lumber, known commercially as 1×6, 2×4, etc.

nonbearing partition: A term used in the building trade when referring to a dividing wall which merely separates space into rooms, but does not carry overhead partitions or floor joists.

nosing: The rounded edge of a stair tread projecting over the riser; also, the projecting part of a buttress. See Fig. 28.

O

offset: A term used in building when referring to a set-off, such as a sunken panel in a wall, or a recess of any kind; also, a horizontal ledge on a wall formed by the diminishing of the thickness of the wall at that point.

on center: A term used in taking measurements, meaning the distance from the center of one structural member to the center of a corresponding member, as in the spacing of studding, girders, joists, or other structural members. Same as *center to center*.

open-string stairs: In the building trade, a term applied to a stairway with a wall on one side and the other side open, so that a protective balustrade or handrail is necessary on the open side. The balustrade is supported at top and bottom by upright posts known as *newel posts*. The construction is such that the treads and risers are visible from the room or hallway into which the stairs lead. See Fig. 28.

out of true: In shopworking and the building trade, a term used when there is a twist or any other irregularity in the alignment of a form; also, a varying from exactness in a structural part.

P

panel: In architecture, a section, or portion, of a wall, ceiling, or other surface, either sunken or raised, enclosed by a framelike border; a term especially applied to woodwork.

panel door: A door with panels or lights.

parapet: In architecture, a protective railing or low wall along the edge of a roof, balcony, bridge, or terrace.

pargeting: A term used by architects when referring to the decoration of a room with plaster work, or stucco, in relief, such as raised oranamental figures; also, plastering on the inside of flues which gives a smooth surface and improves the draft.

parging: A thin coat of plastering applied to rough stone or brick walls for smoothing purposes. See Fig. 22.

paring: A term used by wood turners when referring to a method of wood turning which is opposed to the scraping method commonly employed by patternmakers.

particleboard: A processed wood usually made into panels; it is made from dry wood particles which are bonded together by pressure and heat with a resin bond.

partition: An interior wall separating one portion of a house from another; usually a permanent inside wall which divides a house into various rooms. In residences, partitions often are constructed of studding covered with lath and plaster; in factories, the partitions are made of more

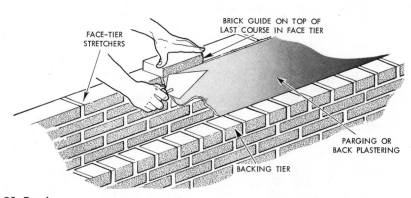

FACE-TIER STRETCHERS

BRICK GUIDE ON TOP OF LAST COURSE IN FACE TIER

PARGING OR BACK PLASTERING

BACKING TIER

Fig. 22. Parging.

durable materials, such as concrete blocks, hollow tile, brick, or heavy glass.

party wall: In architecture, a term used when referring to a wall on the line between adjoining buildings, in which each of the respective owners of the adjacent buildings share the rights and enjoyment of the common wall.

pegboard: A board with holes evenly spaced over its entire surface. May be cut to desired size and used to line closets or hang on walls. Hooks placed in the holes at convenient intervals provide facilities for hanging household objects of almost any size or shape, simplifying storage problems.

pier: One of the pillars supporting an arch; also, a supporting section of wall between two openings; a masonry structure used as an auxiliary to stiffen a wall.

pilaster: A rectangular column attached to a wall or pier; structurally a pier, but treated architecturally as a column with a capital, shaft, and base.

pile: A large timber driven into the ground for the support of a structure or a vertical load. *Piles* are frequently made of the entire trunk of a tree.

pile driver: A machine for driving piles; usually a high vertical framework with appliances attached for raising a heavy mass of iron which, after being lifted to the top of the framework, is allowed to fall, by the force of gravity, on the head of the pile, thus driving it into the ground.

pin knot: A term used by woodworkers when referring to a blemish in boards, consisting of a small knot of ½ inch or less in diameter.

pitch board: In building, a thin piece of board, cut in the shape of a right-angled triangle, used as a guide in forming work. When making cuts for stairs, the *pitch board* serves as a pattern for marking cuts; the shortest side is the height of the riser cut and the next longer side is the width of the tread.

pitch of a roof: The angle, or degree, of slope of a roof from the plate to the ridge. The pitch can be found by dividing the height, or rise, by the span, for example, if the height is 8 feet and the span 16 feet, the pitch is $\frac{8}{16}$ equals ½, then the angle of pitch is 45 degrees.

pith: The central core of a log. The *pith* is surrounded by the *heartwood*.

plan: In architecture, a diagram showing a horizontal view of a building, such as floor plans and sectional plans.

plancier: The underside of an eave or cornice. See Fig. 11.

plane: In woodworking, a flat surface where any line joining two points will lie entirely in the surface; also, a carpenter's tool used for smoothing boards or other wood surfaces.

planing mill: An establishment equipped with woodworking machinery for smoothing rough wood surfaces, cutting, fitting and matching boards with tongued-and-grooved joints; a woodworking mill.

plank: A long, flat, heavy piece of timber thicker than a board; a term commonly applied to a piece of construction material 6 inches or more in width and from 1½ to 6 inches or more in thickness.

plank and beam construction: A system of construction currently used in one-story buildings in which post and beam-framing units are the basic load-bearing members. Fewer framing members are needed, leaving more open space for functional use, for easier installation of large windows, and more flexible placing of free standing walls and partitions. It is also adaptable for prefabricated modular panel installation. Wide roof overhangs, for sun protection, and outdoor living areas are simpler to construct when this framing system is used. Posts and beams may be of wood, structural steel or concrete. Ceiling heights are higher for the same cubage, and it is reported that building is faster and cheaper. Roof deck can double as finished ceiling in the post, beam, and plank variation of the system. Problems include the necessity for extra insulation, difficulty in concealing wiring and duct work, and the necessity for extra care in the choice of materials and in planning. See Fig. 23.

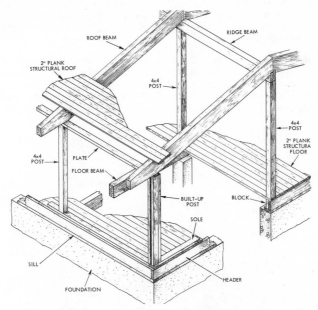

ROOF BEAM

RIDGE BEAM

2" PLANK STRUCTURAL ROOF

4x4 POST

4x4 POST

2" PLANK STRUCTURA FLOOR

4x4 POST

PLATE

FLOOR BEAM

BUILT-UP POST

BLOCK

SOLE

SILL

FOUNDATION

HEADER

Fig. 23. Plank and beam framing.

plan shape: A plan shape is the basic pattern on which a house is laid out. Most commonly used plan shapes are the square, rectangular, T, L, H, U, and split-level patterns. T, L, H, and U plan shapes roughly follow the shape of the alphabet letter by which they are indicated.

plaster: Any pasty material of a mortar-like consistency used for covering walls and ceilings of buildings. Formerly, a widely used type of plastering composed of a mixture of lime, sand, hair, and water. A more durable and popular plastering is now made of Portland cement mixed with sand and water.

plaster board: A rigid insulating board made of plastering material covered on both sides with heavy paper.

plastic veneers: Flexible plastic films with adhesive backs, used to cover various surfaces on which a fine finish is desired. These veneers will adhere to most surfaces, including glass, wood, tile, wallpa-per, most paint, porcelain, and wallboard without plaster core. Raw plaster surfaces, and areas covered with water-base paint, must be covered with shellac or lacquer before the veneer is put on. Some rigid plastics, such as sheets of melamine, are also used for veneering purposes. These rigid plastic sheets are attached to the surfaces desired by means of glues and various other adhesives. By use of these different adhesives, rigid plastics can be fastened to nearly any surface desired. All of these plastic veneers are available in a wide choice of colors and designs.

plastic wood: A manufactured product useful to the building industry. In making wood compounds, choice soft-woods, such as white pine, spruce, and fir, which have been converted into saw-dust, are employed. The sawdust, when ground into wood flour and mixed with the proper adhesives, forms a plastic material used extensively for filling cracks,

381

defects in wood, and for other purposes. Since it dries quickly and hardens upon exposure to air, *plastic wood* can be painted almost immediately.

plate: A term usually applied to a 2 x 4 placed on top of studs in frame walls. It serves as the top horizontal timber upon which the attic joists and roof rafters rest, and to which these members are fas-

tened. See Fig. 4. Also, a flat piece of steel used in conjunction with angle irons, channels, or I beams in the construction of lintels.

platform framing: A type of construction in which the floor platforms are framed independently; also, the second and third floors are supported by studs of only one story in height. See Fig. 24.

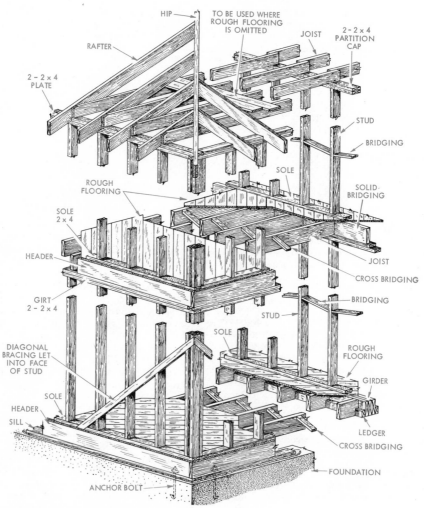

Fig. 24. Platform or western framing.

pliers: A small pincerlike tool having a pair of long, relatively broad jaws which are roughened for gripping and bending wire or for holding small objects. Pliers are sometimes made with nippers at the side of the jaws for cutting off wire.

plinth: The lowest square-shaped part of a column; a course of stones, as at the base of a wall. See *plinth block,* Fig. 25.

plinth block: A small block slightly thicker and wider than the casing for interior trim of a door. It is placed at the bottom of the door trim against which the baseboard or mopboard is butted. See Fig. 25.

plot plan: A plan showing the size of the lot on which the building is to be erected, with all data necessary before excavation for the foundation is begun.

plumb cut: In roof framing, a cut made on a *rafter* parallel to the *ridge board,* at the point where the rafter and ridge board meet.

ply: One thickness of any material used for building up of several layers, as roofing felt or layers of wood, as in laminated woodwork.

plywood: A building material consisting of three or more thin sheets of wood glued together with the grain of adjacent layers, usually at right angles to each other. Usually 3, 5, or 7 ply.

pointing: A term used in masonry for finishing of joints in a brick or stone wall.

post and beam construction: See *plank and beam construction.* When posts are used in the exterior wall and also at the center of the building, the construction may be called "post and beam construction," although "plank and beam" is the more common description.

power hammer: Portable electric, pneumatic, and self-contained gasoline-driven hammers, using a vibratory action principle. They accommodate such tools as chisels, frost wedges, solid drill steel, clay spades, tampers, diggers, asphalt cutters, ground rod drivers, offset trimming spades, plug and feathers, etc. They are used for removing defective brick from walls, hardened putty from steel sash,

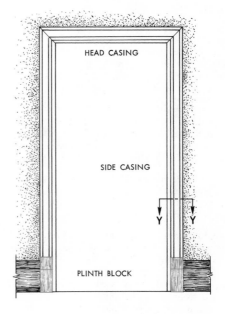

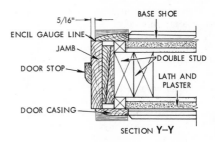

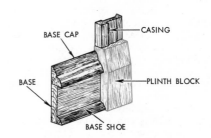

Fig. 25. Plinth block.

and mortar for repointing; for vibrating concrete wall forms, cutting wood, drilling holes in tile floors, digging holes for posts or sewers, and many other applications.

prefabricate: To construct or fabricate all the parts, as of a house, at the factory in advance of selling so that the final construction of the building consists merely of assembling and uniting the standard parts.

prefabricated construction: A building so designed as to involve a minimum of assembly at the site; usually comprising a series of large units or panels manufactured in a factory.

prefabricated houses: Houses prepared in sections in a shop before material is brought to the building site, where it is assembled in a relatively short time.

prefabricated modular units: Units of construction which are prefabricated on a measurement variation base of 4 inches or its multiplies, and can be fitted together on the job with a minimum of adjustments. Modular units include complete window walls, kitchen units complete with installations, as well as masonry, wall panels, and most of the other components of a house. Units are usually designed in such a way that they will fit functionally into a variety of house sizes and plan types.

prestressed concrete: Prestressing is "the imposition of preliminary interval stresses in a structure before working loads are applied, in such a way as to lead to a more favorable state of stress when these loads come into action." Concrete is usually prestressed by means of high strength steel wire incorporated in it. If the wires are placed in tension, and held in this position before the concrete is placed, the process is called *pretensioning*. If the concrete is poured with pockets in it, where the wires can be placed and prestressed after the concrete is poured and cured, the process is called *post-tensioning*. In one type of construction, members are built up of units resembling concrete blocks, with adjacent faces ground smooth. Threaded reinforcing rods are placed in side splines

of the units and extend through washers. Tension is applied to the rods by hydraulic jacks. Pretensioning makes it possible to use much less steel than is needed for structural steel or reinforced concrete buildings. The concrete members can be less bulky. It is also used in making crackless tanks for storing liquids.

priming: The first coat of paint put on for sizing and preserving wood.

purlins: Horizontal timbers supporting the common rafters in roofs, the timbers spanning from truss to truss.

putlog: A crosspiece in a scaffolding, one end of which rests in a hole in a wall; also, horizontal pieces which support the flooring of scaffolding, one end being inserted into *putlog* holes; that is, short timbers on which the flooring of a scaffolding is laid.

Q

quadrant: An instrument usually consisting of a graduated arc of 90 degrees, with an index or vernier; used primarily for measuring altitudes. Sometimes a spirit level or a plumb line is attached to the *quadrant* for determining the vertical or horizontal direction.

quarter sawing: The sawing of logs lengthwise into quarters, with the saw cuts parallel with the medullary rays, then cutting the quarters into boards, as in making quartered oak boards.

queen post: One of the two vertical tie posts in a roof truss, or any similar framed truss.

queen truss: A truss framed with queen posts, that is, two vertical tie posts, distinguished from the king truss which has only one tie post.

R

rabbet: In woodworking, a term used in referring to a groove cut in the surface, or along the edge, of a board, plank, or other timber, so as to receive another board or piece similarly cut.

rabbet joint: A joint which is formed by the fitting together of two pieces of timber which have been rabbeted.

rafter plate: In building construction, the framing member upon which the rafters rest. See Figs. 4 and 26.

rafters: The sloping members of a roof, as the ribs which extend from the ridge or from the hip of a roof to the eaves; used to support the shingles and roof boards. See Figs. 4 and 26.

rafter table: A table found on the face of the blade, or body, of the best-grade steel framing squares. The table gives directly the length per foot of run for a large variety of common rafters.

rail: A horizontal bar of wood or metal used as a guard, as the top member of a balustrade; also, the horizontal member of a door or window. See Fig. 28.

raked joint: In brick masonry, a type of joint which has the mortar raked out to a specified depth while the mortar is still green. See Fig. 19.

rake out: In masonry, the removal of loose mortar by scraping, in preparation for pointing of the joints.

rammer: In building construction, a term applied to an instrument which is used for driving anything by force, as stones or piles, or for compacting earth; in concrete work, a kind of "stomper," used to pack concrete by removing the air bubbles.

random shingles: Shingles of different widths banded together; these often vary from 2½ inches to 12 inches or more in width.

ranger: A horizontal bracing member used in form construction. Also called a *whaler* or *waler*. See Fig. 33.

reflective insulation: Foil-surfaced insulation whose insulating power is determined by the number of its reflective surfaces, and which must be used in connection with an air space. This type of insulation also acts as a vapor barrier.

registers: In building construction, an arrangement of fixtures in floors or walls for admitting or excluding hot or cold air for heating or ventilating purposes.

reinforced: To strengthen by the addition of new material, or extra material, for the reinforcement of concrete, iron or steel rods are embedded to give additional strength.

reinforced concrete: Concrete which has been strengthened by iron or steel bars embedded in it.

reinforced concrete construction: A type of building in which the principal structural members, such as floors, columns, and beams, are made of concrete, which is poured around isolated steel bars, or steel meshwork, in such a way that the two materials act together in resisting force.

reinforcing steel: Steel bars used in concrete construction for giving added strength; such bars are of various sizes and shapes.

return nosing: In the building of stairs, the mitered, overhanging end of a tread outside the balusters. See Fig. 28.

reversed door: A door which opens in the direction opposite to that considered *regular*. A room door opening inward is *regular*, and one opening outward is a *reversed door*. Cupboard doors opening outward are *regular*.

ribbon strip: A term used in building for a board which is nailed to studding for carrying floor joists. See Fig. 4.

ridge: The intersection of two surfaces forming an outward projecting angle, as at the top of a roof where two slopes meet. The highest point of a roof composed of sloping sides. See Fig. 26.

ridge pole: The horizontal member, or timber, at the top of a roof, which receives the upper ends of the rafters.

ridge roof: A roof whose end view is a gable and whose rafters meet in an apex.

right-hand door: If the door swings from you and the hinges are at your right hand, when you face the door from the outside, it is called a *right-hand door*. If the door swings toward you, then it is known as a *reverse right-hand door*.

385

right-hand lock: A door lock constructed for a right-hand door.

right-hand stairway: Stairs where the handrail is to your right as you ascend the stairs.

ring shake: A separation of the wood between the annual growth rings of a tree.

ripping: In woodworking, the sawing or splitting of wood lengthwise of the grain or fiber.

ripsaw: A saw having coarse, chisel-shaped teeth used in cutting wood in the direction of the grain.

rise: The distance through which anything rises, as the *rise* of a stair, the *rise* of a roof. Also, the vertical distance between the springing of an arch and the highest point of the *intrados*. See Fig. 15.

rise and run: A term used by carpenters to indicate the degree of incline.

riser: A vertical board under the tread of a stair step; that is, a board set on edge for connecting the treads of a stairway. See Fig. 28.

rod: A polelike stick of timber used by carpenters as a measuring device for determining the exact height of risers in a flight of stairs; sometimes called a *story rod*.

roof framing: In building, the process, or method, of putting the parts of a roof, such as rafters, ridge, and plates in position.

roof members: In building construction, the various parts or members which compose a roof, as the framing members. The names of important *roof members* are given in Fig. 26.

roof sheathing: Boards which are nailed on roof rafters and over which shingles or other roof covering is laid.

roof truss: The structural support for a roof, consisting of braced timbers or structural iron fastened together for strengthening and stiffening this portion of a building.

room divider: A temporary curtain wall such as a folding partition, or permanent partition, which may or may not reach from floor to ceiling, as a bookcase or cabinet with planter box. These partitions serve to block off activity areas in a room, for various needs, while providing for flexibility of function.

rotunda: A round-shaped building, or circular room, covered by a cupola or dome.

roughcast: A term used in the building trade for a kind of plastering, made of

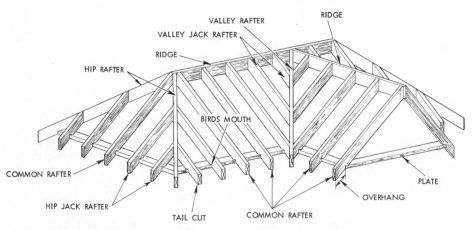

Fig. 26. Roof members.

lime mixed with shells or pebbles, applied to the outside of buildings.

rough floor: A subfloor serving as a base for the laying of the *finished floor* which may be of wood, linoleum, tile, or other suitable material. See Fig. 4.

rough flooring: Materials used for rough floors, usually square-edged lumber size 1x6, though dressed-and-matched boards or shiplap is sometimes used. Rough flooring may be laid either straight or diagonal.

rough hardware: All of the concealed hardware in a house or other building, such as bolts, nails, and spikes which are used in the construction of the building.

roughing-in: In building, a term applied to doing the first or rough work on any part of the construction, as roughing in-plastering, plumbing, and stairs.

rough lumber: Undressed lumber as it comes from the saw.

rough opening: An unfinished window or door opening; any unfinished opening in a building.

rough work: In building construction, the work of constructing the rough skeleton of a building; the rough framework, including the boxing and sheeting. The *rough work* may include making the rough frames for doors and windows and any similar work done in a factory and later moved to the building site ready for installing.

rout: A term in woodworking for cutting or gouging out material with a tool called a *router,* which is a special type of smoothing plane.

router: A two-handled woodworking tool used for smoothing the face of depressed surfaces, such as the bottom of grooves or any other depressions parallel with the surface of a piece of work.

routing: The cutting away of any unecessary parts that would interfere with the usefulness or mar the appearance of a piece of millwork.

rowlock: In masonry, a term applied to a course of bricks laid on edge. Also, the

end of a brick showing on the face of a brick wall in a vertical position. See Fig. 12.

run: In plumbing, that part of a pipe or fitting which continues in the same straight line as the direction of flow in the pipe to which it is connected; in building, a gangway, especially for the passage of wheelbarrows conveying materials from the supply to the part of the structure where they are to be used. In roofs, the horizontal distance between the face of a wall and the ridge of the roof.

run of stairs: A term used when referring to the horizontal part of a stair step, without the nosing; that is, the horizontal distance between the faces of two risers, or the horizontal distance of a flight of stairs. This is found by multiplying the number of steps by the width of the treads. If there are 14 steps each 10 inches wide, then 14×10 equals 140 inches or 11 feet 8 inches, which is the *run of the stairs.*

S

sapwood: The wood just beneath the bark of a tree, that is, the young soft wood consisting of living tissues outside the heartwood.

sash: A framework in which window panes are set.

saw arbor: The spindle, or shaft, on which a circular saw is mounted.

saw bench: A table or framework for carrying a circular saw.

saw gullet: The throat at the bottom of the teeth of a circular saw.

saw gumming: Shaping the teeth of a circular saw. Usually a grinding process.

sawhorse: A rack, or frame, for holding wood while it is being sawed; also, the ordinary trestle on which wood or boards are laid by carpenters for sawing by hand.

scab: A short piece of timber fastened to two other timbers to splice them together.

scabble: The dressing down of the roughest irregularities and projections of stone which is to be used for rubble masonry. A stone ax or scabbling hammer is used for this work.

scaffold: An elevated, and usually temporary, platform for supporting workmen, their tools, and material while working on a building.

scale: An instrument with graduated spaces for measuring; also, a term applied to the outside covering, or coating, of a casing. In lumbering estimating the amount of standing timber.

scaled drawing: A plan made according to a scale, smaller than the work which it represents but to a specified proportion which should be indicated on the drawing.

scantling: A piece of timber of comparatively small dimensions, as a 2x3 or 2x4, used for studding.

scarf joint: The joining of two pieces of timber, then fastening them with straps or bolts.

scoring: To mark with lines, scratches, and grooves across the grain of a piece of wood with any kind of steel instrument, for the purpose of making the surface rough enough to make it a firmer joint when glued.

scratch coat: The first coat of plastering applied to a wall.

SCR brick: A solid masonry unit whose greater thickness permits the use of a single wythe in construction. Its nominal dimensions, which vary from the specified dimensions by the addition of the thickness of the mortar joint with which the unit is designed to be laid (but not more than ½ inch), are 6″ x 2⅔″ x 12″. See Fig. 27.

scribing: Marking and fitting woodwork to an irregular surface.

seasoning of lumber: A term used by woodworkers when referring to the drying out of green lumber. The drying process may be accomplished either naturally by allowing the lumber to dry in the air while

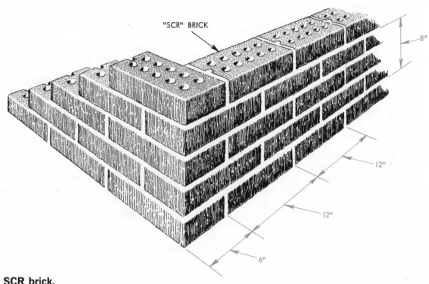

Fig. 27. SCR brick.

sheltered from the weather under a shed, or the wood may be dried artificially in an oven, or kiln, specially prepared for that purpose.

sectional view: A drawing that shows the internal detail of a building, but supposes the building to be cut through in sections to exhibit certain features, such as wall thicknesses, sizes and designs of interior doors, fittings, and thickness of floors or other parts.

set: In woodworking, a term applied to a small tool used for setting nail heads below the surface of a piece of work; also, a term used in connection with the adjusting of some part of a tool, as to *set* saw teeth, or to *set* a plane bit. See *nail set.*

settlement: A term used in the building industry for an unequal sinking or lowering of any part of a structure, which may be caused by the use of unseasoned lumber, by skimping in material, by the weakness of the foundation, or settlement of earth.

shake: A defect in timber such as a fissure or split, causing a separation of the wood between the annual growth rings.

shakes: In the building industry, a term applied to a type of handmade shingles.

sheathing: In construction work, a term usually applied to wide boards nailed to studding or roofing rafters, as a foundation for the covering of the outer surface of the side walls or roof of a house. See Fig. 24.

shingles: Thin pieces of wood, or other material, oblong in shape and thinner at one end, used for covering roofs or walls. The standard thicknesses of wood shingles are described as 4/2, 5/2¼, and 5/2, meaning, respectively, 4 shingles to 2 inches of butt thickness, 5 shingles to 2¼ inches of butt thickness, and 5 shingles to 2 inches of butt thickness. Lengths may be 16, 18, or 24 inches. Wood shingles may be bought in random widths or dimensioned.

shiplap: In carpentry, a term applied to lumber that is edge dressed to make a close rabbeted or lapped joint.

shore: A piece of lumber placed in an oblique direction to support a building temporarily; also, to support as with a prop of stout timber.

shoring: The use of timbers to prevent the sliding of earth adjoining an excavation; also, the timbers used as bracing against a wall for temporary support.

short length: A term used by woodworkers when referring to lumber which measures less than 8 feet in length.

show rafter: An architectural term applied to a short rafter which may be seen below the cornice; often an ornamental rafter.

side cut: Both *hip* and *valley rafters* must have an angle cut, called a *side cut,* to fit against the *ridge* or *common rafter* at the top.

siding: In the building industry, a term applied to boards used for forming the outside walls of frame buildings. See *bevel,* also *drop siding.*

sill: The lowest member beneath an opening, such as a window or door; also, the horizontal timbers which form the lowest members of a frame supporting the superstructure of a house, bridge, or other structure. See Fig. 4.

sill anchor: In building construction, a bolt embedded in the concrete or masonry foundation for the purpose of anchoring the sill to the foundation; sometimes called a *plate anchor.* See *anchor bolt,* Fig. 9.

single-pole switch: An electric device for making or breaking one side of an electric current.

site: The local position of a house or town in relation to its environment.

skirting: The same as baseboard, that is, a finishing board which covers the plastering where it meets the floor of a room.

slab: A relatively thin slice of any material, such as stone, marble, or concrete; also, a term applied to the outside piece cut from a log.

sleeper: A heavy beam or piece of timber laid on, or near, the ground for receiving floor joists and to support the superstructure; also, strips of wood, usually 2x2, laid over a rough concrete floor, to which the finished wood floor is nailed.

sleeper clips: Sheet-metal strips used to anchor wood flooring to concrete.

soffit: The underside of any subordinate member of a building, such as the under surface of an arch, cornice, or stairway.

soffit vent: An opening in the underside of a roof overhang which acts as a passageway into the house for air currents.

softwood: Wood from a group of trees which have needles or scalelike leaves commonly referred to as *conifers,* including cedars, pines, and firs popularly known as evergreens.

soil stack: In a plumbing system, the main vertical pipe which receives waste material from all fixtures.

sole: The horizontal member placed on the sub-flooring in western or platform construction upon which the studs rest.

sound knot: A term used in woodworking when referring to any knot so firmly fixed in a piece of lumber that it will continue to hold its position even when the piece is worked; also, is solid across its face and hard as the wood encircling it.

soundproofing: The application of deadening material to walls, ceilings, and floors to prevent sound from passing through these structural members into other rooms.

spall: A fragment or chip of stone or brick, especially bad or broken brick; in masonry, to reduce an irregular stone block to approximately the desired size by chipping with a stone hammer. Also spelled *spawl.*

span: The distance between the abutments of an arch or the space between two adjoining arches (Fig. 20); also, the distance between the wall, or rafter, plates of a building.

span of a roof or arch: The clear space or distance between two supporting members, as the supporting walls or piers.

specifications: Written instructions to the builder containing all the information pertaining to materials, style, workmanship, fabrication, dimensions, colors, and finishes supplementary to that appearing on the working drawings.

spike: In the building trade, a term commonly applied to a large-sized nail usually made of iron or steel, used as a fastener for heavy lumber.

spike knot: In woodworking, a knot sawed lengthwise.

spire: In architecture, a tapering tower or roof; any elongated structural mass shaped like a cone or pyramid; also, the topmost feature of a steeple.

spirit level: An instrument used for testing horizontal or vertical accuracy of the position of any structural part of a building. The correct position is indicated by the movement of an air bubble in alcohol.

splash block: A small masonry block laid with the top close to the ground surface, to receive drainage of rain water from the roof and carry it away from the building.

splay: An inclined surface, as the slope or bevel at the sides of a door or window; also, to make a beveled surface, or to spread out, or make oblique.

split-level: A house in which two or more floors are usually located directly above one another, and one or more additional floors, adjacent to them, are placed at a different level.

spread footing: A footing whose sides slope gradually outward from the foundation to the base.

springer: In architecture, a stone or other solid piece of masonry forming the impost of an arch; that is, the topmost member of a pillar or pier upon which the weight of the arch rests. See Fig. 20.

square: The multiplying of a number by itself; also, a plane figure of four equal sides, with opposite sides parallel, and all angles, right angles. Shingles for the trade are put up in bundles so packed that 4 bundles of 16- or 18-inch shingles, when laid 5 inches to the weather, will cover a *square* 10 by 10, or 100 square feet, and three bundles of 24-inch shingles will also cover a *square*. An instrument for measuring and laying out work is called a *framing square*. See also *steel square*.

square measure: The measure of areas in square units.

144 square inches = 1 square foot
(sq. in.)   (sq. ft.)

9 square feet = 1 square yard
(sq. yd.)

30¼ square yards = 1 square rod (sq. rd.)

160 square rods = 1 acre (A.)

640 acres = 1 square mile
(sq. mi.)

36 square miles = 1 township
(twp.)

square root: A quantity of which the given quantity is the square, as 4 is the *square root* of 16, the given quantity.

stack partition: A partition wall which carries the stack or soil pipe; sometimes constructed with 2x6 or 2x8 studs, and continuous from first floor to attic lines.

staggered partition: In building, a type of construction used to soundproof walls. Such a partition is made by using two rows of studding, one row supporting the lath and plaster on one side of the wall, and the other row supporting the lath and plaster on the other side of the wall.

staging: In building construction, the same as scaffolding, that is, a temporary structure of posts and boards on which the workmen stand when their work is too high to be reached from the ground.

stair: One step in a flight of stairs. Also called a stairstep. See Fig. 28.

staircase: A flight of steps leading from one floor or story to another above. The term includes landings, newel posts, handrails, and balustrades. See Fig. 28.

stairs: In building, a term applied to a complete flight of steps between two floors. *Straight run stairs* lead directly from one floor to another without a turn; *close string stairs* have a wall on each side; *open string stairs* have one side opening

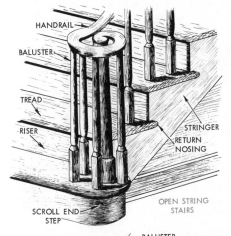

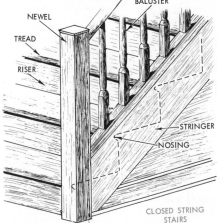

Fig. 28. Open and closed string stairs.

on a hallway or room; *doglegged* or *platform stairs* have a landing near the top or bottom, introduced to change direction.

stair treads: The upper horizontal boards of a flight of steps. See Fig. 28.

stair well: A compartment extending vertically through a building, and in which stairs are placed.

staking out: A term used for the laying out of a building plan by driving stakes into the ground showing the location of the foundation. To insure a clean edge when excavating, the stakes are connected with strong cord indicating the building lines. See *batter boards,* Fig. 5.

standard brick: In masonry, common brick, size 2¼" x 3¾" x 8". Permissible variables are, plus or minus, ¹⁄₁₆" in depth, ⅛" in width, and ¼" in length.

standard modular brick: A brick, size 2⅛" x 3½" x 7½", related to the 4-inch module, every 8 inches in height, if the mortar joint is ½ inch. Thus, 3 bricks, plus 3 one-half-inch joints, add up to an even 8 inches.

starling: A protection about a bridge or pier made by driving piles close together to form an enclosure.

starting board: In form building, the first board nailed in position at the bottom of a foundation form.

starting newel: A post at the bottom of a staircase for supporting the balustrade. See Fig. 28.

starting step: The first step at the bottom of a flight of stairs. See Fig. 28.

steel square: An instrument having at least one right angle and two or more straight edges, used for testing and laying out work for trueness. A term frequently applied to the large framing square used by carpenters.

stepped footings: If a house is built on sloping ground, all the footings cannot be at the same depth, hence they are stepped.

stile: In carpentry, one of the vertical members in a door or sash, into which secondary members are fitted.

stilt house: A house which is constructed on stilts above the ground; used mostly in hot, moist regions and on very uneven ground level sites; provides breeze passage underneath, protection from insects, and space for car.

stirrup or hanger: In building trades, a term applied to any stirruplike drop support attached to a wall to carry the end of a beam or timber, such as the end of a joist. *Stirrups* or *hangers* may also be suspended from a girder as well as from a wall. See *hanger.*

stop: In building, any device which will limit motion beyond a certain point, as a doorstep in a building, usually attached near the bottom of a door and operated by pressure from the foot. See *doorstop.*

story rod: A rod or pole cut to the proposed clear height between finished floor and ceiling. The *story rod* is often marked with minor dimensions, as for door trims.

straightedge: A bar of wood or metal with the edges true and parallel, used for testing straight lines and surfaces; that is, gauging the accuracy of work.

stretcher: In masonry construction, a term applied to a course in which brick or stone lies lengthwise; that is, a brick or stone is laid with its length parallel to the face of the wall. See Fig. 12.

stretcher bond: In masonry, a bond which consists entirely of stretchers, with each vertical joint lying between the centers of the stretchers above and below, so that angle closers are not required. This type of bond is used extensively for internal partition walls which have a thickness of a single tier of brick. See Fig. 8.

string: In building trades, a term applied to the inclined member which supports the treads and risers of a stair. Also called a *stringer.* See Fig. 28.

stringer: A long, heavy, horizontal timber which connects upright posts in a structure and supports a floor; also, the inclined member which supports the treads and risers of a stair. See Fig. 28.

structural clay tile: A term applied to various sizes and kinds of hollow and practically solid building units; molded from surface clay, shale, fire clay, or a mixture of these materials, and laid by masons.

structural glass: A vitreous finishing material used as a covering for masonry walls. It is available in rectangular plates which are held in position by a specially prepared mastic in which the plates are embedded.

stucco: Any of various plasters used as covering for walls; a coating for exterior walls in which cement is largely used; any material used for covering walls which is put on wet, but when dry becomes exceedingly hard and durable.

stud: In building, an upright member, usually a piece of dimension lunmber, 2 x 4 or 2 x 6, used in the framework of a wall. On an inside wall the lath are nailed to the studs. On the outside of a frame wall, the sheathing boards are nailed to the studs. The height of a ceiling is determined by the length or height of the studs. See Figs. 4 and 9.

stud walls: A stud wall consists of verticals usually spaced 16″ apart between top and bottom plate. Stud walls include, or can include, window shapes and headers, and can be preassembled and moved into position.

subbase: In architecture, the lowest part of a structural base, which consists of two or more horizontal members, as the base of a column; also, a *baseboard*.

subfloor: In carpentry, a term applied to a flooring of rough boards laid directly on the joists and serving the purpose of a floor during the process of construction on the building. When all rough construction work is completed, the finish floor is laid over the subfloor. See Fig. 9.

subrail: In building a closed string stair, a molded member called a *subrail* or *shoe* is placed on the top edge of the stair string to receive and carry the lower end of the balusters. See Fig. 28.

substructure: The lower portion of a structure forming the foundation which supports the superstructure of a building.

sump: A pit or depression in a building where water is allowed to accumulate; for example, in a basement floor to collect seepage or a depression in the roof of a building for receiving rain water and delivering it to the downspout. A device used for removing water from such a depression is known as a *sump pump*.

superstructure: The framing above the main supporting level.

supplement of an angle: An angle which is equal to the difference between the given angle and 180 degrees. If the given angle is 165 degrees its supplement is 15 degrees.

surbase: In architecture, a molding above a base, as that immediately above the baseboard of a room; also, a molding or series of moldings, which crown the base of a pedestal.

S4S: An abbreviation for the term *surfaced on four sides.*

surfacing of lumber: In woodworking, symbols are used to indicate how lumber has been surfaced, as *S1E,* surfaced on one edge; *S1S,* surfaced on one side; *S2S,* surfaced on two sides, and so on.

surveying: That branch of applied mathematics dealing with the science of measuring land, the unit of measure being the surveyor's chain, with 80 chains equal to 1 mile.

T

tackle: A construction of blocks and ropes, chains, or cables used for hoisting purposes in heavy construction work. Often spoken of as *block and tackle.*

tail beam or tail joist: Any timber or joist which fits against the header joist.

tailing: In building construction, any projecting part of a stone or brick inserted in a wall.

tail joist: Any building joist with one end fitted against a header joist.

tamp: To pound down, with repeated light strokes, the loose soil thrown in as filling around a wall.

template: A gauge, commonly a thin board or light frame, used as a guide for forming work to be done.

tenon: In carpentry, a piece of lumber or timber cut with a projection, or tongue, on the end for fitting into a mortise. The joint formed by inserting a tenon into a mortise constitutes a so-called *mortise-and-tenon joint.*

termite shield: A protective shield made of noncorrosive metal, placed in or on a foundation wall, or other mass of masonry, or around pipes entering a building, to prevent passage of termites into the structure.

terrace: An elevated level surface of earth supported on one or more faces by a masonry wall, or by a sloping bank covered with turf.

terra cotta: A clay product used for ornamental work on the exterior of buildings; also, used extensively in making vases, and for decorations on statuettes. It is made of hard-baked clay in variable colors with a fine glazed surface.

terrazzo: A type of Venetian marble mosaic in which Portland cement is used as a matrix. Though used in buildings for centuries, *terrazzo* is a modern floor finish, used also for bases, borders, and wainscoating, as well as on stair treads, partitions, and other wall surfaces.

terrazzo flooring: A term used in the building trades for a type of flooring made of small fragments of colored stone, or marble, embedded irregularly in cement. Finally, the surface is given a high polish.

three-way switch: A switch used in house wiring when a light (or lights) is to be turned on or off from two places. A three-way switch must be used at each place.

threshold: In building construction, a term applied to the piece of timber, plank, or stone under a door.

through shake: A separation of wood between annual growth rings, extending between two faces of timber; similar to a *windshake.*

tie: In architecture, anything used to hold two parts together, as a post, rod, or beam.

tie beam: A timber used for tying structural parts together, as in the roof of a building. Any beam which ties together or prevents the spreading apart of the lower ends of the rafters of a roof.

tile: A building material made of fired clay, stone, cement, or glass used for floors, roofing, and drains; also made in varied ornamental designs for decorative work.

tile setting adhesives: Specially formulated glues or mastics, used instead of motarbed,

for tile setting. They are said to be clean, waterproof, less expensive, and faster.

timber connectors: Metal or wood rings and dowels used to tie adjacent structural members together. The *connectors* are placed in precut holes or grooves in the timber-framing members, then the members are drawn together and held firmly in place by bolts.

toeing: In carpentry, the driving of nails or brads obliquely; also, to clinch nails so driven.

toenailing: The driving of a nail, spike, or brad slantingly to the end of a piece of lumber to attach it to another piece, especially as, in laying a floor, to avoid having the heads of the nails show above the surface.

tongue: A projecting rib cut along the edge of a piece of timber so it can be fitted into a groove cut in another piece. Also, the shorter of the two extending arms of the *framing square,* usually 16 inches long and 1½ inches wide. The *blade* of the square forms a right angle with the *tongue.* The *octagon scale* and the *brace measure scale* appear on the faces of the tongue.

tooled joints: In masonry, mortar joints which are specially prepared by compressing and spreading the mortar after it has set slightly. *Tooled joints* present the best weathering properties, and include the *weathered joint, V joint,* and *concave joint.* See Fig. 19.

top plate: In building, the horizontal member nailed to the top of the partition studding.

transit: An instrument, commonly used by surveyors, consisting of four principal parts: (1) a telescope for sighting; (2) a spirit level; (3) a vernier or graduated arc for measuring vertical or horizontal angles; and (4) a tripod with leveling screws for adjusting the instrument.

transom: A term used in building for any small window over a door or another window.

tread: In building, the upper horizontal part of a stair step; that portion of a step on which the foot is placed when mounting the stairs. See Fig. 28.

triangular truss: A popular type of truss used for short spans, especially for roof supports. See *W-truss.*

trim: In carpentry, a term applied to the visible finishing work of the interior of a building, including any ornamental parts of either wood or metal used for covering joints between jambs and plaster around windows and doors. The term may include also the locks, knobs, and hinges on doors.

trimmer: The beam or floor joist into which a header is framed.

trimmer arch: A comparatively flat arch, such as may be used in the construction of a fireplace.

trimmer beam: Usually two joists spiked together around a fireplace opening in floor framing.

trimming joist: A timber, or beam, which supports a header.

trowel: A flat, steel tool used to spread and smooth mortar or plaster. Typical *trowels* are shown in Fig. 29.

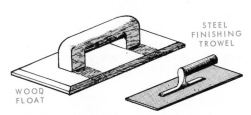

WOOD FLOAT

STEEL FINISHING TROWEL

Fig. 29. Trowels.

truss: A combination of members, such as beams, bars, and ties, usually arranged in triangular units to form a rigid framework for supporting loads over a long span, as in bridges or massive roof construction.

trussed beam: An architectural term applied to a beam stiffened by a truss rod.

tubular scaffolds: Scaffolds for interior and exterior construction work, made of tube steel. These scaffolds are lightweight, offer low wind resistance, and are easily dismantled. They are obtainable in several strengths for varying heights and types of work.

tuck pointing: In masonry, the finishing of joints along the center lines, with a narrow parallel ridge of fine putty or fine lime mortar.

twelfth scale: A scale which divides the inch into 12 parts instead of 16; found usually on the back of the *framing square* along the outside edge. In this scale, one inch equals one foot. The *twelfth scale* makes it possible to reduce layouts to $\frac{1}{12}$ of their regular size and to solve basic right triangle problems.

U

unit length rafter table: A table which appears on the *blade* of the *framing square.* It gives unit lengths of *common rafters* for seventeen different rises, ranging from 2 to 18 inches. It also gives the unit lengths for *hip* or *valley rafters,* difference in lengths of *jack rafters* set 16 inches on center, jack rafters set 24 inches on center, and the *side cuts* for jack and hip rafters.

unsound knot: A term used by woodworkers when referring to a *knot* which is not as solid as the wood in the board surrounding it.

upright: In building, a term applied to a piece of timber which stands upright or in a vertical position, as the vertical pieces at the sides of a doorway or window frame.

V

valley: In architecture, a term applied to a depressed angle formed by the meeting at the bottom of two inclined sides of a roof, as a gutter; also, the space, when viewed from above, between vault ridges.

valley rafter: A rafter disposed in the internal angle of a roof to form a *valley* or depression in the roof. See Fig. 26.

vane: Any flat piece of metal attached to an axis and placed in an elevated position

395

where it can be readily moved by the force of the wind, such as a weathercock on a barn steeple, indicating the direction of the wind.

vapor barrier: Material used to retard the passage of vapor or moisture into walls thus preventing condensation within them. There are different types of vapor barriers, such as membrane which comes in rolls and is applied as a unit in the wall or ceiling, and the paint type which is applied with a brush.

veneer: Thin pieces of wood, or other material, used for finishing purposes to cover an inferior piece of material, thus giving a superior effect and greater strength with reduced cost.

veneer wall: A wall with a masonry facing which is not bonded, but is attached to a wall so as to form an integral part of the wall for purposes of load bearing and stability.

ventilating brick: A brick which has been cored to provide an air passage for ventilating purposes.

ventilation: The free circulation of air in a room or building; a process of changing the air in a room by either natural or artificial means; any provision made for removing contaminated air or gases from a room and replacing the foul air by fresh air.

vent pipe: A flue, or pipe, connecting any interior space in a building with the outer air for purposes of ventilation; any small pipe extending from any of the various plumbing fixtures in a structure to the vent stack.

vent stack: A vertical pipe connected with all vent pipes carrying off foul air or gases from a building. It extends through the roof and provides an outlet for gases and contaminated air, and also aids in maintaining a water seal in the trap.

V & C V: An abbreviation for the term meaning **V** *grooved* and *center* **V** *grooved;* that is, the board is **V** grooved along the edge and also center **V** grooved, on the surface.

vitrified tile: In building construction, pipes made of clay, baked hard and then glazed, so they are impervious to water; used especially for underground drainage.

W

wainscot: The wooden lining of the lower part of an interior wall. Originally, only a superior quality of oak was used for this purpose, but now the term includes other materials.

wainscoting: The materials used in lining the interior of walls; also, the process of applying such materials to walls.

wainscoting cap: A molding at the top of a wainscoting.

waler: Timbers used in form construction to which the ties are fastened, or against which the end of the braces are butted; timbers used for holding forms in line. Same as *whaler.* See Fig. 33.

wallboard: An artificially prepared sheet material, or board, used for covering walls and ceilings as a substitute for wooden boards or plaster. There are many different types of *wallboard* on the market.

wall plates: Horizontal pieces of timber placed on the top of a brick or stone wall under the ends of girders, joists, and other timbers to distribute the weight of the load or pressure of the superstructure, especially the roof.

wall spacers: In concrete work, a type of tie for holding the forms in position while the concrete is being poured, and until it has set. For typical *wall spacers,* see Fig. 30.

wall tie: A device, in any of various shapes, formed of $\frac{1}{4}''$ diameter steel wire, the purpose of which is to bind together the tiers of a masonry wall, particularly those in hollow wall construction. See Fig. 21. Also, a contrivance, usually a metal strip, employed to attach or secure a brick veneer wall to a frame building.

wane: Bark, or lack of bark or wood, from any cause, on edge or corner of a piece of lumber.

warped: In woodworking, a term applied to any piece of timber which has been twisted out of shape and permanently distorted during the process of seasoning.

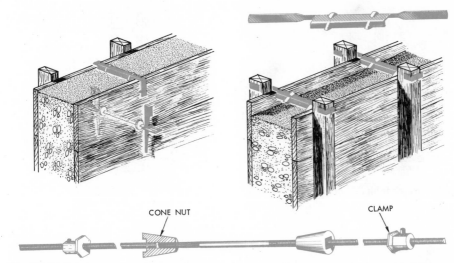

CONE NUT

CLAMP

Fig. 30. Wall spacers.

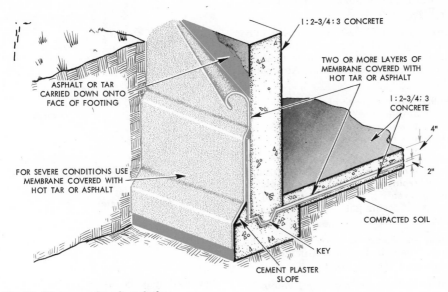

1:2-3/4:3 CONCRETE

TWO OR MORE LAYERS OF
MEMBRANE COVERED WITH
HOT TAR OR ASPHALT

ASPHALT OR TAR
CARRIED DOWN ONTO
FACE OF FOOTING

1:2-3/4:3
CONCRETE

4"

FOR SEVERE CONDITIONS USE
MEMBRANE COVERED WITH
HOT TAR OR ASPHALT

2"

COMPACTED SOIL

CEMENT PLASTER
SLOPE

KEY

Fig. 31. Waterproofing foundation.

waterproofing walls: In concrete work, the making of walls impervious to water, or dampness, by mixing a compound with concrete, or by applying a compound to the surface of the wall. A method of water-proofing the foundations of walls is shown in Fig. 31.

water table: A ledge or slight projection of the masonry or wood construction on

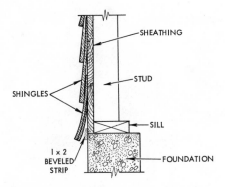

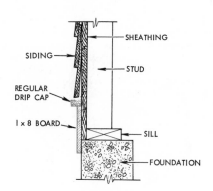

Fig. 32. Water table.

the outside of a foundation wall, or just above, to protect the foundation from rain by throwing the water away from the wall. See Figs. 6 and 32.

weatherboards: Boards shaped so as to be specially adaptable for overlapping at the joints to prevent rain or other moisture from passing through the wall. Also, called *siding.*

weather strip: A piece of metal, wood, or other material used to cover joints around doors and windows to prevent drafts, and to keep out rain and snow.

weep hole: In retaining walls and other similar structures, a small hole through which surplus water drains to the outside, hence preventing damage to the wall by pressure of accumulated water back of or under the structure.

whaler or waler: A horizontal bracing member used in form construction. Also known as a *ranger.* See Fig. 33.

western framing: See *platform framing.*

winders: Treads of steps used in a winding staircase, or where stairs are carried around curves or angles. *Winders* are cut wider at one end than at the other so they can be arranged in a circular form.

window wall: An outside wall, of which a large portion is glass. Glass area may consist of one or more windows. A win-

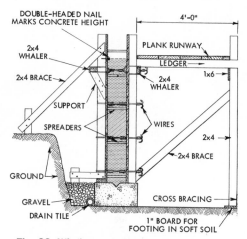

Fig. 33. Whaler or waler.

dow wall may be made up entirely of windows.

windshake: A defect in wood, so-called because of the belief that it is caused by wrenching of the growing tree by the wind. Since there is a separation of the annual rings from each other around the trunk of the tree, this defect is cuplike in appearance and is sometimes known as *cupshake.*

wire ties: Short lengths of wire in various shapes and gauges for reinforcing the bond between two members. They may be embedded in mortar; nailed; twisted around and between masonry, wood, or metal. Wire ties are usually of cement-coated steel or galvanized metal.

withe: In architecture, a term applied to the portion between flues in the same chimney.

woodwork: Interior fittings of wood, such as moldings and staircases; also, work done in or with wood, objects or parts made of wood.

working drawing: In architecture, a drawing or sketch which contains all dimensions and instructions necessary for carrying a job through to a successful completion.

W-truss: A truss commonly used in residential construction; so called because its internal supports form a "W". Sometimes called a *fink truss.*

wythe: In masonry, the partition wall between flues in the same chimney stack. Also spelled *withe.*

Y

year ring: One of the clearly defined rings in a cross section of a tree trunk, showing the amount of annual growth of the tree. Each ring represents one year of growth; also called *growth ring* and *annual ring.* The rings are made up of cells or tubes which convey sap through the tree.

Z

zoning: A term applied to the division of a certain political subdivision into districts which may have different types of regulation. Such a condition is brought about by local ordinance under the police power of a state, granted by specific legislation commonly called an *enabling act.* Zoning laws pertain to the use of land in a particular area.

zonolite concrete: A form of concrete which acts as insulation; used as parts of floor slabs for houses without basements.

Index

Numerals in **bold type** refer to illustrations.

A

Abbreviations, lumber, 160
Abrading tools, 124
Abrasive papers, 124, **125**
Accident prevention
  clothing, safety, 17
  general safety, 15
  hand tool safety, 19
  power tool safety, 20
  safety on job, 14
  tools and safety, 18
Acoustical insulation, 199
Adhesives, 271
  gun, 34, **34**, 275, **277**
  safety rules, 279
Aluminum oxide paper, 125
Anchors
  bolts, 240, **241**
  Dryvin, 241, **242**
  expansion screw, 242
  hammer driven, 243, **245**
  hollow wall screw, 246, **246**
  joist, 240, **241**
  lag expansion shield, **242**, 243
  lead screw, 242, **242**
  machine expansion shield, **242**, 243
  pin bolt drive, 243
  plastic, 242
  powder driven, 243, **245**
  rawlplug, 242
  sleeper clips, 240, **241**

snap-off, 243, **244**
straps, 240, **241**
ties, 240, **241**
toggle bolts, 246, **246**
Angle iron fasteners, 254, **254**
Angle plate fasteners, 254, **254**
Animal glue, 272
Arc, finding center, 66, **66**
Arches, 182, **183, 184**
Architects, 9, 10
Auger bit, 94, **94**
Awl, scratch, **46,** 47

B

Ball bearing hinges, 259, **260**
Bark, 141, **141**
Bark pockets, 149
Barrel bolts, 262, **263**
Bars, wrecking, 42, **42**
Bastard-sawed wood, 145
Battened joint, 170, **171**
Batts, installation, **202, 203, 206, 207, 208**
Beams, box, 180, **180**
Beech, 165
Bevel, T, 49, **49**
Birch
  sweet, 165
  yellow, 165
Blanket insulation, installation, **203, 204, 205**
Blemishes in wood, 148

Blue stain, 153
Bits, see brace and bits
Bit gage, 98, **98**
Blood albumin glue, 273
Boards, 154
Board foot measure, 159, **159**
Bolts
  anchor, 240
  barrel, 262, **263**
  carriage, 238, **239**
  chain, 262, **263**
  cremone, 262, **263**
  door, 262, **262**
  extension flush, 262, **263**
  flush, 262, **263**
  foot, 262, **263**
  handrail, 239, **239**
  lag, 239, **239**
  machine, 238, **239**
  stove, 239, **239**
  surface, 262, **263**
  toggle, 246, **246**
Boring tools, 93
Box beams, 180, **180**
Box nails, 229, **229**
Braces and bits,
  auger bit, 94, **94**
  bit extension, **94,** 95
  brace and bit operation, 97
  corner brace, **93,** 95
  countersink bit, **94,** 96
  expansive bit, **94,** 95
  Forstner bit, **94,** 96
  lock set bit, **94,** 95
  ratchet brace, 93, **93**

safety rules, 96
   screwdriver bit, 37, **94,**
   96
Bracing, metal, 255, **255**
Brad, 224, 229, **229**
Bridging metal, 255, **255**
Building codes, 8
Building components, 180
Building industry, 4
Butt gage, 48, **48**
Butt joint, 168, **170**
Butternut, 165

C

Cabinetmaker, 2
Caliper rule, 52, **53**
Cambium, **141,** 142
Carpenter
   adviser, as an, 5
   apprentice, 4
   journeyman, 4
   modern, 2
   opportunities, 5
   training, 3
Carpentry, definition, 1
Casein glue, 272
Casing nails, 229, **229**
Catches, **264,** 265
Cedar
   Alaska, 162
   northern white, 162
   Port Orford, 162
   western red, 162
Cellulose glue, 274
Celocrete, 220
Center punch, 42, **42**
Chain bolts, 262, **263**
Chain fastener, door, 262,
   263
Chalk line, 44, **44**
Checks in wood, 149, **149**
Chisels
   cold, 119, **122**
   flooring, 119, **122**
   safety rules, cold chisel,
   122

safety rules, wood
   chisels, 119
   socket, 118, **119**
   use of, **120, 121**
Circle, finding center,
   66, **66**
Circumference, finding,
   64, **65**
C clamp, 43, **43**
Clamp nail fasteners, 255,
   255
Clips
   nailing, 251, **251**
   sleeper, 240, **241**
   truss, 248, **249**
   wallboard, 251, **253**
Close grained wood, 144
Closer, door, 263, **263,** 264
Clout nails, **230,** 231
Coarse grained wood, 145
Coated nails, 226
Codes, building and
   zoning, 8
Concrete nails, 229, **229**
Combination square, 52,
   53
Compass saw, 77, **77**
Condensation, 199
Connectors, metal
   framing, 250, **250, 251**
   joist hangers, 251, **251**
   nailing clips, 251, **251**
   plate, 247, **247**
   ring, 247, **247**
   timber, 247, **247**
   truss clips, 248, **249**
   wallboard clips, 251,
   253
Contracts, 11
Coping saw, 77, **77**
Corner angle fasteners,
   254, **254**
Corners, 255, **255**
Corrugated fasteners,
   254, **254**
Cross grain wood, 145, 149
Cross-lap joints, 169, **169**

Cremone bolts, 262, **263**
Cut nails, 223
Cutting tools, 72
Cylindrical locks, 265, **266**
Cypress, 162

D

Dado joint, **168,** 169
Decay, 149
Decay resistance, 149, **150**
Defects in wood, 148
Density, 143, 144
Dimension lumber, 155
Dividers, wing type,
   46, 47
   use of, **47**
Door bolts
   barrel, 262, **263**
   chain, 262, **263**
   cremone, 262, **263**
   extension flush, 262,
   263
   flush, 262, **263**
   foot, 262, **263**
   surface, 262, **263**
Door
   catches, **264,** 265
   chain fasteners, 262,
   263
   closer, hydraulic, **263,**
   264
   closer, pneumatic, 263,
   263
   exit fixture, 262, **263**
   hands, 267, **267**
   holders, **264,** 265
   knocker, **263,** 264
   panic bar, 262, **263**
   stop, **264,** 265
Door hands, 267, **267**
Double head nails, 230,
   230
Dovetailed dado joint,
   168, 169
Dowels, 171

Dowel pin nails, 231, **231**
Doweled joint, 171, **171**
Doweled butt joint, **168,**
169
Drawshave, 106, **107**
Dressed lumber, 155
Dressed size, 158
Drills, hand
breast, 98, **98**
hand, 98, **98**
push, **98,** 99
twist, **98,** 99
Drills, power
auger, **98,** 99
portable, 99, **99,** 100
safety rules, portable,
100
safety rules, stationary,
101
stationary, 101, **101**
Drill press, 101, **101**
safety rules, 102

E

Edge grain wood, 145
Ellipse for pipe openings,
67, **67,** 68
End-lap joint, **168,** 169
Endogens, 142
Epoxy resin glue, 274
Escutcheon pins, 231
Exit door fixture, 262, **263**
Exogens, 142
Extension flush bolt, 262,
263
Extension rule, 50, **51**

F

Factory lumber, 154
Fasteners, metal, for light
carpentry
angle iron, 254, **254**
angle plate, 254, **254**
clamp nails, **254,** 255
corner angle iron, 254,
254

corrugated, 254, **254**
mending plate, 253, **254**
metal corner, 254, **254**
Miklin, 254, **254**
Skotch, 254, **254**
tee, 254, **254**
Fasteners, powder driven,
34, **34**
safety rules, 35
Fiberboard, 189
Files, wood, 122, **123**
safety rules, 122
Fill insulation, 208, **209,**
210, 211
Fillet joint, 171, **171**
Fine grained wood, 145
Financing, 10, **11**
Fir
white, 162
Douglas, 163
Fire retardant insulation,
199
Flat grain wood, 145
Flat-sawed wood, 145,
146
Flexible insulation, 200,
202, 203, 204, 205,
207, 208
Flint paper, 124
Flush bolt, 262, **263**
Foot bolt, 262, **263**
Framing joints, 168, **168**
Framing square
arc, finding center with,
66, **66**
calculating proportions
with, 63, **64**
circle, finding center
with, 66, **66**
circumference, finding
with, 64, **65**
converting square to
octagon, 62, **62**
description, 53
ellipse for pipe open-
ings, 67, **67, 68**
Essex board measure

scale, 58, **59**
gages, 55, **55**
hopper joints, 69, **70**
miter and butt joints,
68, **68, 69**
octagon scale, 60, **61, 62**
pipe capacities, 65, **65**
reduction or enlarge-
ments, 63, **63**
scales, **57**
tables, **57**
testing, 56, **57**
uses, 56
use with circles, 64, **65**
Furring strips, metal, 251,
252, 255

G

Gage
bit, 98, **98**
butt, 48, **48**
marking, 48, **48**
stair, framing square,
55, **55**
use of butt gage, 49
Garnet paper, 124
Glass block insulation, 221
Glue
animal, 272
blood albumin, 273
casein, 272
cellulose, 274
epoxy resin, 274
liquid, 272
safety rules, 279
synthetic resin, 273
vegetable, 273
Glued lumber, 182, **182**
Glued and blocked joint,
168, 169
Goggles, 137
Grading
by use, 154
by manufacture, 155
by size, 155

Grain
  close, **144,** 145
  coarse, 145
  cross, 144, 149
  edge, 145
  fine, 145
  flat, 145
  spiral, 145
  straight, 145
  vertical, 145
Grinders, 133, **134**
  safety rules, 135
Growth rate, 143
  rings, 142
Gum, red, 165
Gun, adhesive, 34, **34,**
    275, **277**
Gypsum wallboard, 192,
    193
  lath, 193

H

Hack saw, **77,** 78
  safety rules, 78
Hammers
  claw, curved, 24, **25**
  claw, straight, 25, **25**
  drywall, 25, **25**
  flooring, 25, **25**
  mallets, 29, **29**
  roofing, 31, **31**
  sledge, 29, **29**
  safety rules, 25
  use, **26, 27**
Hammer fastening tool,
    29, **29**
Hands, door, 267, **267,**
    268
Hangers, joist, 251, **251**
Hardboard, 186, **187,** 188
Hardwood, 140
  uses and working
    qualities, 165
Hardware, finish, 257
Hatchet,
  claw, 27, **28**

half, 28, **28**
  safety rules, 28
  shingle, 28, **28**
Haunched mortise joint,
    168, 169
Heartwood, 141, **141**
Hemlock
  eastern, 163
  western, 163
Hinges
  ball bearing, 259, **260**
  double-action spring
    butt, 261, **261**
  double-action spring
    floor, 260, **261**
  full mortise, 258, **258**
  full surface, 258, **258**
  half mortise, 258, **258**
  half surface, 258, **258**
  invisible, 261, **261**
  loose pin, 258
  offset, 260, **260**
  Olive knuckle butt, 259,
    260
  ornamental, 261, **261**
  parliament butt, 260,
    260
  strap, 260, **260**
  tight pin, 258
  T, 260, **260**
  template, 259
Home
  building and zoning, 8
  electric, gas, phone, 8
  financing, 10, 11
  location, 6
  specifications, 9
  survey, 7
  title, 7
  water and sewerage, 7
Hopper joint, 170, **170**
Housed brace joint, 169

I

Insulating board nails,
    214, 215, 231

Insulation
  acoustical, 199, **200,**
    201
  batt, 201, **202, 203,**
    206, 207, 208
  blanket, 200, **203, 204,**
    205
  condensation, 199
  fill type, 208, **209, 210,**
    211
  fire retardant, 199
  flexible, 200, **202, 203,**
    204, 205, 207, 208
  glass block, 221
  precast, 220, **220**
  reflective, 217, **219**
  rigid, 211, **212, 213,**
    215
  slab, 219, **219**
  spray, 220
  thermal, 197, **198**
  vapor barrier, 209

J

Joints
  battened, **171**
  cross-lap, **169**
  dado, **168,** 169
  dovetailed dado, **168,**
    169
  doweled, 171, **171**
  doweled butt, **168,** 169
  end-lap, **168,** 169
  filleted, 171, **171**
  framing, 168, **168**
  glued and blocked, 169,
    170
  haunched mortise, **168,**
    169
  hopper, 170, **170**
  housed brace, **168,** 169
  lap, **168**
  oblique butt, **168,** 169
  plain butt, 170, **170**
  rabbeted ledge and
    miter, **168,** 170

spliced, **168**
splined, 171, **171**
splined miter, **168**, 169
square butt, 169
tennon, 169
tongue and groove, 171, **171**
Joist hangers, 251, **251**

K

Knife, utility, **46,** 48
safety rules, 48
Knots in wood, 151

L

Lag bolt, 239, **239**
expansion shield, **242,** 243
Laminated lumber, 182
plastics, 194
Layout tools, 44
Lead cap nails, 231, **231**
Level, 45, **45**
Liquid glue, 272
Lineal foot, 160
Locks,
cylindrical, 265, **266**
mortise, 265, **266**
tubular, 265, **266**
Lumber
classification, 154
commercial, 166
dimension, 155
dressed, 155, **156**
factory (shop), 154
glued, 182
glued-laminated, 182
matched, 155, **156**
measurements, 159
molding, 155, **157**
nominal, 158
ordering, 159
patterned, 155, **155**
rough, 155
shiplapped, 155
size classification, 155

structural, 154
worked, 155
working qualities, 161
yard, 154

M

Mahogany, 166
Mallets, 29, **29**
Maple, 165
Masonry nails, 231
Mastic, 271, 274, **275**
safety rules, 279
Matched lumber, 155
Measure, surface, 160
board foot, 159, **159**
Measurements, lumber, 159
Measuring tools, 44
Medullary rays, 139, **141**
Mending plates, 253, **254**
Metal corner, 253, **254**
Metal studs, 191, **192**
Miklin fasteners, 253, **254**
Millman, 2
Miter boxes, 43, **43**
Modified woods, 189
Moisture, 146, **147**
Mortise hinges, 258, **258**
Mortise lock, 265, **266**

N

Nail heads
brad, **223,** 224
deep countersunk, **223,** 224
double, **223,** 224
duplex, **223,** 224
flat, 223, **223**
large flat, **223,** 224
T, **223,** 224
Nail points
blunt, 224, **224**
chisel, 224, **224**
diamond, 224, **224**
duck-bill, 224, **224**
long, 224, **224**

needle, 224, **224**
Nail shanks
annular, 225, **225**
longitudinally grooved, 225, **225**
spiral, 225, **225**
square, 225, **225**
Nails
box, 229, **229**
brad, 229, **229**
casing, 229, **229**
clout, **230,** 231
clamp, **254,** 255
coatings, 226
common, 229, **229**
concrete, 229, **229**
cut, 229, **229**
double head, 230, **230**
dowel pin, 231, **231**
escutcheon pin, **230,** 231
finish, 229, **229**
insulating board, 230, **230**
lead cap, 231, **231**
masonry, 230, **230**
preventing splitting by, 225
ratchet, **230,** 231
roofing, 230, **230, 231**
set, 42, **42**
shingle, 230, **230**
sizes, 226, **227,** 229
sizes and weights, 226, **227**
staples, 231, **231**
tacks, **230,** 231
T, **230,** 231
wire, 223
Nailing
air-operated, 32, **33**
clips, 251, **251**
machine, 31, **31**
safety rules, 33
Nominal size, 158
Non-wood building materials, 191

O

Oak
red, 166
white, **139**, 166
Oblique butt joint, **168**, 169
Offset hinge, 260, **260**

P

Panels, stressed skin, 179, **179**
sandwich, 179
Paring and shaving tools, 103
Parliament butt, 260, **260**
Particleboard, 187
Patterned lumber, 155
Pin hinge, 258
Pinchers, 40, **40**
Pine
southern yellow, 163
longleaf, 163
ponderosa, 164
shortleaf, **139**, 164
sugar, 164
western white, 164
white, 164
Pipes
ellipse for 67, **67, 68**
capacities, 65, **65**
Pith, 141, **141**, 151
Plain butt joint, 170, **170**
Plain-sawed wood, **139**, 145, 146
Planes, hand, 103
block, 105, **105, 110**
bullnose, 106, 107
fiberboard, 106, **107**
fore, 106
forming, 106, **107**
grooving, 106, **107**
jack, 104, **105**
jointer, 105, **105**
rabbet, 106, **107**
router, 106, **107**

safety rules, 109
smoothing, 105, **105**
Stanley smooth, 104
use of, **108, 110**
Planes, power, portable, 111
block, 111, **112**
safety rules, 113
Planes, power, stationary, 115
jointer, 115, **116**
safety rules, 117
Plastics laminated, 194
Pliers
combination, 40, **40**
side cutting, 40, **40**
safety rules, 41
Plumb bob, 44, **44**
Plywood, 174
advantages, 177
box beams, 180, **180**
components, 179, 180
grades, **176**
measurements, 178
types, **175**
uses, 177, **177, 178**
Precast insulation, 220
Prefabricated houses, 181
Processed woods, 186
Punch, center, 42, **42**
Push-pull rule, 50, **51, 52**

R

Rabbeted ledge and miter joint, **168,** 170
Rasps, wood, 122, **123**
safety rules, 122
Ratchet nails, **230**, 231
Redwood, 164
Reflective insulation, 217, **219**
installation, 218
Rigid insulation
application, **212, 213, 215**
description, 211

flat roof, applying, **216**
pitched roof, **215**
wall sheathing, 214
Roofing nails, 230, **230, 231**
Rough lumber, 155
Router, portable, 113, **113, 115**
safety rules, 115
Rule
caliper, 52, **53**
extension, 50, **51**
push-pull, 50, **51, 52**
steel tape, **51, 52**
zig-zag, 50, **50, 51**

S

Safety
accident prevention, 14
clothing, 17
general, 15
goggles, 137
hand tools, 19
job, 14
power tools, 20
protective equipment, 17
tools, 18
Safety rules for
adhesives, 279
braces and bits, 96
chisels, cold, 122
chisels, wood, 119
drill, portable, 100
drill, stationary, 101
drill press, 102
fastener, powder driver, 35
grinder, 135
hammer, 25
hatchet, 28
jointer, 117
knives, 48
nailing machines, 33
plane, hand, 109
plane, portable power, 113

plane, stationary power, 117
pliers, 41
rasps and files, 122
router, 115
sander, belt, portable, 127
sander, belt, stationary, 131
sander, disc, portable, 127
sander, disc, stationary, 131
sander, orbital, 128
saw, band, 92
saw, electric hand, 81
saw, hack, 78
saw, hand, 75
saw, circular, 86
saw, circular blade, 87
saw, radial, 89
saw, sabre and reciprocating, 83
screwdriver, 37
screwdriver, power, 37
snips, tin, 41
stapler, 33
wrenches, 41
Sand paper, 124
Sander, portable power
  belt, 126, **126**
  safety for belt, 127
  orbital, 127, **127, 128**
  safety for orbital, 128
  disc, 128, **129, 131**
  safety for disc, 129
Sander, stationary power
  belt, 130, **130**
  disc, 131, **131**
  safety rules, 131
Sandwich panels, 179
Sapwood, 141, **141**
Saturation point, fiber, 146
Saws, hand
  backsaw, **77**, 78

compass, 77, **77**
coping, 77, **77**
crosscut, 73, **73, 74, 76**
dovetail, 78, **78**
hacksaw, 78, **78**
hacksaw, safety rules, 78
hand, description, 73, **73, 77**
hand, safety rules, 75
keyhole, 77
ripsaw, 74, **75, 76**
Saws, portable power
  electric hand, 78, **79, 80**
  reciprocating, 81, **82**
  sabre, 81, **82**
  safety rules, hand, 81
  safety rules, sabre and reciprocating, 83
Saws, stationary power
  band, 90, **90, 91**
  circular table, 83, **84**
  circular blades, 85
  maintenance, 88
  radial saw, 88, **89**
  safety rules, band, 92
  safety rules, circular, 86
  safety rules, circular blades, 87
  safety rules, radial, 89
Saw set, 78, **78**
Scratch awl, **46,** 47
Screws
  ball head, 235
  drywall, 235, **235, 236**
  finishes, 236
  flathead, 234, **235, 236**
  headless, 234
  hollow-wall, 244
  machine, 238, **238**
  oval head, 234, **235**
  Phillips recessed head, 234, **235**
  roundhead, 234
  self drilling, 235
  sheet metal, 237, **237**
  sizes and shapes, 234

wood, 234
Screwdriver
  bits, **36,** 37, 94
  hand, 36, **36, 37**
  power, 39, **39**
  Phillips, 36, **36**
  ratchet, 36, **37**
  spiral ratchet, 36, **37**
  safety rules, hand, 37
  safety rules, power, 40
  use, **38, 39**
Scriber, 46, **46**
Shake,
  heart, 152, **152**
  star, 152, **152**
  wind, 152, **152**
Shakes (shingles), 158
Shields,
  lag expansion screw, **242,** 243
  machine expansion screw, **242,** 243
Shingles, 158
Shingle nails, 230, **230**
Shiplapped lumber, 155
Slab insulation, 219
Sledge hammer, 29, **29**
Snips, tin, **40,** 41
  safety rules, 41
Softwoods, 140
  uses and working qualities, 162
Specifications, building, 9
Spiral grain, 145
Splined joint, 171, **171**
Splined miter joint, **168,** 169
Split in wood, 153
Spokeshave, 106, **107**
Spray insulation, 220
Spring butt hinge, 261, **261**
Spring floor hinge, 260, **261**
Springwood, 143
Spruce, 165

Square butt joint, 169,
169
Squares, shingle, 158
Square
combination, 52, **53**
framing, 54, **55,** 56
try, 53, **53**
try and miter, 53, **53**
Straight grained wood,
145
Stair framing square
gages, 55, **55**
Staplers
air, 32
electric, 32, **33**
mechanical, 30, **30**
portable air, 31, **32**
roofing, 30
safety rules, 33
Staples, 231, **232, 233,
234**
Straightedge, 45, **45**
Strap hinge, 260, **260**
Steel tape, **51,** 52
Stressed skin panels,
179, **179**
Strips, furring, metal, 255
Strips, wood, 154
Structural lumber, 154
Studs, metal, 192
Summerwood, 143
Supporting tools, 43
Surface bolt, 262, **263**
Surface hinges, 258, **258**
Synthetic resin glue, 273

T

Tacks, **230,** 231
Tape, steel, **51,** 52
T-bevel, 49, **49**
T-fastener, 254, **254**
T-hinge, 260, **260**
T-nail, **230,** 231
Template hinge, 259
Tennon joint, 169
Thermal insulation, 197
Ties, metal, 240, **241**

Tongue and groove joint,
171, **171**
Tool boxes, 24, **24**
Tool kit, apprentice, 23,
23
Tools
abrading, 124
boring, 93
cutting, 72
classification, 24
hammering and
percussion, 24
layout and measuring,
44
paring and shaving, 103
supporting and holding,
43
Trammel points, 49, **49**
Truss clips, 248, **249**
Trusses, 184, **185**
Try and miter square,
53, **53**
Try square, 53, **53**
Tubular lock, 265, **266**

V

Vapor barrier, 209
Vegetable glue, 273
Ventilators, 269, **269**
Vertical grain wood, 145
Vinyl materials, 194
Vise, 43, **43**

W

Wallboard, 192, **193**
clips, 251, **253**
Walnut, black, 166
Wane, 153
Warping, 153, **153**
Whetstone, 136
Wire nails, 223
Wood
bastard-sawed, 145
blemishes, 148
blue stain, 153

checks, 149
close-grained, 144
coarse-grained, 145
cross grain, 141
defects, 148
dense, 143
edge grain, 145
fine-grained, 145
flat-grained, **139,** 145
flat-sawed, 146, **146**
grading, 154
grain, 145
growth, 143
holes in, 151
knots, 151
modified, 189
moisture, 146, **147**
plain-sawed, **139,** 145,
146
processed, 186
products, 173
quarter-sawed, **139,**
145, **146**
rays, 139, **141**
rings, **141,** 142
shakes, 152, **152**
spiral grain, 145
split in, 153
spring, 143
straight grain, 145
summer, 143
treatments, 190
uses and working
qualities of, 161
vertical grain, 145
wane, 153
warping, 153, **153**
Worked lumber, 155
Wrecking bars, 42, **42**
Wrenches, adjustable, 41,
41, 42
safety rules, 41

Z

Zig-zag rule, 50, **50, 51**
Zoning, 8

The Making of This Book

A book is a familiar product often taken for granted by readers who are not acquainted with the intricate steps that intervene between the original manuscript and the finished volume.

In the preparation of a modern textbook, skills highly perfected through centuries are combined with the latest findings of present-day science. A book is at once an achievement of art, craftsmanship, and technology. This work is the result of the coordinated efforts of the following specialists:

Editorial	W. RAHY PAUL: *Editor in Chief*—Former teacher of Science and Practical Arts—School Administrator—Training Officer U. S. Air Force.
	ROBERT PUTNAM: *Editor Building Series*—Extensive Experience in Architectural and Building Trades field. ELDRED GREEN, *Copy Editor.*
Illustrations	ARTHUR BURKE: *Head, Illustration Department*—Author of Architectural books.
	GORDON L. RUEDGER: *Illustration Coordinator.*
	KOOROSH JAMALPUR, CARL HUDSON, JR., MICHAEL CIANCANELLI, *Technical Illustrators.*
Production	PAUL WARRINGTON: *Production Manager*—Specialist in Book Production.

The team listed above, representing over 100 years of experience in education and vocational publishing, hope that their contribution will help both teachers and students to attain their educational goals.

D. N. McCARL, *President*
American Technical Society